CONGRESS AT YOUR FINGERTIPS

MW00608464

Qty		Total
	Standard Congressional Directories	
	Alpha Congressional Directories	
	VA (6%) and DC (5.75%) add sales tax	
	Shipping	
	Subtotal	
	TOTAL	

Pricing Information

Qty	Standard	Alpha
Single	$18	$21
2-5	$17	$20
6-25	$16	$19
26-50	$15	$18
51-99	$14	$17
100+	$13	$16

Shipping Rates

Total books ordered....add	
Single	$5
2-5	$9
6-10	$14
11-20	$22
21-35	$32
36-50	$45
51+	$60

Orders of 100+ can be personalized with your name, logo and inserts. Call for details and special rates.

Payment/Billing Information

❑ Payment enclosed. Checks payable to *Capitol Advantage, LLC.*
❑ Please bill my credit card: ❑ MasterCard ❑ Visa ❑ AmEx. ❑ Disc.

(Credit card payment processed upon shipment of order).

Card #_____ Exp. Date _____

Name on Card _____

Signature _____

SEND ORDER TO:

Signature (required):_____

Name: _____Title: _____

Organization: _____

Address: _____

City:_____ State:_____ ZIP: _____

Phone:_____E-mail: _____

20121004b

CONGRESS AT YOUR FINGERTIPS
PO Box 309 · Newington, VA 22122
T 703 550 9500 **T** 877 827 3321 toll free **F** 703 550 0406
CongressAtYourFingertips.com

CQ ROLL CALL

CQ Roll Call provides essential intelligence and grassroots advocacy resources to take action.

LEGISLATIVE TRACKING

Whether you track legislation at the federal or state levels, CQ Roll Call's services can be customized to meet your information needs and budget. CQ.com is our signature online legislative tracking service, covering and analyzing every legislative action in Congress. CQ StateTrack provides both legislative tracking and regulatory monitoring in all 50 states and the District of Columbia.

NEWS, INSIGHTS & ANALYSIS

CQ Roll Call delivers the timely news, expert analysis and in-depth information about Congress, politics and government. Without agenda, bias or spin, we make critical information accessible and understandable.

ADVOCACY TOOLS

CQ Roll Call's advocacy solutions deliver the legislative intelligence and innovative tools to help you manage and mobilize your membership with greater efficiency. When it comes to grassroots mobilization, congressional relationship management, and PAC management and compliance, we can help you manage your grassroots program with ease and accuracy.

For more information and product trials,
visit www.cqrollcall.com
or call 800 432 2250, ext. 6599.

Table of Contents

Congressional Office Buildings

U.S. SENATE

Dirksen Senate Office Building (SD)
1st & C Sts., NE
- Opened October 1958
- 712,910 sq. ft.

Hart Senate Office Building (SH)
2nd & C Sts., NE
- Opened November 1982
- 1,019,750 sq. ft.

Russell Senate Office Building (SR)
1st & C Sts., NE
- Opened March 1909
- 658,250 sq. ft.

Senate addresses are Washington, DC 20510

U.S. HOUSE

Cannon House Office Building (CHOB)
1st St. & Independence Ave., SE
- Room numbers are 3 digits
- Opened January 1908
- 671,921 sq. ft.

Longworth House Office Building (LHOB)
Independence & New Jersey Aves., SE
- Room numbers are 4 digits and begin with 1
- Opened April 1933
- 599,675 sq. ft.

Rayburn House Office Building (RHOB)
Independence Ave. & S. Capitol St., SW
- Room numbers are 4 digits and begin with 2
- Opened February 1965
- 2,375,000 sq. ft.

House addresses are Washington, DC 20515

OTHER BUILDINGS
Ford House Office Building (FHOB) - 300 D St., SW
U.S. Capitol (H- or S-)
U.S. Capitol Visitor Center (CVC)

Photos Courtesy of the Architect of the Capitol

Key Telephone Numbers

US Capitol Switchboard	202-224-3121
Architect of the Capitol	202-228-1793
Capitol Visitor Center	202-226-8000
Congressional Budget Office	202-226-2600
Congressional Record Index (GPO)	202-512-0275
Congressional Research Service	202-707-5700
Federal Register	202-741-6000
Library of Congress	202-707-5000
Congressional Accessibility Services	202-224-4048
House Bill Status	202-225-1772
Senate Bill Records	202-224-2120

Key Legislative Websites

Currently on the House Floor .... clerk.house.gov/floorsummary/floor.html

US Senate Calendar of Business .... www.senate.gov/floor/index.htm

Congress.gov .... www.congress.gov

Key Media Websites

ABC News	abcnews.go.com
CBS News	www.cbsnews.com
Congressional Quarterly	www.cq.com
CNN	www.cnn.com
C-SPAN	www.c-span.org
FOX News Channel	www.foxnews.com
The Hill	thehill.com
Los Angeles Times	www.latimes.com
MSNBC	www.msnbc.com
NBC News	nbcnews.com
The New York Times	www.nytimes.com
Politico	www.politico.com
Roll Call	www.rollcall.com
USA TODAY	www.usatoday.com
The Wall Street Journal	online.wsj.com
The Washington Examiner	washingtonexaminer.com
The Washington Post	www.washingtonpost.com
The Washington Times	www.washingtontimes.com

Party Information

Democratic National Committee 202-863-8000
www.democrats.org

Democratic Congressional Campaign Committee 202-863-1500
www.dccc.org

Democratic Senatorial Campaign Committee 202-224-2447
www.dscc.org

Democratic Governors Association 202-772-5600
www.democraticgovernors.org

Republican National Committee 202-863-8500
www.gop.com

National Republican Congressional Committee 202-479-7000
www.nrcc.org

National Republican Senatorial Committee 202-675-6000
www.nrsc.org

Republican Governors Association 202-662-4140
www.rga.org

Information in directory updated to March 3, 2017.

© Copyright 2017 **CQ-Roll Call, Inc.**

PO Box 309, Newington, VA 22122, 703-550-9500

The White House

1600 Pennsylvania Ave., NW • Washington, DC 20500
www.whitehouse.gov

President Donald J. Trump   **456-1414**

Bio: b. 6/14/46, New York, NY; BS Univ. of PA, 1968;
Businessman; Presbyterian

Chief of Staff to the President –
   Reince Priebus   456-1414

Vice President Mike Pence   **456-9000**

Bio: b. 6/7/59, Columbus, IN; JD Univ. of IN, 1986;
Radio Talk Show Host; Christian

Chief of Staff to the Vice President –
   Josh Pitcock   456-9000
Press Secretary to the Vice President –
   Marc Lotter   456-5249

First Lady Melania Trump   **456-7064**

Bio: b. 4/26/70, Novo Mesto, Yugoslavia; Attended
Univ. of Ljubljana; Model; Christian

Chief of Staff to the First Lady –
   Lindsay Reynolds   456-7064
Press Secretary to the First Lady – Vacant   456-6313

EXECUTIVE OFFICES OF THE PRESIDENT

Cabinet Secretary-Bill McGinley...456-2572

Acting Communications Director-Sean Spicer 456-2580

Counselor to the President-Kellyanne Conway.............................456-1414

White House Counsel-Don McGahn 456-2632

Domestic Policy Council-Andrew Bremberg..................................456-5594

*Environmental Protection Agency-Scott Pruitt 564-4700

Intergovernmental Affairs-Rick Dearborn 456-1414

Legislative Affairs-Marc Short...456-2230

*Management and Budget-Mick Mulvaney 395-3080

Acting National Drug Control Policy-Kemp Chester......................395-6700

National Economic Council-Gary Cohn 456-1337

National Intelligence Director-Dan Coats# 703-733-8600

National Security Advisor-H.R. McMaster.....................................456-9491

Presidential Personnel-John DeStefano 456-9713

Press Secretary-Sean Spicer 456-2673

Public Engagement-Vacant 456-1414

Scheduling and Advance-George Gigicos.....................................456-5325

Senior Advisor to the President for Policy-Stephen Miller...............456-1414

Senior Advisor to the President-Jared Kushner.............................456-1414

Senior Counselor to the President-Steve Bannon..........................456-1414

*U.S. Ambassador to the UN-Nikki R. Haley 212-415-4404

*U.S. Trade Representative-Robert Lighthizer# 395-6890

*CABINET RANK

Nomination still pending before the Senate as of press time.

Area code for all numbers is 202 unless otherwise specified

The Cabinet

Department of Agriculture (USDA) **202-720-3631**

1400 Independence Ave., SW   www.usda.gov
Washington, DC 20250

Secretary Sonny Perdue#

Bio: b. 6/20/1946; Perry, GA; Baptist; DVM Univ. of GA, 1971; USAF, 1971-74; Fertilizer and Grain Business Owner; Veterinarian; m. Mary

Director of Communications—Vacant 202-720-4623

Department of Commerce (DOC) **202-482-2112**

1401 Constitution Ave., NW   www.commerce.gov
Washington, DC 20230

Secretary Wilbur Ross

Bio: b. 11/28/37; Weehawken, NJ; Unspecifed; MA Harvard Univ., 1961; Private Equity Firm Founder; Investment Banker; m. Hilary

Dep. Director of Public Affairs—
Areaka Faye-McFadden 202-482-4883

Department of Defense (DOD) **703-692-7100**

1400 Defense Pentagon   www.defense.gov
Washington, DC 20301

Secretary James Mattis

Bio: b. 9/8/50; Pullman, WA; Unspecifed; BA Central WA Univ., 1971; USMC, 1969-2013; Marine Corps Officer; single

Assistant Secretary for Public Affairs—Vacant 703-697-9312

Department of Education (ED) **202-401-3000**

400 Maryland Ave., SW   www.ed.gov
Washington, DC 20202

Secretary Betsy DeVos

Bio: b. 1/8/1958; Holland, MI; Non-denominational Christian; BA Calvin College, 1979; Education Policy Activist; Investment Firm Chair; m. Dick

Assistant Secretary for Communications and Outreach—
Vacant.. 202-401-2000

Department of Energy (DOE) **202-586-5000**

1000 Independence Ave., SW   www.energy.gov
Washington, DC 20585

Secretary Rick Perry

Bio: b. 3/4/1950; Paint Creek, TX; Methodist; BS TX A&M Univ., 1972; USAF, 1972-77; Farmer; Rancher; m. Anita

Director of Public Affairs—Vacant 202-586-4940

Nomination still pending before the Senate as of press time.

The Cabinet (cont'd)

Department of Health and Human Services (HHS) 202-690-7000

200 Independence Ave., SW   www.hhs.gov
Washington, DC 20201

Secretary Tom Price

Bio: b. 10/8/54 Lansing, MI; Presbyterian; MD Univ.
of MI, 1979; Surgeon; m. Elizabeth

Dep. Assistant Secretary for Public Affairs—Bill Hall 202-690-7850

Department of Homeland Security (DHS) 202-282-8000

Nebraska Ave. Center, NW   www.dhs.gov
Washington, DC 20528

Secretary John F. Kelly

Bio: b. 5/11/50; Boston, MA; Roman Catholc; BA Univ.
of MA, Boston, 1979; USMC, 1970-72 and 1976-2016;
USMCR, 1972-76; Marine Corps Officer; m. Karen

Assistant Secretary for Public Affairs—Vacant 202-282-8010

**Department of Housing and
  Urban Development (HUD) 202-708-0417**

451 7th St., SW   www.hud.gov
Washington, DC 20410

Secretary Ben Carson

Bio: b. 9/18/51; Detroit, MI; Seventh Day Adventist;
MD Univ. of MI, 1977; Physician; Public Speaker;
m. Candy

Gen. Dep. Assistant Secretary for Public Affairs—
  Jereon Brown 202-708-0980

Department of the Interior (DOI) 202-208-7351

1849 C St., NW   www.doi.gov
Washington, DC 20240

Secretary Ryan Zinke

Bio: b. 11/1/61 Bozeman, MT; Lutheran - Missouri
Synod; MS Univ. of San Diego, 2003; USN, 1985-
2008; Navy Officer, Technology Consulting Company
Owner; m. Lolita

Director of Communications—Vacant 202-208-6416

Department of Justice (DOJ) 202-514-2001

950 Pennsylvania Ave., NW   www.justice.gov
Washington, DC 20530

Attorney General Jeff Sessions

Bio: b. 12/24/46 Hybart, AL; Methodist; JD Univ. of
AL, 1973; USAR, 1973-86; Attorney; m. Mary

Acting Director, Office of Public Affairs—Peter Carr 202-514-2007

Nomination still pending before the Senate as of press time.

The Cabinet (cont'd)

Department of Labor (DOL) **202-693-6000**

200 Constitution Ave., NW   www.dol.gov
Washington, DC 20210

Secretary R. Alexander Acosta#

Bio: b. 1/16/69 Miami, FL; JD Harvard Univ.; Law
School Dean; Attorney; Investment Bank Associate;
m. Jan

Dep. Assistant Secretary, Office of Public Affairs—
Stephen Barr 202-693-4676

Department of State (DOS) **202-647-5291**

2201 C St., NW   www.state.gov
Washington, DC 20520

Secretary Rex Tillerson

Bio: b. 5/23/52; Wichita Falls, TX; Christian; BS Univ.
of TX, 1975; Oil Company CEO; Oil Production
Engineer; m. Ronda St. Clair

Acting Assistant Secretary for Public Affairs—
Susan Stevenson..202-647-6607

Department of Transportation (DOT) **202-366-4000**

1200 New Jersey Ave., SE   www.dot.gov
Washington, DC 20590

Secretary Elaine Chao

Bio: b. 3/26/53; Taipei, Taiwan; Non-denominational
Christian; MBA Harvard Univ., 1979; United Way
President, Banker, Transportation Dept. Official; m.
Mitch McConnell

Director of Public Affairs—Vacant 202-366-4570

Department of the Treasury (TREAS) **202-622-2000**

1500 Pennsylvania Ave., NW   www.treasury.gov
Washington, DC 20220

Secretary Steven Mnuchin

Bio: b. 12/21/62; New York, NY; Jewish; BA Yale
Univ., 1985; Movie Producer; Hedge Fund Manager;
Investment Banker; eng.

Assistant Secretary, Public Affairs—Vacant................. 202-622-2910

Department of Veterans Affairs (VA) **202-461-4800**

810 Vermont Ave., NW   www.va.gov
Washington, DC 20420

Secretary David Shulkin

Bio: b. 6/22/1959; Bala Cynwyd, PA; Jewish; MD,
Medical College of PA, 1986; Hospital System President; Physician; m. Merle Bari

Assistant Secretary for Public Affairs—Vacant 202-461-7500

Nomination still pending before the Senate as of press time.

Selected Agencies

Alcohol, Tobacco, Firearms and Explosives, ... **202-648-7777**
Bureau of (DOJ)
99 New York Ave. NE, Washington, DC 20226   www.atf.gov

Census, Bureau of the (DOC) **301-763-4636**
4600 Silver Hill Rd., Suitland, MD 20746   www.census.gov

Centers for Disease Control and Prevention (HHS) **404-639-3311**
1600 Clifton Rd., Atlanta, GA 30333   www.cdc.gov

Centers for Medicare and Medicaid Services (HHS) **410-786-3000**
7500 Security Blvd., Baltimore, MD 21244   www.cms.gov

Central Intelligence Agency **703-482-0623**
1000 Colonial Farm Rd., McLean, VA 22101   www.cia.gov

Consumer Product Safety Commission **301-504-7923**
4330 East-West Hwy., Bethesda, MD 20814   www.cpsc.gov

Customs and Border Protection, Bureau of (DHS) **877-227-5511**
1300 Pennsylvania Ave., NW, Washington, DC 20229   www.cbp.gov

Defense Advanced Research Projects Agency (DOD) **703-526-6630**
675 North Randolph St., Arlington, VA 22203   www.darpa.mil

Drug Enforcement Administration (DOJ) **202-307-1000**
600 Army Navy Dr., Arlington, VA 22202   www.dea.gov

Environmental Protection Agency **202-272-0167**
1200 Pennsylvania Ave., NW, Washington, DC 20004   www.epa.gov

Equal Employment Opportunity Commission **202-663-4900**
131 M St., NE, Washington, DC 20507   www.eeoc.gov

Export-Import Bank of the United States **202-565-3946**
811 Vermont Ave., NW, Washington, DC 20571   www.exim.gov

Farm Credit Administration **703-883-4056**
1501 Farm Credit Dr., McLean, VA 22102   www.fca.gov

Federal Aviation Administration (DOT) **866-835-5322**
800 Independence Ave., SW, Washington, DC 20591   www.faa.gov

Federal Bureau of Investigation (DOJ) **202-324-3000**
935 Pennsylvania Ave., NW, Washington, DC 20535   www.fbi.gov

Federal Communications Commission **888-225-5322**
445 12th St., SW, Washington, DC 20554   www.fcc.gov

Federal Deposit Insurance Corporation **877-275-3342**
550 17th St., NW, Washington, DC 20429   www.fdic.gov

Federal Election Commission **202-694-1000**
999 E St., NW, Washington, DC 20463   www.fec.gov

Federal Emergency Management Agency (DHS) **202-646-2500**
500 C St., SW, Washington, DC 20472   www.fema.gov

Federal Energy Regulatory Commission (DOE) **202-502-6088**
888 First St., NE, Washington, DC 20426   www.ferc.gov

Federal Highway Administration (DOT) **202-366-4000**
1200 New Jersey Ave., SE, Washington, DC 20590   www.fhwa.dot.gov

Federal Railroad Administration (DOT) **202-493-6024**
1200 New Jersey Ave., SE, Washington, DC 20590   www.fra.dot.gov

Federal Reserve System **202-452-3000**
20th St. & Constitution Ave., NW, Washington, DC 20551   federalreserve.gov

Federal Student Aid, Office of (ED) **319-337-5665**
830 First St., NE, Washington, DC 20202   www.studentaid.ed.gov

Federal Trade Commission **202-326-2222**
600 Pennsylvania Ave., NW, Washington, DC 20580   www.ftc.gov

Federal Transit Administration (DOT) **202-366-4000**
1200 New Jersey Ave., SE, Washington, DC 20590   www.fta.dot.gov

Fish and Wildlife Service (DOI) **800-344-9453**
1849 C St., NW, Washington, DC 20240   www.fws.gov

Food and Drug Administration (HHS) **888-463-6332**
10903 New Hampshire Ave., Silver Spring, MD 20993   www.fda.gov

Forest Service (USDA) **202-205-8333**
1400 Independence Ave., SW, Washington, DC 20250   www.fs.fed.us

General Services Administration 202-501-0800
1800 F St., Washington, DC 20405   www.gsa.gov

Government Accountability Office 202-512-3000
441 G St., NW, Washington, DC 20548   www.gao.gov

Government Printing Office 202-512-1800
732 N. Capitol St., NW, Washington, DC 20401   www.gpo.gov

Internal Revenue Service (TREAS) 202-622-9511
1111 Constitution Ave., NW, Washington, DC 20224   www.irs.gov

International Monetary Fund 202-623-7000
700 19th St., NW, Washington, DC 20431   www.imf.org

Land Management, Bureau of (DOI) 202-208-3801
1849 C St., NW, Washington, DC 20240   www.blm.gov

National Aeronautics and Space Administration 202-358-0000
300 E St., SW, Washington, DC 20546   www.nasa.gov

National Endowment for the Humanities 202-606-8400
400 7th St., SW, Washington, DC 20506   www.neh.gov

National Endowment for the Arts 202-682-5400
400 7th St., SW, Washington, DC 20506   www.arts.gov

National Highway Traffic Safety Administration (DOT) 888-327-4236
1200 New Jersey Ave., SE, Washington, DC 20590   www.nhtsa.gov

National Institute of Standards and Technology (DOC) 301-975-6478
100 Bureau Dr., Gaithersburg, MD 20899   www.nist.gov

National Institutes of Health (HHS) 301-496-4000
9000 Rockville Pike, Bethesda, MD 20892   www.nih.gov

National Oceanic and Atmospheric 202-482-6090
Administration (DOC)
1401 Constitution Ave., NW, Washington, DC 20230   www.noaa.gov

National Park Service (DOI) 202-208-3818
1849 C St., NW, Washington, DC 20240-0001   www.nps.gov

National Science Foundation 703-292-5111
4201 Wilson Blvd., Arlington, VA 22230   www.nsf.gov

National Telecommunications and Information 202-482-2000
Administration (DOC)
1401 Constitution Ave., NW, Washington, DC 20230   www.ntia.doc.gov

Occupational Safety and Health 202-693-2000
Administration (DOL)
200 Constitution Ave., NW, Washington, DC 20210   www.osha.gov

Pension Benefit Guaranty Corporation 202-326-4000
1200 K St., NW, Washington, DC 20005-4026   www.pbgc.gov

Personnel Management, Office of 202-606-1800
1900 E. St., NW, Washington, DC 20415   www.opm.gov

Securities and Exchange Commission 202-942-8088
100 F St., NE, Washington, DC 20549   www.sec.gov

Small Business Administration 800-827-5722
409 3rd St., SW, Washington, DC 20416   www.sba.gov

Smithsonian Institution 202-633-1000
1000 Jefferson Dr., SW, Washington, DC 20560   www.si.edu

Social Security Administration 800-772-1213
6401 Security Blvd., Baltimore, MD 21235   www.ssa.gov

Surgeon General, Office of the (HHS) 240-276-8853
1101 Wooton Pkwy., Rockville, MD 20852   www.surgeongeneral.gov

U.S. Agency for International Development 202-712-4810
1300 Pennsylvania Ave., NW, Washington, DC 20523   www.usaid.gov

U.S. Army Corps of Engineers (DOD) 202-761-0011
441 G St., NW, Washington, DC 20314   www.usace.army.mil

U.S. Postal Service 800-275-8777
475 L'Enfant Plz., SW, Washington, DC 20260   www.usps.gov

The Supreme Court

United States Supreme Court Building
1 First St., NE
Washington, DC 20543
202-479-3000
www.supremecourt.gov

Chief Justice

John G. Roberts
Nominated Chief Justice by President G.W. Bush, 2005
b. 1/27/55 Buffalo, NY; JD Harvard Univ., 1979; m. Jane

Associate Justices

Anthony M. Kennedy
Nominated by President Reagan, 1988
b. 7/23/36 Sacramento, CA; LLB Harvard Univ., 1961;
CAARNG, 1961; m. Mary

Clarence Thomas
Nominated by President G.H.W. Bush, 1991
b. 6/23/48 Pin Point, GA; JD Yale Univ., 1974; m. Virginia

Ruth Bader Ginsburg
Nominated by President Clinton, 1993
b. 3/15/33 Brooklyn, NY; LLB Columbia Univ., 1959;
wid.

Stephen G. Breyer
Nominated by President Clinton, 1994
b. 8/15/38 San Francisco, CA; LLB Harvard Univ., 1964;
m. Joanna

Samuel A. Alito
Nominated by President G.W. Bush, 2005
b. 4/1/50 Trenton, NJ; JD Yale Univ., 1975; USAR, 1972-
80; m. Martha-Ann

Sonia Sotomayor
Nominated by President Obama, 2009
b. 6/25/54 Bronx, NY; JD Yale Univ., 1979; single

Elena Kagan
Nominated by President Obama, 2010
b. 4/28/60 New York, NY; JD Harvard Univ., 1986; single

Neil Gorsuch#
Nominated by President Trump, 2017
b. 8/29/67 Denver, CO; JD Harvard Univ., 1991; m.
Louise

Nomination still pending before the Senate as of press time.

US Senate

www.senate.gov

Leadership

President .... Mike Pence, Vice President	
Director for Legis. Affairs	Jonathan Hiler
Office: S-212	Phone: 224-2424
President Pro Tempore .... Orrin G. Hatch (R-UT)	
Office: S-125	Phone: 224-9400
Majority Leader .... Mitch McConnell (R-KY)	
Chief of Staff	Sharon Soderstrom
Office: S-230	Phone: 224-3135
Majority Whip .... John Cornyn (R-TX)	
Chief of Staff	Monica Popp
Office: S-208	Phone: 224-2708
Republican Policy Committee .... John Barrasso (R-WY)	
Chair	
Staff Director	Dan Kunsman
Office: SR-347	Phone: 224-2946
Republican Conference Chair .... John Thune (R-SD)	
Staff Director	Brendon Plack
Office: SH-405	Phone: 224-2764
Minority Leader .... Charles E. Schumer (D-NY)	
Chief of Staff	Mike Lynch
Office: S-221	Phone: 224-2158
Minority Whip .... Richard J. Durbin (D-IL)	
Chief of Staff	Pat Souders
Office: S-321	Phone: 224-9447
Assistant Leader .... Patty Murray (D-WA)	
Chief of Staff	Mike Spahn
Office: S-312	Phone: 224-0238
Democratic Policy Committee Chair ..... Debbie Stabenow (D-MI)	
Chief of Staff	Matt VanKuiken
Office: SH-731	Phone: 224-4822

Officers

Secretary of the Senate
Julie E. Adams
S-312, 224-3622

Sergeant at Arms
Frank J. Larkin
S-151, 224-2341

Majority Secretary
Laura Dove
S-337, 224-3835

Minority Secretary
Gary Myrick
S-309, 224-3735

Parliamentarian
Elizabeth MacDonough
S-132, 224-6128

Chaplain
Dr. Barry C. Black
S-332, 224-2510

Senate Historian
Betty K. Koed
SH-201, 224-6900

Key Offices

Document Room SH-B04/224-7701
Cloak Room .... (D) 224-4691, (R) 224-6191
Floor Information .... (D) 224-8541, (R) 224-8601
Press Gallery S-316/224-0241
Postal Operations, Senate 224-5353

Area code for all numbers is 202

Senate Re-election Schedule

Up for Re-election in 2018

Democrats (23)
Baldwin, Tammy (WI)
Brown, Sherrod (OH)
Cantwell, Maria (WA)
Cardin, Benjamin L. (MD)
Carper, Thomas R. (DE)
Casey, Bob (PA)
Donnelly, Joe (IN)
Feinstein, Dianne (CA)
Gillibrand, Kirsten (NY)
Heinrich, Martin (NM)
Heitkamp, Heidi (ND)
Hirono, Mazie K. (HI)
Kaine, Tim (VA)
Klobuchar, Amy (MN)
Manchin, Joe, III (WV)
McCaskill, Claire (MO)
Menendez, Robert (NJ)
Murphy, Christopher S. (CT)
Nelson, Bill (FL)
Stabenow, Debbie (MI)
Tester, Jon (MT)
Warren, Elizabeth (MA)
Whitehouse, Sheldon (RI)

Independents (2)
King, Angus (ME)
Sanders, Bernard (VT)

Republicans (9)
Barrasso, John (WY)
Corker, Bob (TN)
Cruz, Ted (TX)
Fischer, Deb (NE)
Flake, Jeff (AZ)
Hatch, Orrin G. (UT)
Heller, Dean (NV)
Strange, Luther (AL)*
Wicker, Roger (MS)

Up for Re-election in 2020

Democrats (11)
Booker, Cory (NJ)
Coons, Chris (DE)
Durbin, Richard J. (IL)
Franken, Al (MN)
Markey, Edward J. (MA)
Merkley, Jeff (OR)
Peters, Gary (MI)
Reed, Jack (RI)
Shaheen, Jeanne (NH)
Udall, Tom (NM)
Warner, Mark (VA)

Republicans (21)
Alexander, Lamar (TN)
Capito, Shelley Moore (WV)
Cassidy, Bill (LA)
Cochran, Thad (MS)
Collins, Susan (ME)
Cornyn, John (TX)
Cotton, Tom (AR)
Daines, Steve (MT)
Enzi, Michael B. (WY)
Ernst, Joni (IA)
Gardner, Cory (CO)
Graham, Lindsey (SC)
Inhofe, James M. (OK)
McConnell, Mitch (KY)
Perdue, David (GA)
Risch, Jim (ID)
Roberts, Pat (KS)
Rounds, Michael (SD)
Sasse, Ben (NE)
Sullivan, Dan (AK)
Tillis, Thom (NC)

Up for Re-election in 2022

Democrats (10)
Bennet, Michael (CO)
Blumenthal, Richard (CT)
Cortez Masto, Catherine (NV)
Duckworth, Tammy (IL)
Harris, Kamala (CA)
Hassan, Maggie (NH)
Leahy, Patrick J. (VT)
Murray, Patty (WA)
Schatz, Brian (HI)
Schumer, Charles E. (NY)
Van Hollen, Chris (MD)
Wyden, Ron (OR)

Republicans (24)
Blunt, Roy (MO)
Boozman, John (AR)
Burr, Richard M. (NC)
Crapo, Michael D. (ID)
Grassley, Charles E. (IA)
Hoeven, John (ND)
Isakson, Johnny (GA)
Johnson, Ron (WI)
Kennedy, John N. (LA)
Lankford, James (OK)
Lee, Mike (UT)
McCain, John (AZ)
Moran, Jerry (KS)
Murkowski, Lisa (AK)
Paul, Rand (KY)
Portman, Rob (OH)
Rubio, Marco (FL)
Scott, Tim (SC)
Shelby, Richard C. (AL)
Thune, John (SD)
Toomey, Patrick J. (PA)
Young, Todd (IN)

*Special election

Members of the Senate

Party Ratio: 52 Republicans/46 Democrats/2 Independents

	Seniority in Party	Office	Phone (202)	Page
Alexander, Lamar (R-TN)	14	SD-455	224-4944	120
Baldwin, Tammy (D-WI)	31	SH-709	224-5653	138
Barrasso, John (R-WY)	20	SD-307	224-6441	140
Bennet, Michael (D-CO)	24	SR-261	224-5852	42
Blumenthal, Richard (D-CT)	29	SH-706	224-2823	44
Blunt, Roy (R-MO)	23	SR-260	224-5721	84
Booker, Cory (D-NJ)	40	SD-359	224-3224	91
Boozman, John (R-AR)	26	SH-141	224-4843	30
Brown, Sherrod (D-OH)	14	SH-713	224-2315	105
Burr, Richard M. (R-NC)	16	SR-217	224-3154	101
Cantwell, Maria (D-WA)	11	SH-511	224-3441	134
Capito, Shelley Moore (R-WV)	38	SR-172	224-6472	137
Cardin, Benjamin L. (D-MD)	13	SH-509	224-4524	72
Carper, Thomas R. (D-DE)	9	SH-513	224-2441	46
Casey, Bob (D-PA)	15	SR-393	224-6324	112
Cassidy, Bill (R-LA)	39	SH-520	224-5824	69
Cochran, Thad (R-MS)	2	SD-113	224-5054	82
Collins, Susan (R-ME)	9	SD-413	224-2523	71
Coons, Chris (D-DE)	28	SR-127A	224-5042	46
Corker, Bob (R-TN)	19	SD-425	224-3344	120
Cornyn, John (R-TX)	15	SH-517	224-2934	122
Cortez Masto, Catherine (D-NV)	46	SD-B40A	224-3542	89
Cotton, Tom (R-AR)	42	SR-124	224-2353	31
Crapo, Michael D. (R-ID)	11	SD-239	224-6142	56
Cruz, Ted (R-TX)	36	SR-404	224-5922	123
Daines, Steve (R-MT)	43	SH-320	224-2651	86
Donnelly, Joe (D-IN)	32	SH-720	224-4814	61
Duckworth, Tammy (D-IL)	43	SH-524	224-2854	58
Durbin, Richard J. (D-IL)	5	SH-711	224-2152	58
Enzi, Michael B. (R-WY)	10	SR-379A	224-3424	140
Ernst, Joni (R-IA)	47	SR-111	224-3254	64
Feinstein, Dianne (D-CA)	2	SH-331	224-3841	32
Fischer, Deb (R-NE)	37	SR-454	224-6551	87
Flake, Jeff (R-AZ)	35	SR-413	224-4521	28
Franken, Al (D-MN)	26	SH-309	224-5641	80
Gardner, Cory (R-CO)	40	SR-354	224-5941	42
Gillibrand, Kirsten (D-NY)	25	SR-478	224-4451	96
Graham, Lindsey (R-SC)	13	SR-290	224-5972	117
Grassley, Charles E. (R-IA)	3	SH-135	224-3744	64
Harris, Kamala (D-CA)	45	SH-112	224-3553	32
Hassan, Maggie (D-NH)	44	SR-B85	224-3324	90
Hatch, Orrin G. (R-UT)	1	SH-104	224-5251	129
Heinrich, Martin (D-NM)	35	SH-303	224-5521	94
Heitkamp, Heidi (D-ND)	38	SH-516	224-2043	104
Heller, Dean (R-NV)	33	SH-324	224-6244	89
Hirono, Mazie K. (D-HI)	34	SH-370	224-6361	55
Hoeven, John (R-ND)	28	SR-338	224-2551	104
Inhofe, James M. (R-OK)	7	SR-205	224-4721	108
Isakson, Johnny (R-GA)	18	SR-131	224-3643	52
Johnson, Ron (R-WI)	30	SH-328	224-5323	138
Kaine, Tim (D-VA)	36	SR-231	224-4024	132
Kennedy, John N. (R-LA)	51	SR-B11	224-4623	69
King, Angus (I-ME)		SH-133	224-5344	71
Klobuchar, Amy (D-MN)	17	SH-302	224-3244	80

Members of the Senate

	Seniority in Party	Office	Phone (202)	Page
Lankford, James (R-OK)	41	SH-316	224-5754	108
Leahy, Patrick J. (D-VT)	1	SR-437	224-4242	131
Lee, Mike (R-UT)	32	SR-361A	224-5444	129
Manchin, Joe III (D-WV)	27	SH-306	224-3954	137
Markey, Edward J. (D-MA)	39	SD-255	224-2742	75
McCain, John (R-AZ)	6	SR-218	224-2235	28
McCaskill, Claire (D-MO)	16	SH-503	224-6154	84
McConnell, Mitch (R-KY)	4	SR-317	224-2541	67
Menendez, Robert (D-NJ)	12	SH-528	224-4744	91
Merkley, Jeff (D-OR)	23	SH-313	224-3753	110
Moran, Jerry (R-KS)	24	SD-521	224-6521	66
Murkowski, Lisa (R-AK)	12	SH-522	224-6665	27
Murphy, Christopher S. (D-CT)	33	SH-136	224-4041	44
Murray, Patty (D-WA)	3	SR-154	224-2621	134
Nelson, Bill (D-FL)	8	SH-716	224-5274	47
Paul, Rand (R-KY)	31	SR-167	224-4343	67
Perdue, David (R-GA)	45	SR-383	224-3521	52
Peters, Gary (D-MI)	41	SH-724	224-6221	77
Portman, Rob (R-OH)	25	SR-448	224-3353	105
Reed, Jack (D-RI)	6	SH-728	224-4642	116
Risch, Jim (R-ID)	22	SR-483	224-2752	57
Roberts, Pat (R-KS)	8	SH-109	224-4774	65
Rounds, Mike (R-SD)	44	SH-502	224-5842	119
Rubio, Marco (R-FL)	29	SR-284	224-3041	47
Sanders, Bernie (I-VT)		SD-332	224-5141	131
Sasse, Ben (R-NE)	48	SR-386A	224-4224	87
Schatz, Brian (D-HI)	30	SH-722	224-3934	55
Schumer, Charles E. (D-NY)	7	SH-322	224-6542	95
Scott, Tim (R-SC)	34	SH-717	224-6121	117
Shaheen, Jeanne (D-NH)	21	SH-506	224-2841	90
Shelby, Richard C. (R-AL)	5	SR-304	224-5744	25
Stabenow, Debbie (D-MI)	10	SH-731	224-4822	77
Strange, Luther (R-AL)	52	SD-G12	224-4124	25
Sullivan, Dan (R-AK)	49	SH-702	224-3004	27
Tester, Jon (D-MT)	19	SH-311	224-2644	86
Thune, John (R-SD)	17	SD-511	224-2321	119
Tillis, Thom (R-NC)	46	SD-185	224-6342	101
Toomey, Patrick J. (R-PA)	27	SR-248	224-4254	112
Udall, Tom (D-NM)	20	SH-531	224-6621	94
Van Hollen, Chris (D-MD)	42	SD-B40C	224-4654	73
Warner, Mark (D-VA)	22	SR-475	224-2023	132
Warren, Elizabeth (D-MA)	37	SH-317	224-4543	75
Whitehouse, Sheldon (D-RI)	18	SH-530	224-2921	116
Wicker, Roger (R-MS)	21	SD-555	224-6253	83
Wyden, Ron (D-OR)	4	SD-221	224-5244	110
Young, Todd (R-IN)	50	SR-B33	224-5623	62

SD .... Dirksen Building .... 1st & C Sts., NE
SH .... Hart Building .... 2nd & C Sts., NE
SR .... Russell Building .... 1st & C Sts., NE

House of Representatives

Leadership

Speaker .... **Paul D. Ryan (R-1st WI)**
Chief of Staff   Jonathan Burks
Office: H-232   Phone: 225-0600

Majority Leader .... **Kevin McCarthy (R-23rd CA)**
Chief of Staff   Barrett Karr
Office: H-107   Phone: 225-4000

Majority Whip .... **Steve Scalise (R-1st LA)**
Chief of Staff   Brett Horton
Office: H-329   Phone: 225-0197

Republican Policy Committee .... **Luke Messer (R-6th IN)**
  Chair
Chief of Staff   Douglas Menorca
Office: 1230 LHOB   Phone: 225-3021

Republican Conference Chair .... **Cathy McMorris Rodgers**
Chief of Staff   **(R-5th WA)**
Office: 202A CHOB   Jeremy Deutsch
                                                  Phone: 225-5107

Minority Leader .... **Nancy Pelosi (D-12th CA)**
Chief of Staff   Nadeam Elshami
Office: H-204   Phone: 225-0100

Minority Whip .... **Steny H. Hoyer (D-5th MD)**
Chief of Staff   Alexis Covey-Brandt
Office: H-148   Phone: 225-3130

Assistant Democratic Leader .... **James E. Clyburn (D-6th SC)**
Chief of Staff   Yelberton Watkins
Office: H-132   Phone: 226-3210

Democratic Caucus Chair .... **Joseph Crowley (D-14th NY)**
Chief of Staff   Kate Keating
Office: 1420 LHOB   Phone: 225-1400

Officers

Clerk of the House   **Inspector General**
Karen L. Haas   Theresa Grafenstine
H-154, 225-7000   386 FHOB, 226-1250

Chief Administrative Officer   **Chaplain**
Philip G. Kiko   Rev. Patrick J. Conroy
HB-30, 225-6969   HB-25, 225-2509

Sergeant at Arms   **House Historian**
Paul D. Irving   Matthew Wasniewski
H-124, 225-2456   B56 CHOB, 226-5525

Parliamentarian
Thomas J. Wickham, Jr.
H-209, 225-7373

Key Offices

Legislative Resource Center 135 CHOB/226-5200
Cloak Room .... (D) 225-7330, (R) 225-7350
Floor Information .... (D) 225-7400, (R) 225-2020
Press Gallery H-315/225-3945
Postal Operations, House 226-3764

Area code for all numbers is 202

Members of the House of Representatives

Party Ratio: 237 Republicans/193 Democrats/5 Vacancies

	Seniority in Party	Office	Phone (202)	Page
Abraham, Ralph (R-5th LA)	169	417	225-8490	70
Adams, Alma (D-12th NC)	155	222	225-1510	103
Aderholt, Robert B. (R-4th AL)	21	235	225-4876	26
Aguilar, Pete (D-31st CA)	157	1223	225-3201	37
Allen, Rick W. (R-12th GA)	170	426	225-2823	54
Amash, Justin (R-3rd MI)	91	114	225-3831	78
Amodei, Mark (R-2nd NV)	136	332	225-6155	89
Arrington, Jodey C. (R-19th TX)	214	1029	225-4005	126
Babin, Brian (R-36th TX)	171	316	225-1555	129
Bacon, Don (R-2nd NE)	215	1516	225-4155	88
Banks, Jim (R-3rd IN)	216	509	225-4436	62
Barletta, Lou (R-11th PA)	92	2049	225-6511	114
Barr, Andy (R-6th KY)	138	1427	225-4706	68
Barragán, Nanette (D-44th CA)	171	1320	225-8220	40
Barton, Joe L. (R-6th TX)	5	2107	225-2002	124
Bass, Karen (D-37th CA)	109	2241	225-7084	38
Beatty, Joyce (D-3rd OH)	121	133	225-4324	105
Bera, Ami (D-7th CA)	122	1431	225-5716	33
Bergman, Jack (R-1st MI)	217	414	225-4735	77
Beyer, Don Jr. (D-8th VA)	158	1119	225-4376	133
Biggs, Andy (R-5th AZ)	218	1626	225-2635	29
Bilirakis, Gus (R-12th FL)	62	2112	225-5755	49
Bishop, Mike (R-8th MI)	172	428	225-4872	79
Bishop, Rob (R-1st UT)	36	123	225-0453	130
Bishop, Sanford D. Jr. (D-2nd GA)	21	2407	225-3631	53
Black, Diane (R-6th TN)	93	1131	225-4231	121
Blackburn, Marsha (R-7th TN)	37	2266	225-2811	121
Blum, Rod (R-1st IA)	173	1108	225-2911	64
Blumenauer, Earl (D-3rd OR)	39	1111	225-4811	111
Blunt Rochester, Lisa (D-At Large DE)	172	1123	225-4165	46
Bonamici, Suzanne (D-1st OR)	115	439	225-0855	110
Bordallo, Madeleine Z. (D-At Large GU)		2441	225-1188	142
Bost, Mike (R-12th IL)	174	1440	225-5661	60
Boyle, Brendan F. (D-13th PA)	159	1133	225-6111	114
Brady, Kevin (R-8th TX)	49	1011	225-4901	124
Brady, Robert A. (D-1st PA)	22	2004	225-4731	112
Brat, Dave (R-7th VA)	168	1628	225-2815	133
Bridenstine, Jim (R-1st OK)	139	216	225-2211	109
Brooks, Mo (R-5th AL)	94	2400	225-4801	26
Brooks, Susan W. (R-5th IN)	140	1030	225-2276	62
Brown, Anthony G. (D-4th MD)	173	1505	225-8699	73
Brownley, Julia (D-26th CA)	123	1019	225-5811	37
Buchanan, Vern (R-16th FL)	63	2104	225-5015	50
Buck, Ken (R-4th CO)	175	1130	225-4676	43
Bucshon, Larry (R-8th IN)	95	1005	225-4636	63
Budd, Ted (R-13th NC)	219	118	225-4531	103
Burgess, Michael C. (R-26th TX)	38	2336	225-7772	127
Bustos, Cheri (D-17th IL)	124	1009	225-5905	61
Butterfield, G.K. (D-1st NC)	68	2080	225-3101	101
Byrne, Bradley (R-1st AL)	167	119	225-4931	25
Calvert, Ken (R-42nd CA)	12	2205	225-1986	39
Capuano, Michael E. (D-7th MA)	50	1414	225-5111	76
Carbajal, Salud (D-24th CA)	174	212	225-3601	36
Cárdenas, Tony (D-29th CA)	125	1510	225-6131	37
Carson, André (D-7th IN)	93	2135	225-4011	63

Rooms with 3 numbers ....CHOB, 1st St. & Independence Ave., SE
Rooms with 4 numbers beginning with 1 ....LHOB, Independence & New Jersey Aves., SE
Rooms with 4 numbers beginning with 2 ...RHOB, Independence Ave. & S. Capitol St., SW

Members of the House of Representatives

	Seniority in Party	Office	Phone (202)	Page
Carter, Earl L. "Buddy" (R-1st GA)	176	432	225-5831	52
Carter, John (R-31st TX)	39	2110	225-3864	128
Cartwright, Matt (D-17th PA)	126	1034	225-5546	115
Castor, Kathy (D-14th FL)	79	2052	225-3376	49
Castro, Joaquin (D-20th TX)	127	1221	225-3236	126
Chabot, Steve (R-1st OH)	26	2371	225-2216	105
Chaffetz, Jason (R-3rd UT)	73	2236	225-7751	130
Cheney, Liz (R-At Large WY)	220	416	225-2311	140
Chu, Judy (D-27th CA)	105	2423	225-5464	37
Cicilline, David (D-1st RI)	110	2244	225-4911	116
Clark, Katherine M. (D-5th MA)	154	1415	225-2836	76
Clarke, Yvette D. (D-9th NY)	80	2058	225-6231	97
Clay, William Lacy (D-1st MO)	56	2428	225-2406	84
Cleaver, Emanuel II (D-5th MO)	69	2335	225-4535	85
Clyburn, James E. (D-6th SC)	22	242	225-3315	118
Coffman, Mike (R-6th CO)	74	2443	225-7882	43
Cohen, Steve (D-9th TN)	81	2404	225-3265	122
Cole, Tom (R-4th OK)	40	2467	225-6165	109
Collins, Chris (R-27th NY)	141	1117	225-5265	100
Collins, Doug (R-9th GA)	142	1504	225-9893	54
Comer, James R. (R-1st KY)	213	1513	225-3115	68
Comstock, Barbara (R-10th VA)	177	229	225-5136	133
Conaway, K. Michael (R-11th TX)	49	2430	225-3605	124
Connolly, Gerald E. (D-11th VA)	97	2238	225-1492	134
Conyers, John Jr. (D-13th MI)	1	2426	225-5126	79
Cook, Paul (R-8th CA)	143	1222	225-5861	34
Cooper, Jim (D-5th TN)	20	1536	225-4311	121
Correa, Lou (D-46th CA)	175	1039	225-2965	40
Costa, Jim (D-16th CA)	70	2081	225-3341	35
Costello, Ryan A. (R-6th PA)	178	326	225-4315	113
Courtney, Joe (D-2nd CT)	82	2348	225-2076	45
Cramer, Kevin (R-At Large ND)	144	1717	225-2611	104
Crawford, Rick (R-1st AR)	96	2422	225-4076	31
Crist, Charlie (D-13th FL)	176	427	225-5961	49
Crowley, Joseph (D-14th NY)	51	1035	225-3965	98
Cuellar, Henry (D-28th TX)	71	2209	225-1640	127
Culberson, John (R-7th TX)	30	2161	225-2571	124
Cummings, Elijah E. (D-7th MD)	38	2163	225-4741	74
Curbelo, Carlos (R-26th FL)	179	1404	225-2778	51
Davidson, Warren (R-8th OH)	212	1004	225-6205	106
Davis, Danny K. (D-7th IL)	40	2159	225-5006	59
Davis, Rodney (R-13th IL)	145	1740	225-2371	60
Davis, Susan A. (D-53rd CA)	57	1214	225-2040	41
DeFazio, Peter A. (D-4th OR)	6	2134	225-6416	111
DeGette, Diana (D-1st CO)	41	2111	225-4431	42
Delaney, John (D-6th MD)	128	1632	225-2721	74
DeLauro, Rosa (D-3rd CT)	16	2413	225-3661	45
DelBene, Suzan (D-1st WA)	116	2442	225-6311	135
Demings, Val B. (D-10th FL)	177	238	225-2176	49
Denham, Jeff (R-10th CA)	97	1730	225-4540	34
Dent, Charlie (R-15th PA)	50	2082	225-6411	115
DeSantis, Ron (R-6th FL)	146	1524	225-2706	48
DeSaulnier, Mark (D-11th CA)	160	115	225-2095	34
DesJarlais, Scott (R-4th TN)	98	2301	225-6831	121
Deutch, Ted (D-22nd FL)	107	2447	225-3001	51
Diaz-Balart, Mario (R-25th FL)	41	440	225-4211	51
Dingell, Debbie (D-12th MI)	161	116	225-4071	79
Doggett, Lloyd (D-35th TX)	34	2307	225-4865	128
Donovan, Dan (R-11th NY)	209	1541	225-3371	97
Doyle, Mike (D-14th PA)	35	239	225-2135	114

Members of the House of Representatives

	Seniority in Party	Office	Phone (202)	Page
Duffy, Sean P. (R-7th WI)	99	2330	225-3365	139
Duncan, Jeff (R-3rd SC)	8	2229	225-5301	118
Duncan, John J. Jr. (R-2nd TN)	100	2207	225-5435	121
Dunn, Neal (R-2nd FL)	221	423	225-5235	47
Ellison, Keith (D-5th MN)	83	2263	225-4755	81
Emmer, Tom (R-6th MN)	180	315	225-2331	81
Engel, Eliot L. (D-16th NY)	11	2462	225-2464	98
Eshoo, Anna G. (D-18th CA)	23	241	225-8104	35
Espaillat, Adriano (D-13th NY)	178	1630	225-4365	98
Esty, Elizabeth (D-5th CT)	129	221	225-4476	45
Evans, Dwight (D-2nd PA)	169	1105	225-4001	112
Farenthold, Blake (R-27th TX)	101	2331	225-7742	127
Faso, John J. (R-19th NY)	222	1616	225-5614	99
Ferguson, Drew (R-3rd GA)	223	1032	225-5901	53
Fitzpatrick, Brian (R-8th PA)	224	514	225-4276	113
Fleischmann, Chuck (R-3rd TN)	102	2410	225-3271	121
Flores, Bill (R-17th TX)	103	2440	225-6105	125
Fortenberry, Jeff (R-1st NE)	51	1514	225-4806	88
Foster, Bill (D-11th IL)	108	1224	225-3515	60
Foxx, Virginia (R-5th NC)	52	2262	225-2071	102
Frankel, Lois (D-21st FL)	130	1037	225-9890	50
Franks, Trent (R-8th AZ)	42	2435	225-4576	30
Frelinghuysen, Rodney (R-11th NJ)	17	2306	225-5034	93
Fudge, Marcia L. (D-11th OH)	95	2344	225-7032	107
Gabbard, Tulsi (D-2nd HI)	131	1433	225-4906	56
Gaetz, Matt (R-1st FL)	225	507	225-4136	47
Gallagher, Mike (R-8th WI)	226	1007	225-5665	139
Gallego, Ruben (D-7th AZ)	162	1218	225-4065	29
Garamendi, John (D-3rd CA)	106	2438	225-1880	33
Garrett, Tom (R-5th VA)	227	415	225-4711	133
Gibbs, Bob (R-7th OH)	104	2446	225-6265	106
Gohmert, Louie (R-1st TX)	53	2243	225-3035	123
Gonzalez, Vicente (D-15th TX)	179	113	225-2531	125
Gonzalez-Colon, Jenniffer (R-At Large PR)		1529	225-2615	143
Goodlatte, Robert W. (R-6th VA)	13	2309	225-5431	133
Gosar, Paul (R-4th AZ)	105	2057	225-2315	29
Gottheimer, Josh (D-5th NJ)	180	213	225-4465	92
Gowdy, Trey (R-4th SC)	106	2418	225-6030	118
Granger, Kay (R-12th TX)	23	1026	225-5071	125
Graves, Garret (R-6th LA)	181	430	225-3901	70
Graves, Sam (R-6th MO)	31	1135	225-7041	85
Graves, Tom (R-14th GA)	88	2078	225-5211	55
Green, Al (D-9th TX)	72	2347	225-7508	124
Green, Gene (D-29th TX)	24	2470	225-1688	127
Griffith, Morgan (R-9th VA)	107	2202	225-3861	133
Grijalva, Raúl M. (D-3rd AZ)	63	1511	225-2435	29
Grothman, Glenn (R-6th WI)	182	1217	225-2476	139
Guthrie, Brett (R-2nd KY)	75	2434	225-3501	68
Gutiérrez, Luis V. (D-4th IL)	25	2408	225-8203	58
Hanabusa, Colleen (D-1st HI)	119	422	225-2726	56
Harper, Gregg (R-3rd MS)	76	2227	225-5031	83
Harris, Andy (R-1st MD)	108	1533	225-5311	73
Hartzler, Vicky (R-4th MO)	109	2235	225-2876	85

Rooms with 3 numbers ....CHOB, 1st St. & Independence Ave., SE
Rooms with 4 numbers beginning with 1 .... LHOB, Independence & New Jersey Aves., SE
Rooms with 4 numbers beginning with 2 .... RHOB, Independence Ave. & S. Capitol St., SW

Members of the House of Representatives

	Seniority in Party	Office	Phone (202)	Page
Hastings, Alcee L. (D-20th FL)	26	2353	225-1313	50
Heck, Denny (D-10th WA)	132	425	225-9740	136
Hensarling, Jeb (R-5th TX)	43	2228	225-3484	123
Herrera Beutler, Jaime (R-3rd WA)	110	1107	225-3536	135
Hice, Jody B. (R-10th GA)	183	324	225-4101	54
Higgins, Brian (D-26th NY)	73	2459	225-3306	100
Higgins, Clay (R-3rd LA)	228	1711	225-2031	70
Hill, French (R-2nd AR)	184	1229	225-2506	31
Himes, Jim (D-4th CT)	98	1227	225-5541	45
Holding, George (R-2nd NC)	147	1110	225-3032	101
Hollingsworth, Trey (R-9th IN)	229	1641	225-5315	63
Hoyer, Steny H. (D-5th MD)	2	1705	225-4131	73
Hudson, Richard (R-8th NC)	148	429	225-3715	102
Huffman, Jared (D-2nd CA)	133	1406	225-5161	33
Huizenga, Bill (R-2nd MI)	111	2232	225-4401	78
Hultgren, Randy (R-14th IL)	112	2455	225-2976	60
Hunter, Duncan (R-50th CA)	77	2429	225-5672	41
Hurd, Will (R-23rd TX)	185	317	225-4511	126
Issa, Darrell (R-49th CA)	32	2269	225-3906	40
Jackson Lee, Sheila (D-18th TX)	36	2187	225-3816	126
Jayapal, Pramila (D-7th WA)	181	319	225-3106	136
Jeffries, Hakeem (D-8th NY)	134	1607	225-5936	97
Jenkins, Evan H. (R-3rd WV)	186	1609	225-3452	137
Jenkins, Lynn (R-2nd KS)	78	1526	225-6601	66
Johnson, Bill (R-6th OH)	113	1710	225-5705	106
Johnson, Eddie Bernice (D-30th TX)	27	2468	225-8885	128
Johnson, Hank (D-4th GA)	84	2240	225-1605	53
Johnson, Mike (R-4th LA)	230	327	225-2777	70
Johnson, Sam (R-3rd TX)	11	2304	225-4201	123
Jones, Walter B. (R-3rd NC)	18	2333	225-3415	101
Jordan, Jim (R-4th OH)	64	2056	225-2676	106
Joyce, David (R-14th OH)	149	1124	225-5731	107
Kaptur, Marcy (D-9th OH)	3	2186	225-4146	106
Katko, John (R-24th NY)	187	1620	225-3701	100
Keating, William (D-9th MA)	111	2351	225-3111	76
Kelly, Mike (R-3rd PA)	114	1707	225-5406	113
Kelly, Robin (D-2nd IL)	153	1239	225-0773	58
Kelly, Trent (R-1st MS)	210	1721	225-4306	83
Kennedy, Joseph P. III (D-4th MA)	135	434	225-5931	75
Khanna, Ro (D-17th CA)	182	513	225-2631	35
Kihuen, Ruben (D-4th NV)	183	313	225-9894	89
Kildee, Dan (D-5th MI)	136	227	225-3611	78
Kilmer, Derek (D-6th WA)	137	1520	225-5916	135
Kind, Ron (D-3rd WI)	42	1502	225-5506	139
King, Peter T. (R-2nd NY)	14	339	225-7896	96
King, Steve (R-4th IA)	44	2210	225-4426	65
Kinzinger, Adam (R-16th IL)	115	2245	225-3635	60
Knight, Steve (R-25th CA)	188	1023	225-1956	36
Krishnamoorthi, Raja (D-8th IL)	184	515	225-3711	59
Kuster, Ann McLane (D-2nd NH)	138	137	225-5206	91
Kustoff, David (R-8th TN)	231	508	225-4714	122
Labrador, Raúl R. (R-1st ID)	116	1523	225-6611	57
LaHood, Darin (R-18th IL)	211	1424	225-6201	61
LaMalfa, Doug (R-1st CA)	150	322	225-3076	32
Lamborn, Doug (R-5th CO)	65	2402	225-4422	43
Lance, Leonard (R-7th NJ)	79	2352	225-5361	93
Langevin, Jim (D-2nd RI)	58	2077	225-2735	116
Larsen, Rick (D-2nd WA)	59	2113	225-2605	135
Larson, John B. (D-1st CT)	52	1501	225-2265	44

Members of the House of Representatives

	Seniority in Party	Office	Phone (202)	Page
Latta, Bob (R-5th OH)	69	2448	225-6405	106
Lawrence, Brenda (D-14th MI)	163	1213	225-5802	80
Lawson, Al (D-5th FL)	185	1337	225-0123	48
Lee, Barbara (D-13th CA)	48	2267	225-2661	34
Levin, Sander M. (D-9th MI)	4	1236	225-4961	79
Lewis, Jason (R-2nd MN)	7	418	225-2271	81
Lewis, John (D-5th GA)	232	343	225-3801	53
Lieu, Ted (D-33rd CA)	164	236	225-3976	38
Lipinski, Daniel (D-3rd IL)	74	2346	225-5701	58
LoBiondo, Frank A. (R-2nd NJ)	19	2427	225-6572	92
Loebsack, Dave (D-2nd IA)	85	1527	225-6576	64
Lofgren, Zoe (D-19th CA)	37	1401	225-3072	35
Long, Billy (R-7th MO)	117	2454	225-6536	85
Loudermilk, Barry (R-11th GA)	189	329	225-2931	54
Love, Mia (R-4th UT)	190	217	225-3011	130
Lowenthal, Alan (D-47th CA)	139	125	225-7924	40
Lowey, Nita M. (D-17th NY)	12	2365	225-6506	98
Lucas, Frank D. (R-3rd OK)	16	2405	225-5565	109
Luetkemeyer, Blaine (R-3rd MO)	80	2230	225-2956	85
Luján, Ben Ray (D-3rd NM)	99	2231	225-6190	95
Lujan Grisham, Michelle (D-1st NM)	140	214	225-6316	94
Lynch, Stephen F. (D-8th MA)	62	2268	225-8273	76
MacArthur, Tom (R-3rd NJ)	191	506	225-4765	92
Maloney, Carolyn B. (D-12th NY)	28	2308	225-7944	98
Maloney, Sean Patrick (D-18th NY)	141	1027	225-5441	99
Marchant, Kenny (R-24th TX)	54	2369	225-6605	127
Marino, Tom (R-10th PA)	118	2242	225-3731	114
Marshall, Roger (R-1st KS)	233	312	225-2715	66
Massie, Thomas (R-4th KY)	137	2453	225-3465	68
Mast, Brian (R-18th FL)	234	2182	225-3026	50
Matsui, Doris (D-6th CA)	77	2311	225-7163	33
McCarthy, Kevin (R-23rd CA)	66	2421	225-2915	36
McCaul, Michael (R-10th TX)	55	2001	225-2401	124
McClintock, Tom (R-4th CA)	81	2312	225-2511	33
McCollum, Betty (D-4th MN)	60	2256	225-6631	81
McEachin, A. Donald (D-4th VA)	186	314	225-6365	132
McGovern, Jim (D-2nd MA)	43	438	225-6101	75
McHenry, Patrick T. (R-10th NC)	56	2334	225-2576	103
McKinley, David B. (R-1st WV)	119	2239	225-4172	137
McMorris Rodgers, Cathy (R-5th WA)	57	1314	225-2006	135
McNerney, Jerry (D-9th CA)	86	2265	225-1947	34
McSally, Martha (R-2nd AZ)	192	510	225-2542	29
Meadows, Mark (R-11th NC)	151	1024	225-6401	103
Meehan, Patrick (R-7th PA)	120	2305	225-2011	113
Meeks, Gregory W. (D-5th NY)	47	2234	225-3461	96
Meng, Grace (D-6th NY)	142	1317	225-2601	97
Messer, Luke (R-6th IN)	152	1230	225-3021	63
Mitchell, Paul (R-10th MI)	235	211	225-2106	79
Moolenaar, John (R-4th MI)	193	117	225-3561	78
Mooney, Alex (R-2nd WV)	194	1232	225-2711	137
Moore, Gwen (D-4th WI)	75	2252	225-4572	139
Moulton, Seth (D-6th MA)	165	1408	225-8020	76
Mullin, Markwayne (R-2nd OK)	153	1113	225-2701	109
Murphy, Stephanie (D-7th FL)	187	1237	225-4035	48
Murphy, Tim (R-18th PA)	45	2332	225-2301	115

Rooms with 3 numbers ....CHOB, 1st St. & Independence Ave., SE
Rooms with 4 numbers beginning with 1 ....LHOB, Independence & New Jersey Aves., SE
Rooms with 4 numbers beginning with 2 ...RHOB, Independence Ave. & S. Capitol St., SW

Members of the House of Representatives

	Seniority in Party	Office	Phone (202)	Page
Nadler, Jerrold (D-10th NY)	19	2109	225-5635	97
Napolitano, Grace F. (D-32nd CA)	53	1610	225-5256	38
Neal, Richard E. (D-1st MA)	13	341	225-5601	75
Newhouse, Dan (R-4th WA)	195	1318	225-5816	135
Noem, Kristi (R-At Large SD)	122	2457	225-2801	119
Nolan, Rick (D-8th MN)	96	2366	225-6211	82
Norcross, Donald (D-1st NJ)	156	1531	225-6501	92
Norton, Eleanor Holmes (D-At Large DC)		2136	225-8050	141
Nunes, Devin (R-22nd CA)	46	1013	225-2523	36
O'Halleran, Tom (D-1st AZ)	188	126	225-3361	28
Olson, Pete (R-22nd TX)	82	2133	225-5951	126
O'Rourke, Beto (D-16th TX)	143	1330	225-4831	125
Palazzo, Steven M. (R-4th MS)	123	2349	225-5772	83
Pallone, Frank Jr. (D-6th NJ)	10	237	225-4671	92
Palmer, Gary (R-6th AL)	196	330	225-4921	26
Panetta, Jimmy (D-20th CA)	189	228	225-2861	36
Pascrell, Bill Jr. (D-9th NJ)	44	2370	225-5751	93
Paulsen, Erik (R-3rd MN)	83	127	225-2871	81
Payne, Donald M. Jr. (D-10th NJ)	117	132	225-3436	93
Pearce, Steve (R-2nd NM)	61	2432	225-2365	95
Pelosi, Nancy (D-12th CA)	9	233	225-4965	34
Perlmutter, Ed (D-7th CO)	87	1410	225-2645	43
Perry, Scott (R-4th PA)	154	1207	225-5836	113
Peters, Scott (D-52nd CA)	144	1122	225-0508	41
Peterson, Collin C. (D-7th MN)	17	2204	225-2165	82
Pingree, Chellie (D-1st ME)	100	2162	225-6116	71
Pittenger, Robert (R-9th NC)	155	224	225-1976	102
Plaskett, Stacey (D-At Large VI)		331	225-1790	143
Pocan, Mark (D-2nd WI)	145	1421	225-2906	138
Poe, Ted (R-2nd TX)	58	2132	225-6565	123
Poliquin, Bruce (R-2nd ME)	197	1208	225-6306	72
Polis, Jared (D-2nd CO)	101	1727	225-2161	42
Posey, Bill (R-8th FL)	84	2150	225-3671	48
Price, David E. (D-4th NC)	15	2108	225-1784	102
Quigley, Mike (D-5th IL)	104	2458	225-4061	59
Radewagen, Aumua Amata Coleman (R-At Large AS)		1339	225-8577	141
Raskin, Jamie (D-8th MD)	190	431	225-5341	74
Ratcliffe, John (R-4th TX)	198	325	225-6673	123
Reed, Tom (R-23rd NY)	89	2437	225-3161	99
Reichert, Dave (R-8th WA)	60	1127	225-7761	136
Renacci, James B. (R-16th OH)	124	328	225-3876	108
Rice, Kathleen (D-4th NY)	166	1508	225-5516	96
Rice, Tom (R-7th SC)	156	223	225-9895	118
Richmond, Cedric L. (D-2nd LA)	112	420	225-6636	70
Roby, Martha (R-2nd AL)	125	442	225-2901	26
Roe, Phil (R-1st TN)	85	336	225-6356	120
Rogers, Harold (R-5th KY)	3	2406	225-4601	68
Rogers, Mike D. (R-3rd AL)	47	2184	225-3261	26
Rohrabacher, Dana (R-48th CA)	9	2300	225-2415	40
Rokita, Todd (R-4th IN)	126	2439	225-5037	62
Rooney, Francis (R-19th FL)	236	120	225-2536	50
Rooney, Tom (R-17th FL)	86	2160	225-5792	50
Rosen, Jacky (D-3rd NV)	191	413	225-3252	89
Roskam, Peter (R-6th IL)	67	2246	225-4561	59
Ros-Lehtinen, Ileana (R-27th FL)	10	2206	225-3931	51
Ross, Dennis A. (R-15th FL)	127	436	225-1252	49
Rothfus, Keith (R-12th PA)	157	1205	225-2065	114

Members of the House of Representatives

	Seniority in Party	Office	Phone (202)	Page
Rouzer, David (R-7th NC)	199	424	225-2731	102
Roybal-Allard, Lucille (D-40th CA)	29	2083	225-1766	39
Royce, Ed (R-39th CA)	15	2310	225-4111	39
Ruiz, Raul (D-36th CA)	146	1319	225-5330	38
Ruppersberger, C.A. Dutch (D-2nd MD)	64	2416	225-3061	73
Rush, Bobby L. (D-1st IL)	30	2188	225-4372	58
Russell, Steve (R-5th OK)	200	128	225-2132	109
Rutherford, John (R-4th FL)	237	230	225-2501	48
Ryan, Paul D. (R-1st WI)	27	1233	225-3031	138
Ryan, Tim (D-13th OH)	65	1126	225-5261	107
Sablan, Gregorio Kilili Camacho (D-th MP)		2411	225-2646	142
Sánchez, Linda T. (D-38th CA)	66	2329	225-6676	38
Sanford, Mark (R-1st SC)	72	2211	225-3176	117
Sarbanes, John (D-3rd MD)	88	2444	225-4016	73
Scalise, Steve (R-1st LA)	71	2338	225-3015	69
Schakowsky, Jan (D-9th IL)	54	2367	225-2111	59
Schiff, Adam B. (D-28th CA)	61	2372	225-4176	37
Schneider, Brad (D-10th IL)	170	1432	225-4835	59
Schrader, Kurt (D-5th OR)	102	2431	225-5711	111
Schweikert, David (R-6th AZ)	128	2059	225-2190	29
Scott, Austin (R-8th GA)	129	2417	225-6531	54
Scott, David (D-13th GA)	67	225	225-2939	54
Scott, Robert C. (D-3rd VA)	31	1201	225-8351	132
Sensenbrenner, Jim (R-5th WI)	2	2449	225-5101	139
Serrano, José E. (D-15th NY)	14	2354	225-4361	98
Sessions, Pete (R-32nd TX)	24	2233	225-2231	128
Sewell, Terri A. (D-7th AL)	113	2201	225-2665	26
Shea-Porter, Carol (D-1st NH)	120	1530	225-5456	90
Sherman, Brad (D-30th CA)	45	2181	225-5911	37
Shimkus, John (R-15th IL)	25	2217	225-5271	60
Shuster, Bill (R-9th PA)	34	2079	225-2431	114
Simpson, Mike (R-2nd ID)	28	2084	225-5531	57
Sinema, Kyrsten (D-9th AZ)	147	1725	225-9888	30
Sires, Albio (D-8th NJ)	78	2342	225-7919	93
Slaughter, Louise M. (D-25th NY)	8	2469	225-3615	100
Smith, Adam (D-9th WA)	46	2264	225-8901	136
Smith, Adrian (R-3rd NE)	68	320	225-6435	88
Smith, Christopher H. (R-4th NJ)	4	2373	225-3765	92
Smith, Jason (R-8th MO)	166	1118	225-4404	86
Smith, Lamar (R-21st TX)	6	2409	225-4236	126
Smucker, Lloyd K. (R-16th PA)	238	516	225-2411	115
Soto, Darren (D-9th FL)	192	1429	225-9889	48
Speier, Jackie (D-14th CA)	94	2465	225-3531	35
Stefanik, Elise (R-21st NY)	201	318	225-4611	99
Stewart, Chris (R-2nd UT)	158	323	225-9730	130
Stivers, Steve (R-15th OH)	130	1022	225-2015	107
Suozzi, Tom (D-3rd NY)	193	226	225-3335	96
Swalwell, Eric (D-15th CA)	148	129	225-5065	35
Takano, Mark (D-41st CA)	149	1507	225-2305	39
Taylor, Scott (R-2nd VA)	239	412	225-4215	132
Tenney, Claudia (R-22nd NY)	240	512	225-3665	99
Thompson, Bennie (D-2nd MS)	33	2466	225-5876	83
Thompson, Glenn (R-5th PA)	87	124	225-5121	113
Thompson, Mike (D-5th CA)	55	231	225-3311	33

Rooms with 3 numbers ....CHOB, 1st St. & Independence Ave., SE
Rooms with 4 numbers beginning with 1 ....LHOB, Independence & New Jersey Aves., SE
Rooms with 4 numbers beginning with 2 ...RHOB, Independence Ave. & S. Capitol St., SW

Members of the House of Representatives

	Seniority in Party	Office	Phone (202)	Page
Thornberry, Mac (R-13th TX)	20	2208	225-3706	125
Tiberi, Pat (R-12th OH)	33	1203	225-5355	107
Tipton, Scott (R-3rd CO)	131	218	225-4761	43
Titus, Dina (D-1st NV)	118	2464	225-5965	89
Tonko, Paul (D-20th NY)	103	2463	225-5076	99
Torres, Norma J. (D-35th CA)	167	1713	225-6161	38
Trott, Dave (R-11th MI)	202	1722	225-8171	79
Tsongas, Niki (D-3rd MA)	92	1714	225-3411	75
Turner, Michael R. (R-10th OH)	48	2368	225-6465	107
Upton, Fred (R-6th MI)	7	2183	225-3761	78
Vacant (34th CA)		1226	225-6235	38
Vacant (6th GA)		100	225-4501	53
Vacant (4th KS)		436	225-6216	66
Vacant (At Large MT)		113	225-3211	87
Vacant (5th SC)		2419	225-5501	118
Valadao, David (R-21st CA)	159	1728	225-4695	36
Vargas, Juan C. (D-51st CA)	150	1605	225-8045	41
Veasey, Marc (D-33rd TX)	151	1519	225-9897	128
Vela, Filemon (D-34th TX)	152	437	225-9901	128
Velázquez, Nydia M. (D-7th NY)	32	2302	225-2361	97
Visclosky, Peter J. (D-1st IN)	5	2328	225-2461	62
Wagner, Ann (R-2nd MO)	160	435	225-1621	85
Walberg, Tim (R-7th MI)	90	2436	225-6276	78
Walden, Greg (R-2nd OR)	29	2185	225-6730	111
Walker, Mark (R-6th NC)	203	1305	225-3065	102
Walorski, Jackie (R-2nd IN)	161	419	225-3915	62
Walters, Mimi (R-45th CA)	204	215	225-5611	40
Walz, Tim (D-1st MN)	89	2313	225-2472	81
Wasserman Schultz, Debbie (D-23rd FL)	76	1114	225-7931	51
Waters, Maxine (D-43rd CA)	18	2221	225-2201	39
Watson Coleman, Bonnie (D-12th NJ)	168	1535	225-5801	93
Weber, Randy (R-14th TX)	162	1708	225-2831	125
Webster, Daniel (R-11th FL)	132	1210	225-1002	49
Welch, Peter (D-At Large VT)	90	2303	225-4115	131
Wenstrup, Brad (R-2nd OH)	163	2419	225-3164	105
Westerman, Bruce (R-4th AR)	205	130	225-3772	31
Williams, Roger (R-25th TX)	164	1323	225-9896	127
Wilson, Frederica S. (D-24th FL)	114	2445	225-4506	51
Wilson, Joe (R-2nd SC)	35	1436	225-2452	118
Wittman, Rob (R-1st VA)	70	2055	225-4261	132
Womack, Steve (R-3rd AR)	133	2412	225-4301	31
Woodall, Rob (R-7th GA)	134	1724	225-4272	53
Yarmuth, John (D-3rd KY)	91	131	225-5401	68
Yoder, Kevin (R-3rd KS)	135	2433	225-2865	66
Yoho, Ted (R-3rd FL)	165	511	225-5744	47
Young, David (R-3rd IA)	206	240	225-5476	65
Young, Don (R-At Large AK)	1	2314	225-5765	27
Zeldin, Lee (R-1st NY)	207	1517	225-3826	96

Rooms with 3 numbers ....CHOB, 1st St. & Independence Ave., SE
Rooms with 4 numbers beginning with 1 ....LHOB, Independence & New Jersey Aves., SE
Rooms with 4 numbers beginning with 2 ...RHOB, Independence Ave. & S. Capitol St., SW

2017 Congressional Schedule and Calendar

JANUARY

S	M	T	W	T	F	S
1	2	3	4	5	6	7
8	9	10	11	12	13	14
15	16	17	18	19	20	21
22	23	24	25	26	27	28
29	30	31				

Jan. 1: New Year's Day
Jan. 3: House and Senate Convenes
Jan. 16: Martin Luther King, Jr. Day
Jan. 16: Recess (Senate & House)
Jan. 17-19: Recess (House)
Jan. 25-27: Recess (House)

FEBRUARY

S	M	T	W	T	F	S
			1	2	3	4
5	6	7	8	9	10	11
12	13	14	15	16	17	18
19	20	21	22	23	24	25
26	27	28				

Feb. 5: Super Bowl Sunday
Feb. 9-10: Recess (House)
Feb. 14: Valentine's Day
Feb. 20: Presidents' Day
Feb. 20-24: Recess (Senate & House)

MARCH

S	M	T	W	T	F	S
			1	2	3	4
5	6	7	8	9	10	11
12	13	14	15	16	17	18
19	20	21	22	23	24	25
26	27	28	29	30	31	

March 3-6: Recess (House)
March 12: Daylight Saving Time starts
March 13: Recess (House)
March 16-17: Recess (Senate)
March 17: St. Patrick's Day
March 24: Recess (House)
March 31: Recess (House)

APRIL

S	M	T	W	T	F	S
						1
2	3	4	5	6	7	8
9	10	11	12	13	14	15
16	17	18	19	20	21	22
23/30	24	25	26	27	28	29

April 7: Recess (House)
April 9: Palm Sunday
April 10: First Day of Passover
April 10-21: Recess (Senate & House)
April 16: Easter
April 18: Tax Day
April 24: Recess (House)

MAY

S	M	T	W	T	F	S
	1	2	3	4	5	6
7	8	9	10	11	12	13
14	15	16	17	18	19	20
21	22	23	24	25	26	27
28	29	30	31			

May 5: Cinco de Mayo
May 5-15: Recess (Senate & House)
May 14: Mother's Day
May 26: First day of Ramadan
May 26: Recess (House)
May 29: Memorial Day
May 29-June 2: Recess
   (Senate & House)

JUNE

S	M	T	W	T	F	S
				1	2	3
4	5	6	7	8	9	10
11	12	13	14	15	16	17
18	19	20	21	22	23	24
25	26	27	28	29	30	

June 5: Recess (House)
June 14: Flag Day
June 18: Father's Day
June 19: Recess (House)

Congressional recess dates are in red.

2017 Congressional Schedule and Calendar

JULY

S	M	T	W	T	F	S
						1
2	3	4	5	6	7	8
9	10	11	12	13	14	15
16	17	18	19	20	21	22
23/30	24/31	25	26	27	28	29

July 3-7: Recess (Senate & House)
July 4: Independence Day
July 10: Recess (House)
July 21: Recess (House)
July 31-Sept. 4: Recess
    (Senate & House)

AUGUST

S	M	T	W	T	F	S
		1	2	3	4	5
6	7	8	9	10	11	12
13	14	15	16	17	18	19
20	21	22	23	24	25	26
27	28	29	30	31		

SEPTEMBER

S	M	T	W	T	F	S
					1	2
3	4	5	6	7	8	9
10	11	12	13	14	15	16
17	18	19	20	21	22	23
24	25	26	27	28	29	30

Sept. 4: Labor Day
Sept. 15-20: Recess (House)
Sept. 20: First day of Rosh Hashanah
Sept. 21-22: Recess (Senate & House)
Sept. 29: First day of Yom Kippur
Sept. 29: Recess (House)

OCTOBER

S	M	T	W	T	F	S
1	2	3	4	5	6	7
8	9	10	11	12	13	14
15	16	17	18	19	20	21
22	23	24	25	26	27	28
29	30	31				

Oct. 6: Recess (House)
Oct. 9: Columbus Day
Oct. 9: Recess (Senate & House)
Oct. 10-13: Recess (Senate)
Oct. 16-20: Recess (House)
Oct. 27-30: Recess (House)
Oct. 31: Halloween

NOVEMBER

S	M	T	W	T	F	S
			1	2	3	4
5	6	7	8	9	10	11
12	13	14	15	16	17	18
19	20	21	22	23	24	25
26	27	28	29	30		

Nov. 5: Daylight Saving Time ends
Nov. 7: Election Day
Nov. 10: Recess (Senate & House)
Nov. 11: Veterans Day
Nov. 17: Recess (House)
Nov. 20-24: Recess (Senate & House)
Nov. 23: Thanksgiving Day
Nov. 27: Recess (House)

DECEMBER

S	M	T	W	T	F	S
					1	2
3	4	5	6	7	8	9
10	11	12	13	14	15	16
17	18	19	20	21	22	23
24/31	25	26	27	28	29	30

Dec. 4: Recess (House)
Dec. 12: First day of Chanukah
Dec. 15: Recess (House)
Dec. 18-31: Recess
    (Senate & House)
Dec. 24: Christmas Eve
Dec. 25: Christmas Day
Dec. 31: New Year's Eve

Congressional recess dates are in red.
Senate and House Target Adjournment: TBD

Guide To Using This Book

State Name
State Website

Pop.: 2015 est. (Census) **Rank:** #
Caucasian: % **African-Am.:** %
Nat. Am.: % **Asian:** % **Other:** %
Hisp.: %*
Area: sq. mi. **Rank:** #
Reg. Voters: #
Dem: % **Rep:** % **Other:** %

Number of U.S. House Seats:
Dem./Rep.

State Legislature
Website
Senate: D/R House: D/R
Session Dates

*Hispanic origin is a category
separate from race. People of
Hispanic origin will also be
included in another racial category.*

CONGRESS
AT YOUR
FINGERTIPS®

IMAGE OF
CONGRESSIONAL
DISTRICT MAP

STANDARD
VERSION

Governor Photo	Name (Party)		Phone Number
	Next Election: Year	Term/Last Election %	Fax Number

Blue frame denotes Democrats

Red frame denotes Republicans

Purple frame denotes Independents

twitter

Bio: Birthdate Birthplace; Religion; Highest Degree
Achieved, School, Year; Military Service; Previous
Profession; Marital Status, Spouse's Name

Capital Address
Washington Office: Phone Number

CHAMBER HEADING

Member Photo	Name (Party-District)		Phone Number
	Address Term/Election % CQ Vote Studies* Fax Number		
	Website Address		twitter

Blue frame denotes Democrats

Red frame denotes Republicans

Purple frame denotes Independents

Staff Title ....Staff Name **Staff Title** ....Staff Name
Staff Title ....Staff Name **Staff Title** ....Staff Name
Bio: Birthdate Birthplace; Religion; Highest Degree Achieved,
School, Year; Military Service; Previous Profession; Marital
Status, Spouse's Name
Comm.: Committee Assignments
Dist. Offices: City, Phone Number

* CQ VOTE STUDIES: % Agreed with President/% Agreed with Party/Participation %

Congressional Quarterly has analyzed the roll call voting patterns of members of Congress since 1953. The three principal studies involve:

- The frequency with which lawmakers vote with the president when he clearly indicates his preferences (Presidential Support).
- The frequency with which they vote with their party, on occasions when a majority of Republicans oppose a majority of Democrats (Party Unity).
- And the frequency with which they show up and cast "yea" or "nay" votes (Voting Participation).

Vote study numbers are for 2016.

Commonly used staff titles:

Appt:	Appointment Secretary	**LD:**	Legislative Director
AD:	Administrative Director	**OM:**	Office Manager
CD:	Communications Director	**PD:**	Policy Director
CO:	Chief of Operations	**Press:**	Press Secretary
CoS:	Chief of Staff	**Sr Adv:**	Senior Advisor
Dep CoS:	Deputy Chief of Staff	**Sch:**	Scheduler
EA:	Executive Assistant	**Sr LA:**	Senior Legislative Assistant
LC:	Legislative Counsel	**Sr PA:**	Senior Policy Advisor

ALABAMA
alabama.gov

Pop.: 4,858,979   **Rank:** 24th
Caucasian: 70%   **African-Am.:** 27%
Nat. Am.: 1%   **Asian:** 1%
Other: 2%   **Hisp.:** 4%
Reg. Voters: 3,214,917
Party registration not required
Land Area: 50,645 sq. mi.   **Rank:** 28th

Number of US House Seats: 6 Rep./1 Dem.

State Legislature
legislature.state.al.us
Senate: 26R/8D/1 Other
House: 72R/31D/2Vac
Session: 02/02/17 – 5/31/2017

Gov. Robert Bentley (R)   334-242-7100
Next Election: 2018 2nd Term/64%   Fax: 334-353-0004
twitter governorbentley
Bio: b. 2/3/43 Columbiana, AL; Baptist; MD Univ. of AL, 1968; USAF; Dermatologist; div.
State Capitol, 600 Dexter Avenue, Montgomery, AL 36130-2751
Washington Office: 202-220-1379

SENATE

Richard C. Shelby (R)   202-224-5744
SR-304   6th Term/64%   52/94/94   twitter SenShelby
shelby.senate.gov
CoS .... Katie Britt **LD** .... Dayne Cutrell
Appt .... Anne Caldwell **CD** .... Torrie Matous
Bio: b. 5/6/34 Birmingham, AL; Presbyterian; LLB Univ. of AL, 1963; Attorney; m. Annette
Comm.: Appropriations; Banking, Housing & Urban Affairs; Environment & Public Works; Rules & Administration (Chair)
Dist. Offices: Tuscaloosa, 205-759-5047; Mobile, 251-694-4164; Montgomery, 334-223-7303; Birmingham, 205-731-1384; Huntsville, 256-772-0460

Luther Strange (R)   202-224-4124
SD-G12   1st Term/Appt.   Fax: 224-3149
strange.senate.gov   twitter lutherstrange
CoS .... Kevin Turner **LD** .... Vacant
Sch .... Melissa Chambers **CD** .... Vacant
Bio: b. 3/1/53 Birmingham, AL; Episcopalian; JD Tulane Univ., 1979; Attorney, Lobbyist; m. Melissa
Comm.: Agriculture, Nutrition, & Forestry; Armed Services; Budget; Energy & Natural Resources
Dist. Offices: TBA

HOUSE

Bradley Byrne (R-1st)   202-225-4931
119 CHOB   3rd Term/Unc.   7/98/97   Fax: 225-0562
byrne.house.gov   twitter RepByrne
CoS .... Alex Schriver **LD** .... Chad Carlough
Sch .... Holly Lewis **CD** .... Seth Morrow
Bio: b. 2/16/55 Mobile, AL; Episcopal; JD Univ. of AL, 1980; Attorney; m. Rebecca
Comm.: Armed Services; Education & the Workforce; Rules
Dist. Offices: Mobile, 251-690-2811; Summerdale, 251-989-2664

ALABAMA

Martha Roby (R-2nd)   **202-225-2901**
442 CHOB   4th Term/54%   9/96/94   Fax: 225-8913
roby.house.gov   twitter RepMarthaRoby
CoS ....Vacant   **LD** ....Mike Albares
Sch .... Kate Hollis   **CD** .... Todd Stacy
Bio: b. 7/26/76 Montgomery, AL; Presbyterian; JD Samford Univ., 2001; Attorney; m. Riley
Comm.: Appropriations; Judiciary
Dist. Offices: Dothan, 334-794-9680; Montgomery, 334-277-9113; Andalusia, 334-428-1129

Mike D. Rogers (R-3rd)   **202-225-3261**
2184 RHOB   8th Term/67%   9/96/96   Fax: 226-8485
mikerogers.house.gov   twitter RepMikeRogersAL
CoS ....Chris Brinson   **LD** ....Whitney Verett
Sch ....Jacie Coressel   **Press**.........Shea Snider Miller
Bio: b. 7/16/58 Hammond, IN; Baptist; JD Birmingham School of Law, 1991; Attorney, Worker Assistance Program Director; m. Beth
Comm.: Agriculture; Armed Services; Homeland Security
Dist. Offices: Anniston, 256-236-5655; Opelika, 334-745-6221

Robert B. Aderholt (R-4th) *ADD-er-holt*   **202-225-4876**
235 CHOB   11th Term/Unc.   7/96/98   Fax: 225-5587
aderholt.house.gov   twitter Robert_Aderholt
CoS .... Brian Rell   **LD** .... Mark Dawson
Sch ....Chris Lawson   **CD** ....Brian Rell
Bio: b. 7/22/65 Haleyville, AL; Congregationalist; JD Samford Univ., 1990; Attorney, Gubernatorial Aide; m. Caroline
Comm.: Appropriations
Dist. Offices: Jasper, 205-221-2310; Cullman, 256-734-6043; Gadsden, 256-546-0201; Tuscumbia, 256-381-3450

Mo Brooks (R-5th)   **202-225-4801**
2400 RHOB   4th Term/67%   8/95/99   Fax: 225-4392
brooks.house.gov   twitter RepMoBrooks
CoS ....Mark Pettitt   **LD** .... Mark Pettitt
Sch .... Kelly Zams   **Press**............Annalyse Keller
Bio: b. 4/29/54 Charleston, SC; Christian Non-Denominational; JD Univ. of AL, 1978; Attorney, County Prosecutor; m. Martha
Comm.: Armed Services; Foreign Affairs; Science, Space & Technology
Dist. Offices: Huntsville, 256-551-0190; Decatur, 256-355-9400; Florence, 256-718-5155

Gary Palmer (R-6th)   **202-225-4921**
330 CHOB   2nd Term/75%   7/99/99   Fax: 225-2082
palmer.house.gov   twitter USRepGaryPalmer
CoS .... William Smith   **LD** ....Cari Fike
Sch ....Nonie Brown   **Press**...................Cate Cullen
Bio: b. 5/14/54 Hackleburg, AL; Christian; BS Univ. of AL, 1977; Think Tank Executive, Industrial Engineer; m. Ann
Comm.: Budget; Oversight & Government Reform; Science, Space & Technology
Dist. Offices: Birmingham, 205-968-1290; Clanton, 205-280-6846; Oneonta, 205-274-2136

Terri A. Sewell (D-7th) *SUE-ell*   **202-225-2665**
2201 RHOB   4th Term/Unc.   85/93/94   Fax: 226-9567
sewell.house.gov   twitter RepTerriSewell
CoS ....Shashrina Thomas   **LD** .... Cachavious English
Sch ....Perry Hamilton   **CD** ...Christopher Mackenzie
Bio: b. 1/1/65 Huntsville, AL; African Methodist Episcopal; JD Harvard Univ., 1992; Attorney; single
Comm.: Ways & Means ; Select Intelligence
Dist. Offices: Birmingham, 205-254-1960; Selma, 334-877-4414; Montgomery, 334-262-1919; Tuscaloosa, 205-752-5380

ALASKA
alaska.gov

Pop.: 738,432   **Rank:** 48th
Caucasian: 67%   **African-Am.:** 4%
Nat. Am.: 15%   **Asian:** 6%   **Other:** 9%
Hisp.: 7%
Reg. Voters: 533,145
Dem.: 14%   **Rep.:** 27%   **Other:** 59%
Land Area: 570,641 sq. mi.   **Rank:** 1st

1   .Fairbanks

Anchorage.

Juneau ★

Number of US House Seats: 1 Rep.

State Legislature
legis.state.ak.us
Senate: 14R/6D   House: 21R/17D/2 Other
Session: 01/17/17 – 4/16/2017

Gov. Bill Walker (I)   907-465-3500
Next Election: 2018   1st Term/48%   Fax: 907-465-3532
twitter akgovbillwalker
Bio: b. 4/16/51 Fairbanks, AK; Presbyterian; JD Univ. of Puget Sound, 1983; Attorney, Business Owner; m. Donna
State Capitol, 3rd Floor, Juneau, AK 99811-0001
Washington Office: 202-624-5858

SENATE

Lisa Murkowski (R)   202-224-6665
SH-522   4th Term/44%   48/73/95   Fax: 224-5301
murkowski.senate.gov   twitter lisamurkowski
CoS ....Michael Pawlowski **LD** .... Garrett Boyle
Sch ....Kristen **CD** .... Karina Petersen
Daimler-Nothdurft
Bio: b. 5/22/57 Ketchikan, AK; Catholic; JD Willamette Univ., 1985; Attorney; m. Verne Martell
Comm.: Appropriations; Energy & Natural Resources (Chair); Health, Education, Labor & Pensions; Indian Affairs
Dist. Offices: Anchorage, 907-271-3735; Fairbanks, 907-456-0233; Wasilla, 907-376-7665; Ketchikan, 907-225-6880; Kenai, 907-283-5808; Juneau, 907-586-7277

Dan Sullivan (R)   202-224-3004
SH-702   1st Term/48%   44/89/96   Fax: 224-6501
sullivan.senate.gov   twitter SenDanSullivan
CoS .... Joe Balash **LD** ....Erik Elam
Sch .... Avery Fogets **CD** ....Michael Anderson
Bio: b. 11/13/64 Fairview Park, OH; Catholic; JD/MSFS Georgetown Univ., 1993; USMC, 1993-97; USMCR, 1997-present; White House Aide, Attorney, Author; m. Julie Fate Sullivan
Comm.: Armed Services; Commerce, Sciences & Transportation; Environment & Public Works; Veterans' Affairs
Dist. Offices: Anchorage, 907-271-5915; Wasilla, 907-357-9956; Juneau, 907-586-7277; Fairbanks, 907-456-0261; Kenai, 907-283-4000; Ketchikan, 907-225-6880

HOUSE

Don Young (R-At Large)   202-225-5765
2314 RHOB   23rd Term/50%   10/96/95   Fax: 225-0425
donyoung.house.gov   twitter repdonyoung
CoS .... Pamela Day **LD** ....Alex Ortiz
Sch ....Paula Conru **Press**..... Matthew Shuckerow
Bio: b. 6/9/33 Meridian, CA; Episcopal; BA Chico St. Col., 1958; USA, 1955-57; Teacher, Riverboat Captain; m. Anne Garland Walton
Comm.: Natural Resources; Transportation & Infrastructure
Dist. Offices: Anchorage, 907-271-5978; Fairbanks, 907-456-0210; Juneau, 907-586-7400

ARIZONA
az.gov

Pop.: 6,828,065 **Rank:** 14th
Caucasian: 84% **African-Am.:** 5%
Nat. Am.: 5% **Asian:** 3%
Other: 3% **Hisp.:** 31%
Reg. Voters: 3,646,122
Dem.: 29% **Rep.:** 36% **Other:** 35%
Land Area: 113,594 sq. mi. **Rank:** 6th

Number of US House Seats:
5 Rep./4 Dem.

State Legislature
azleg.gov
Senate: 17R/13D House: 35R/25D
Session: 01/09/17 – 4/22/2017

Gov. Doug Ducey (R)   602-542-4331
Next Election: 2018 1st Term/53%   Fax: 602-542-1381
twitter dougducey
Bio: b. 4/9/64 Toledo, OH; Catholic; BS AZ St. Univ., 1986;
Businessman; m. Angela
1700 West Washington Street, Phoenix, AZ 85007

SENATE

John McCain (R)   202-224-2235
SR-218 6th Term/53% 54/89/98 Fax: 228-2862
boozman.senate.gov   *twitter* SenJohnMcCain
CoS .... Pablo Carrillo **LD** .... Joe Donoghue
Sch .... Ellen Cahill **CD** .... Julie Tarallo
Bio: b. 8/29/36 Panama Canal Zone; Episcopal; BS U.S.
Naval Acad., 1958; USN, 1958-81; Naval Officer; m. Cindy
Comm.: Armed Services (Chair); Homeland Security &
Governmental Affairs; Indian Affairs
Dist. Offices: Phoenix, 602-952-2410; Prescott, 928-445-
0833; Tucson, 520-670-6334

Jeff Flake (R)   202-224-4521
SR-413 1st Term/49% 62/90/95 Fax: 228-0515
mccain.senate.gov   *twitter* jefflake
CoS .... Chandler Morse **LD** .... Sarah Towles
Sch .... MS Meagan Shepherd **CD** .... Jason Samuels
Bio: b. 12/31/62 Snowflake, AZ; Mormon; MA Brigham Young
Univ., 1987; Association Executive, Lobbyist; m. Cheryl
Comm.: Energy & Natural Resources; Foreign Relations;
Judiciary; Special Aging
Dist. Offices: Phoenix, 602-840-1891; Tucson, 520-575-8633

HOUSE

Tom O'Halleran (D-1st)   202-225-3361
126 CHOB 1st Term/52%   Fax: 225-3462
ohalleran.house.gov   *twitter* RepOHalleran
CoS .... Jeremy Nordquist **LD** .... Xenia Ruiz
Sch .... Willa Prescott **CD** .... Cody Uhing
Bio: b. 1/24/46 Chicago, IL; Catholic; Lobbyist, Bond Trader,
Officer; m. Pat
Comm.: Agriculture; Armed Services
Dist. Offices: Casa Grande, 520-316-0839; Flagstaff, 928-
210-8165

Arizona

Martha McSally (R-2nd)   **202-225-2542**
510 CHOB   2nd Term/57%   7/94/100   Fax: 225-0378
mcsally.house.gov   twitter repmcsally
CoS ....Justin Roth **LD**...............Pace McMullan
Sch .... Zoe Aguillard **CD** ....Patrick Ptak
Bio: b. 3/22/66 Warwick, RI; Christian; MPP Harvard Univ., 1990; USAF, 1988-2010; College Instructor, Air Force Officer; single
Comm.: Armed Services; Homeland Security
Dist. Offices: Tucson, 520-881-3588; Sierra Vista, 520-459-3115

Raúl M. Grijalva (D-3rd) *gree-HAHL-va* **202-225-2435**
1511 LHOB   8th Term/Unc.   98/99/87   Fax: 225-1541
grijalva.house.gov   twitter RepRaulGrijalva
CoS ....Amy Emerick **LD**.................Kelsey Mishkin
Sch ....Cristina Villa **CD** ....Dan Lindner
Bio: b. 2/19/48 Tucson, AZ; Catholic; BA Univ. of AZ, 1987; Public Official, University Dean; m. Mona
Comm.: Education & the Workforce; Natural Resources (Rnk. Mem.)
Dist. Offices: Tucson, 520-622-6788; Somerton, 928-343-7933; Avondale, 623-536-3388

Paul Gosar (R-4th) *go-SAR*   **202-225-2315**
2057 RHOB   4th Term/72%   6/97/98   Fax: 226-9739
gosar.house.gov   twitter repgosar
CoS .... Tom Van Flein **LD**................. Trevor Pearson
Sch ....Leslie Foti **CD** ....Steven Smith
Bio: b. 11/27/58 Rock Springs, WY; Catholic; DDS Creighton Univ., 1985; Dentist; m. Maude
Comm.: Natural Resources; Oversight & Government Reform
Dist. Offices: Prescott, 928-445-1683; San Tan Valley, 480-882-2697

Andy Biggs (R-5th)   **202-225-2635**
1626 LHOB   1st Term/63%   Fax: 226-4386
biggs.house.gov   twitter RepAndyBiggsAZ
CoS .... Deborah Weigel **LD**..................... Kate Labord
EA ....Maggie Woodin **CD** ....Daniel Stefanski
Bio: b. 11/7/58 Tuscon; Mormon; MA AZ St. Univ., 1999; Attorney; m. Cindy
Comm.: Judiciary; Science, Space & Technology
Dist. Offices: Mesa, 480-699-8239

David Schweikert (R-6th)   **202-225-2190**
2059 RHOB   4th Term/62%   7/98/99   Fax: 225-0096
schweikert.house.gov   twitter repdavid
CoS ....Oliver Schwab **LD**...... Katherina Dimenstein
OM .... Ashley Sylvester **Press**............ Ashley Sylvester
Bio: b. 3/3/62 Los Angeles, CA; Catholic; MBA AZ St. Univ., 2005; Real Estate Company Owner, Financial Consultant; m. Joyce
Comm.: Ways & Means; Joint Economic
Dist. Offices: Scottsdale, 480-946-2411

Ruben Gallego (D-7th)   **202-225-4065**
1218 LHOB   2nd Term/74%   98/99/99   Fax: None
rubengallego.house.gov   twitter reprubengallego
CoS ....David Montes **LD**...................Matthew Lee
Sch .... Abigail O'Brien **CD** ....Christina Carr
Bio: b. 11/20/79 Chicago, IL; Catholic; AB Harvard Univ., 2004; USMCR, 2000-06; Public Affairs Consultant, City Council Aide; sep. Kate
Comm.: Armed Services; Natural Resources
Dist. Offices: Phoenix, 602-256-0551

ARIZONA

Trent Franks (R-8th)　　　　　　**202-225-4576**
2435 RHOB　8th Term/69%　8/99/96　Fax: 225-6328
franks.house.gov　　　　　　**twitter** RepTrentFranks
CoS .... Jonathan Hayes　**LD** ....Bobby Cornett
Sch ....Lisa Teschler　**CD** .... Destiny Edwards
Bio: b. 6/19/57 Uravan, CO; Baptist; Attended Ottawa Univ., 1989-90; Oil Company Executive, Commentator; m. Josephine
Comm.: Armed Services; Judiciary
Dist. Offices: Glendale, 623-776-7911

Kyrsten Sinema (D-9th)
KEER-sten SIN-eh-ma (like "cinema")　**202-225-9888**
1725 LHOB　3rd Term/61%　51/72/97　Fax: 225-9731
sinema.house.gov　　　　　　**twitter** repsinema
CoS .... Meg Joseph　**LD** ....Alyssa Marois
Sch ....Kate Gonzales　**CD** ....Macey Matthews
Bio: b. 7/12/76 Tucson, AZ; None; PhD AZ St. Univ., 2012; Attorney, College Instructor, Social Worker; single
Comm.: Financial Services
Dist. Offices: Phoenix, 602-956-2285

ARKANSAS
arkansas.gov

Pop.: 2,978,204　**Rank:** 33rd
Caucasian: 80%　**African-Am.:** 16%
Nat. Am.: 1%　**Asian:** 2%
Other: 2%　**Hisp.:** 7%
Reg. Voters: 1,703,609
Party registration not required
Land Area: 52,035 sq. mi.
Rank: 27th

Number of US House Seats: 4 Rep.

State Legislature
arkleg.state.ar.us
Senate: 24R/11D　House: 76R/24D
Session: 01/09/17 – 3/9/2017

Gov. Asa Hutchinson (R)　　　**501-682-2345**
Next Election: 2018　1st Term/55%　Fax: 501-682-1382
twitter asahutchinson

Bio: b. 12/3/50 Bentonville, AR; Southern Baptist; JD Univ. of AR, 1975; Attorney; m. Susan

State Capitol, Room 250, Little Rock, AR 72201
Washington Office: 202-220-1329

SENATE

John Boozman (R) *BOZE-man*　　**202-224-4843**
SH-141　2nd Term/60%　50/91/99　Fax: 228-1371
flake.senate.gov　　　　　　**twitter** JohnBoozman
CoS ....Helen Tolar　**LD** .... Toni-Marie Higgins
Sch ....Kelsi Daniell　**CD** .... Sara Lasure
Bio: b. 12/10/50 Shreveport, LA; Baptist; OD Southern Col. of Optometry, 1977; Optometrist, Rancher; m. Cathy
Comm.: Agriculture, Nutrition & Forestry; Appropriations; Budget; Environment & Public Works; Veterans' Affairs; Joint Printing
Dist. Offices: Little Rock, 501-372-7153; Ft. Smith, 479-573-0189; Lowell, 479-725-0400; Mountain Home, 870-424-0129; Jonesboro, 870-268-6925; Stuttgart, 870-672-6941; El Dorado, 870-863-4641

ARKANSAS

Tom Cotton (R)   **202-224-2353**
SR-124   1st Term/56%   44/96/94   Fax: None
501-223-9105
cotton.senate.gov   **twitter** sentomcotton
CoS ....Doug Coutts **LD** ....John Martin
Sch ....Chloe Pickle **CD** ....Caroline Rabbitt
Bio: b. 5/13/77 Dardanelle, AR; Methodist; JD Harvard Univ., 2002; USA, 2004-09; Management Consultant, Attorney; m. Anna
Comm.: Armed Services; Banking, Housing, & Urban Affairs; Select Intelligence; Joint Economic
Dist. Offices: Little Rock, 501-223-9081; Springdale, 479-751-0879; El Dorado, 870-864-8582; Jonesboro, 870-933-6223

HOUSE

Rick Crawford (R-1st)   **202-225-4076**
2422 RHOB   4th Term/77%   8/99/96   Fax: 225-5602
crawford.house.gov   **twitter** RepRickCrawford
CoS ....Jonah Shumate **LD** ....Chris Jones
Sch ....Courtney Handey **Press**.................James Arnold
Bio: b. 1/22/66 Homestead AFB, FL; Southern Baptist; BS AR St. Univ., 1996; USA, 1985-89; Broadcaster, Ag News Service Owner; m. Stacy
Comm.: Agriculture; Transportation & Infrastructure; Select Intelligence
Dist. Offices: Jonesboro, 870-203-0540; Cabot, 501-843-3043; Mountain Home, 870-424-2075

French Hill (R-2nd)   **202-225-2506**
1229 LHOB   2nd Term/58%   7/97/99   Fax: 225-5903
hill.house.gov   **twitter** RepFrenchHill
CoS ....A. Brooke Bennett **LD** ....Peter Comstock
Sch ....Anna Wilbourn **CD** ....Mike Siegel
Bio: b. 12/5/56 Little Rock, AR; Catholic; BS Vanderbilt Univ., 1979; Bank Executive, White House Aide, Congressional Aide; m. Martha
Comm.: Financial Services
Dist. Offices: Little Rock, 501-324-5941; Conway, 501-358-3481

Steve Womack (R-3rd)   **202-225-4301**
2412 RHOB   4th Term/77%   7/97/100   Fax: 225-5713
womack.house.gov   **twitter** rep_stevewomack
CoS ....Beau Walker **LD** .... Adrielle Churchill
Sch ....Aimee Rosen **CD** ....Claire Burghoff
Bio: b. 2/18/57 Russellville, AR; Southern Baptist; BA AR Tech Univ., 1979; ARNG, 1979-2009; Securities Broker, Radio Station Manager; m. Terri
Comm.: Appropriations; Budget
Dist. Offices: Rogers, 479-464-0446; Harrison, 870-741-6900; Ft. Smith, 479-424-1146

Bruce Westerman (R-4th)   **202-225-3772**
130 CHOB   2nd Term/74%   9/99/99   Fax: 225-1314
westerman.house.gov   **twitter** RepWesterman
CoS ....Vivian Moeglein **LD** ....Jonathan Shuffield
Sch ....Darbie Koykendall **Press**...................Ryan Saylor
Bio: b. 11/18/67 Hot Springs, AR; Southern Baptist; MF Yale Univ., 2001; Agricultural Engineer; m. Sharon
Comm.: Budget; Natural Resources; Transportation & Infrastructure
Dist. Offices: Hot Springs, 501-609-9796; El Dorado, 870-864-8946; Pine Bluff, 870-536-8178; Ozark, 479-667-0075

CALIFORNIA
ca.gov

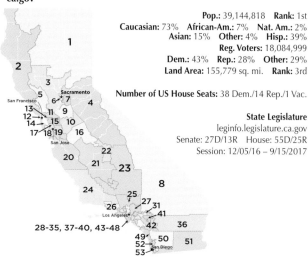

Pop.: 39,144,818   **Rank:** 1st
Caucasian: 73%   **African-Am.:** 7%   **Nat. Am.:** 2%
Asian: 15%   **Other:** 4%   **Hisp.:** 39%
Reg. Voters: 18,084,999
Dem.: 43%   **Rep.:** 28%   **Other:** 29%
Land Area: 155,779 sq. mi.   **Rank:** 3rd

Number of US House Seats: 38 Dem./14 Rep./1 Vac.

State Legislature
leginfo.legislature.ca.gov
Senate: 27D/13R   House: 55D/25R
Session: 12/05/16 – 9/15/2017

Gov. Jerry Brown (D)   **916-445-2841**
Next Election: 2018   4th Term/60%   Fax: 916-558-3160
twitter jerrybrowngov

Bio: b. 4/7/38 San Francisco, CA; Catholic; LLB Yale Univ.,
1964; Public Official; m. Anne Gust

State Capitol Building, Suite 1173, Sacramento, CA 95814
Washington Office: 202-624-5270

SENATE

Dianne Feinstein (D) *FINE-stine*   **202-224-3841**
SH-331   5th Term/63%   93/89/98   Fax: 228-3954
feinstein.senate.gov   twitter senfeinstein
CoS .... Steve Haro   **LD** .... John Watts
Sch .... Chesna Foord   **CD** .... Tom Mentzer
Bio: b. 6/22/33 San Francisco, CA; Jewish; AB Stanford Univ.,
1955; Public Official; m. Richard Blum
Comm.: Appropriations; Judiciary (Rnk. Mem.); Rules &
Administration; Select Intelligence
Dist. Offices: San Francisco, 415-393-0707; Fresno, 559-485-
7430; Los Angeles, 310-914-7300; San Diego, 619-231-9712

Kamala D. Harris (D) *COM-uh-la*   **202-224-3553**
SH-112   1st Term/62%   Fax: 224-0454
harris.senate.gov   twitter KamalaHarris
CoS .... Nathan Barankin   **LD** .... Clint Odom
Sch .... Shaeda Ahmadi   **Press** .... Tyrone Gayle
Bio: b. 10/20/64 Oakland, CA; Baptist; JD Univ. of CA - Hast-
ings, 1989; Attorney; m. Doug Emhoff
Comm.: Budget; Environment & Public Works; Homeland
Security & Governmental Affairs; Select Intelligence
Dist. Offices: Los Angeles, 213-894-5000; San Diego,
619-239-3884; Sacramento, 916-448-2787; San Francisco,
916-448-2787

HOUSE

Doug LaMalfa (R-1st)   **202-225-3076**
322 CHOB   3rd Term/59%   9/99/96   Fax: 226-0852
lamalfa.house.gov   twitter replamalfa
CoS .... Mark Spannagel   **LD** .... Kevin Eastman
Sch .... Meredith Kroft   **CD** .... Parker Williams
Bio: b. 7/2/60 Oroville, CA; Christian; BS CA Poly St. Univ.,
1982; Farmer; m. Jill
Comm.: Agriculture; Natural Resources; Transportation &
Infrastructure
Dist. Offices: Oroville, 530-534-7100; Redding, 530-223-
5898; Auburn, 530-878-5035

CALIFORNIA

Jared Huffman (D-2nd)　　　　　**202-225-5161**
1406 LHOB　3rd Term/76%　98/99/98　Fax: 225-5163
huffman.house.gov　　　　　　　twitter rephuffman
CoS .... Ben Miller **LD** .... Logan Ferree
Sch .... Kellie Luke **CD** .... Alexa Shaffer
Bio: b. 2/18/64 Independence, MO; Not Stated; JD Boston
Col., 1990; Attorney; m. Susan
Comm.: Natural Resources; Transportation & Infrastructure
Dist. Offices: San Rafael, 415-258-9657; Eureka, 707-407-
3585; Ft. Bragg, 707-962-0933; Petaluma, 707-981-8967;
Ukiah, 707-671-7449

John Garamendi (D-3rd)　　　　**202-225-1880**
2438 RHOB　5th Term/59%　87/95/97　Fax: 225-5914
garamendi.house.gov　　　　　twitter RepGaramendi
Acting CoS .... Emily Burns **LD** .... Garrett Durst
Sch .... Nicole McAllister **CD** .... Donald Lathbury
Bio: b. 1/24/45 Camp Blanding, FL; Christian; MBA Harvard
Univ., 1970; Public Official, Rancher; m. Patti
Comm.: Armed Services; Transportation & Infrastructure
Dist. Offices: Davis, 530-753-5301; Fairfield, 707-438-1822;
Yuba City, 530-329-8865

Tom McClintock (R-4th)　　　　**202-225-2511**
2312 RHOB　5th Term/62%　7/97/100　Fax: 225-5444
mcclintock.house.gov　　　　twitter RepMcClintock
CoS .... Igor Birman **LD** .... Chris Tudor
Sch .... Rachel Long **CD** .... Jennifer Cressy
Bio: b. 7/10/56 Bronxville, NY; Baptist; BA Univ. of CA -
Los Angeles, 1978; Public Policy Analyst, State Legislative
Aide; m. Lori
Comm.: Budget; Natural Resources
Dist. Offices: Roseville, 916-786-5560

Mike Thompson (D-5th)　　　　**202-225-3311**
231 CHOB　10th Term/77%　98/98/99　Fax: 225-4335
mikethompson.house.gov　　　twitter RepThompson
CoS .... Melanie Rhinehart **LD** .... Jennifer Goedke
　　　　　　Van Tassell
Sch .... Blair Mallin **Press** .... Amanda Schoen
Bio: b. 1/24/51 St. Helena, CA; Catholic; MA CA St. Univ.
- Chico, 1996; USA, 1969-73; Grape Farmer, Public Of-
ficial; m. Janet
Comm.: Ways & Means
Dist. Offices: Napa, 707-226-9898; Vallejo, 707-645-1888;
Santa Rosa, 707-542-7182

Doris Matsui (D-6th)　　　　　**202-225-7163**
2311 RHOB　7th Term/75%　98/99/99　Fax: 225-0566
matsui.house.gov　　　　　　twitter DorisMatsui
CoS .... Julie Eddy **LD** .... Margaret McCarthy
Sch .... McKinley Krongaus **Press** .... Lauren Dart
Bio: b. 9/25/44 Poston, AZ; Methodist; BA Univ. of CA -
Berkeley, 1966; Lobbyist, White House Aide; wid.
Comm.: Energy & Commerce
Dist. Offices: Sacramento, 916-498-5600

Ami Bera (D-7th) *AH-mi BEAR-uh*　**202-225-5716**
1431 LHOB　3rd Term/51%　80/92/99　Fax: 226-1298
bera.house.gov　　　　　　twitter RepBera
CoS .... Chad Obermiller **LD** .... Erin O'Quinn
Sch .... Marguerite Biagi **CD** .... Annie Ellison
Bio: b. 3/2/65 Los Angeles, CA; Unitarian; MD Univ. of CA
- Irvine, 1991; Physician, Professor; m. Janine
Comm.: Foreign Affairs; Science, Space & Technology
Dist. Offices: Sacramento, 916-635-0505

CALIFORNIA

Paul Cook (R-8th)   **202-225-5861**
1222 LHOB   3rd Term/64%   6/97/97   Fax: 225-6498
cook.house.gov   twitter RepPaulCook
CoS ....John Sobel **LD** .... Tim Itnyre
Sch ....Bert Johnson **CD** ....Michael Fresquez
Bio: b. 3/3/43 Meriden, CT; Catholic; MA Univ. of CA - Riverside, 2000; USMC, 1966-92; Professor, Marine Corps Officer; m. Jeanne
Comm.: Armed Services; Foreign Affairs; Natural Resources
Dist. Offices: Apple Valley, 760-247-1815

Jerry McNerney (D-9th)   **202-225-1947**
2265 RHOB   6th Term/57%   94/97/99   Fax: 225-4060
mcnerney.house.gov   twitter RepMcNerney
CoS ....Nicole Alioto **LD** ....Patrick Arness
Sch .... Teresa Frison **CD** .... Vacant
Bio: b. 6/18/51 Albuquerque, NM; Catholic; PhD Univ. of NM, 1981; Wind Engineer, Entrepreneur; m. Mary
Comm.: Energy & Commerce; Science, Space & Technology
Dist. Offices: Stockton, 209-476-8552; Antioch, 925-754-0716

Jeff Denham (R-10th)   **202-225-4540**
1730 LHOB   4th Term/52%   8/93/99   Fax: 225-3402
denham.house.gov   twitter RepJeffDenham
CoS ....Jason Larrabee **LD** .... Bret Manley
Sch .... Carol Kresse **Press**............. Jessica McFaul
Bio: b. 7/29/67 Hawthorne, CA; Presbyterian; BA CA Poly St. Univ., 1992; USAF, 1984-88; USAFR, 1988-2000; Business Owner; m. Sonia
Comm.: Agriculture; Natural Resources; Transportation & Infrastructure
Dist. Offices: Modesto, 209-579-5458

Mark DeSaulnier (D-11th) *de-SAWN-yay* **202-225-2095**
115 CHOB   2nd Term/71%   98/99/99   Fax: 225-5609
desaulnier.house.gov   twitter RepDeSaulnier
CoS .... Betsy Arnold Marr **LD** ....Mark Copeland
Sch .... Alexandra Fox **CD** ....Betsy Arnold Marr
Bio: b. 3/31/52 Lowell, MA; Catholic; BA Col. of the Holy Cross, 1974; Restaurateur; div.
Comm.: Education & the Workforce; Oversight & Government Reform; Transportation & Infrastructure
Dist. Offices: Richmond, 510-620-1000; Walnut Creek, 925-933-2660

Nancy Pelosi (D-12th)   **202-225-4965**
233 CHOB   16th Term/82%   98/99/88   Fax: 225-8259
pelosi.house.gov   twitter nancypelosi
CoS ....Robert Edmonson **LD** ....Dick Meltzer
Sch ....Kelsey Smith **Dep. CoS**.......Drew Hammill
Bio: b. 3/26/40 Baltimore, MD; Catholic; AB Trinity Col. (DC), 1962; Public Relations Consultant; m. Paul
Comm.: Minority Leader
Dist. Offices: San Francisco, 415-556-4862

Barbara Lee (D-13th)   **202-225-2661**
2267 RHOB   11th Term/90%   98/100/92   Fax: 225-9817
lee.house.gov   twitter repbarbaralee
CoS ....Julie Little Nickson **LD** ....Emma Mehrabi
Sch ....Christopher Livingston **CD** ....Christopher Huntley
Bio: b. 7/16/46 El Paso, TX; Baptist; MSW Univ. of CA - Berkeley, 1975; Congressional Aide; div.
Comm.: Appropriations; Budget
Dist. Offices: Oakland, 510-763-0370

CALIFORNIA

Jackie Speier (D-14th) *SPEAR* **202-225-3531**
2465 RHOB   6th Term/81%   96/98/93   Fax: 226-4183
speier.house.gov   twitter RepSpeier
CoS ....Josh Connolly   **LD** ....Miriam Goldstein
Sch .... Angela Chasebi   **CD** .... Tracy Manzer
Bio: b. 5/14/50 San Francisco, CA; Catholic; JD Univ. of CA - Hastings, 1976; Attorney, Congressional Aide; m. Barry Dennis
Comm.: Armed Services; Select Intelligence
Dist. Offices: San Mateo, 650-342-0300

Eric Swalwell (D-15th) **202-225-5065**
129 CHOB   3rd Term/73%   96/98/93   Fax: 226-3805
swalwell.house.gov   twitter repswalwell
CoS .... Ricky Le   **LD** ....Andrew Ginsburg
Sch .... Carly Reed   **CD** ....Josh Richman
Bio: b. 11/16/80 Sac City, IA; Christian; JD Univ. of MD, 2006; County Prosecutor; m. Brittany
Comm.: Judiciary; Select Intelligence
Dist. Offices: Pleasanton, 925-460-5100; Hayward, 510-370-3322

Jim Costa (D-16th) **202-225-3341**
2081 RHOB   7th Term/55%   57/69/95   Fax: 225-9308
costa.house.gov   twitter RepJimCosta
CoS .... Juan Lopez   **LD** ....Scott Petersen
Sch .... Claudia Santiago   **Press**.............Kristina Solberg
Bio: b. 4/13/52 Fresno, CA; Catholic; BA CA St. Univ. - Fresno, 1974; Public Official, Government Relations Executive; single
Comm.: Agriculture; Natural Resources
Dist. Offices: Fresno, 559-495-1620; Merced, 209-384-1620

Ro Khanna (D-17th) **202-225-2631**
513 CHOB   1st Term/59%   Fax: 225-2699
khanna.house.gov   twitter RepRoKhanna
CoS .... Pete Spiro   **LD** ....Chris Schloesser
Sch ....Angela Valles   **CD** .... Liz Bartolomeo
Bio: b. 9/13/76 Philadelphia, PA; Hindu; JD Yale Univ., 2001; Attorney; m. Ritu
Comm.: Armed Services; Budget
Dist. Offices: Santa Clara, 408-436-2720

Anna G. Eshoo (D-18th) **202-225-8104**
241 CHOB   13th Term/72%   96/98/99   Fax: 225-8890
eshoo.house.gov   twitter RepAnnaEshoo
Dist. CoS .... Karen Chapman   **LD** .... Matthew McMurray
Sch .... Anna Perry   **Press**.................Emma Crisci
Bio: b. 12/13/42 New Britain, CT; Catholic; AA Canada Col., 1975; Public Official, State Legislative Aide; div.
Comm.: Energy & Commerce
Dist. Offices: Palo Alto, 650-323-2984

Zoe Lofgren (D-19th) *ZO LOFF-gren* **202-225-3072**
1401 LHOB   12th Term/74%   96/98/98   Fax: 225-3336
lofgren.house.gov   twitter RepZoeLofgren
CoS ....Stacey Leavandosky   **LD** .... Stacey Leavandosky
Sch .... Andrew DeLuca   **CD** .... Peter Whippy
Bio: b. 12/21/42 San Mateo, CA; Lutheran; JD Univ. of Santa Clara, 1975; Attorney, Professor, Congressional Aide; m. John Marshall Collins
Comm.: House Administration; Judiciary; Science, Space & Technology; Joint Library
Dist. Offices: San Jose, 408-271-8700

Jimmy Panetta (D-20th) **202-225-2861**
228 CHOB   1st Term/71%   98/98/88   Fax: 225-6791
panetta.house.gov   twitter RepJimmyPanetta
CoS .... Tom Tucker **LD** .... Debbie Merrill
Sch .... Rose Leopold **Press**...................Sarah Davey
Bio: b. 10/1/69 Washington; Catholic; JD Santa Clara, 1996;
USNR, 2003-11; Deputy DA; m. Carrie McIntryre
Comm.: Agriculture; Natural Resources
Dist. Offices: Salinas, 831-424-2229; Santa Cruz, 831-
429-1976

David Valadao (R-21st) *val-a-DAY-oh* **202-225-4695**
1728 LHOB   3rd Term/58%   7/93/99   Fax: 225-3196
valadao.house.gov   twitter repdavidvaladao
CoS .... Cole Rojewski **LD** ....Kristina Dunklin
Sch .... Allison Rosa **CD** .... Anna Vetter
Bio: b. 4/14/77 Hanford, CA; Catholic; Attended Col. of the
Sequoias, 1996-98; Dairy Farmer; m. Terra
Comm.: Appropriations
Dist. Offices: Hanford, 559-582-5526; Bakersfield, 661-
864-7736

Devin Nunes (R-22nd) *NEW-ness* **202-225-2523**
1013 LHOB   8th Term/68%   9/96/99   Fax: 225-3404
nunes.house.gov   twitter DevinNunes
CoS ....Anthony Ratekin **LD** ....Jilian Plank
Sch .... Jennifer Morrow **CD** .... Jack Langer
Bio: b. 10/1/73 Tulare, CA; Catholic; MS CA Poly St. Univ.,
1996; Farmer, USDA Program Administrator; m. Elizabeth
Comm.: Ways & Means, Select Intelligence (Chair); Joint
Taxation
Dist. Offices: Visalia, 559-733-3861; Clovis, 559-323-5235

Kevin McCarthy (R-23rd)   **202-225-2915**
2421 RHOB   6th Term/71%   8/98/97   Fax: 225-2908
kevinmccarthy.house.gov   twitter GOPLeader
CoS .... James Min **LD** ....Kyle Lombardi
Sch .... Alexandra Gourdikian **CD** ....Mike Long
Bio: b. 1/26/65 Bakersfield, CA; Baptist; MBA CA St. Univ.
- Bakersfield, 1994; Congressional Aide, Sandwich Store
Owner; m. Judy
Comm.: Majority Leader
Dist. Offices: Bakersfield, 661-327-3611

Salud Carbajal *sa-LOOD car-ba-HALL* **202-225-3601**
  (D-24th)
212 CHOB   1st Term/54%   Fax: 225-5632
carbajal.house.gov   twitter RepCarbajal
CoS ....Jeremy Tittle **LD** .... Nancy Juarez
Sch ....Erin Sandlin **CD** .... Tess Whittlesey
Bio: b. 9/18/64 Moroleon, Mexico; Catholic; MA Fielding
U, 1994; USMCR, 1984-92; Aide; m. Gina
Comm.: Armed Services; Budget
Dist. Offices: San Luis Obispo, 805-546-8348; Santa Barbara,
805-546-8348

Steve Knight (R-25th)   **202-225-1956**
1023 LHOB   2nd Term/54%   6/98/99   Fax: 226-0683
knight.house.gov   twitter SteveKnight25
CoS ....Jeanette Whitener **LD** .... Vacant
Sch ....Andrea Grace **CD** ....Daniel Outlaw
Bio: b. 12/17/66 Edwards AFB, CA; Catholic; AA Antelope
Valley Col., 2006; USA, 1985-87; USAR, 1987-93; Police
Officer; m. Lily
Comm.: Armed Services; Science, Space & Technology;
Small Business
Dist. Offices: Palmdale, 661-441-0320

Julia Brownley (D-26th)   202-225-5811
1019 LHOB   3rd Term/60%   83/94/99   Fax: 225-1100
juliabrownley.house.gov   twitter JuliaBrownley26
CoS .... Lenny Young   **LD** .... Sharon Wagener
Sch .... Eva Gavrish   **CD** .... Darwin Pham
Bio: b. 8/28/52 Aiken, SC; Episcopal; MBA American Univ., 1979; Public Official, Businesswoman; div.
Comm.: Transportation & Infrastructure; Veterans' Affairs
Dist. Offices: Oxnard, 805-379-1779; Thousand Oaks, 805-379-1779

Judy Chu (D-27th)   202-225-5464
2423 RHOB   5th Term/65%   96/100/95   Fax: 225-5467
chu.house.gov   twitter RepJudyChu
CoS .... Linda Shim   **LD** .... Sonali Desai
Sch .... Joanna Barrett   **Press** .... Ben Suarato
Bio: b. 7/7/53 Los Angeles, CA; Not Stated; PhD CA School of Professional Psychology, 1979; Professor, Public Official; m. Mike Eng
Comm.: Small Business; Ways & Means
Dist. Offices: Pasadena, 626-304-0110; Claremont, 909-625-5394

Adam B. Schiff (D-28th)   202-225-4176
2372 RHOB   9th Term/77%   98/98/97   Fax: 225-5828
schiff.house.gov   twitter RepAdamSchiff
CoS .... Jeff Lowenstein   **LD** .... Joe Jankiewicz
Appt .... Christopher Hoven   **CD** .... Patrick Boland
Bio: b. 6/22/60 Framingham, MA; Jewish; JD Harvard Univ., 1985; Attorney, Federal Prosecutor; m. Eve
Comm.: Select Intelligence (Rnk. Mem.)
Dist. Offices: Burbank, 818-450-2900

Tony Cárdenas (D-29th)   202-225-6131
1510 LHOB   3rd Term/75%   88/97/89   Fax: 225-0819
cardenas.house.gov   twitter repcardenas
CoS .... Miguel Franco   **LD** .... Jacqueline Usyk
Sch .... Mark Foley   **CD** .... Francesca Amodeo
Bio: b. 3/31/63 San Fernando, CA; Christian; BS Univ. of CA - Santa Barbara, 1986; Real Estate Company Owner, Insurance Agent; m. Norma
Comm.: Energy & Commerce
Dist. Offices: Panorama City, 818-781-7407

Brad Sherman (D-30th)   202-225-5911
2181 RHOB   11th Term/72%   91/95/98   Fax: 225-5879
bradsherman.house.gov   twitter BradSherman
CoS .... Don MacDonald   **LD** .... Lauren Wolman
Sch .... Ashley Pennington   **CD** .... Shane Seaver
Bio: b. 10/24/54 Los Angeles, CA; Jewish; JD Harvard Univ., 1979; Attorney, Accountant; m. Lisa
Comm.: Financial Services; Foreign Affairs
Dist. Offices: Sherman Oaks, 818-501-9200

Pete Aguilar (D-31st)   202-225-3201
1223 LHOB   2nd Term/55%   80/91/99   Fax: 226-6962
aguilar.house.gov   twitter reppeteaguilar
CoS ...... Boris Medzhibovsky   **LD** .... Becky Cornell
Sch .... Danielle Giulino   **CD** .... Sarah Weinstein
Bio: b. 6/19/79 Fontana, CA; Catholic; BS Univ. of Redlands, 2001; Public Affairs Firm Owner, Gubernatorial Aide; m. Alisha
Comm.: Appropriations
Dist. Offices: San Bernardino, 909-890-4445

Grace F. Napolitano (D-32nd)   **202-225-5256**
1610 LHOB   10th Term/62%   98/100/94   Fax: 225-0027
napolitano.house.gov   *twitter* gracenapolitano
CoS ....Daniel Chao **LD** ....Joe Sheehy
Sch .... Joseph Ciccone **Press**............ Jerry O'Donnell
Bio: b. 12/4/36 Brownsville, TX; Catholic; HS Diploma; Public Official, Transportation Claims Agent; m. Frank
Comm.: Natural Resources; Transportation & Infrastructure
Dist. Offices: El Monte, 626-350-0150

Ted Lieu (D-33rd) *LOO*   **202-225-3976**
236 CHOB   2nd Term/66%   93/98/85   Fax: 225-4099
lieu.house.gov   *twitter* reptedlieu
CoS ....Marc Cevasco **Sr PA** ....Corey Jacobson
Sch .... Jackie Conley **CD** ....Jack d'Annibale
Bio: b. 3/29/69 Taipei, Taiwan; Catholic; JD Georgetown Univ., 1994; USAF, 1995-99; USAFR, 2000-present; Attorney; m. Betty Chim
Comm.: Foreign Affairs; Judiciary
Dist. Offices: Los Angeles, 323-651-1040; Manhattan Beach, 310-321-7664

OPEN SEAT

Vacant (34th)   **202-225-6235**
1226 LHOB
Rep. Xavier Becerra (D) resigned on January 24, 2017. A special election has been scheduled for June, 6, 2017.

Norma J. Torres (D-35th)   **202-225-6161**
1713 LHOB   2nd Term/71%   92/96/98   Fax: 225-8671
torres.house.gov   *twitter* NormaJTorres
CoS ....Dana Cohen **LD** ....Justin Vogt
Sch ....Bambi Yingst **CD** ....Anna Gonzalez
Bio: b. 4/23/65 Escuintla, Guatemala; Catholic; BA National Labor Col., 2012; Emergency Dispatcher; m. Louis
Comm.: Foreign Affairs; Natural Resources
Dist. Offices: Ontario, 909-481-6474

Raul Ruiz (D-36th)   **202-225-5330**
1319 LHOB   3rd Term/61%   83/93/99   Fax: 225-1238
ruiz.house.gov   *twitter* CongressmanRuiz
CoS ....Sarah Rubinfield **LD** .... Erin Doty
Sch .... Lauren Heasley **Press**...Alexandra Macfarlane
Bio: b. 8/25/72 Zacatecas, Mexico; Seventh-Day Adventist; MPH Harvard Univ., 2007; Physician; m. Monica Rivers
Comm.: Energy & Commerce
Dist. Offices: Palm Desert, 760-424-8888; Hemet, 951-765-2304

Karen Bass (D-37th)   **202-225-7084**
2241 RHOB   4th Term/82%   100/99/88   Fax: 225-2422
bass.house.gov   *twitter* RepKarenBass
CoS ....Carrie Kohns **LD** ....Janice Bashford
Sch .... Bridget Brennan **Press**.................... Zach Seidl
Bio: b. 10/3/53 Los Angeles, CA; Baptist; BS CA St. Univ. - Dominguez Hills, 1990; College Instructor, Physician Assistant; div.
Comm.: Foreign Affairs; Judiciary
Dist. Offices: Los Angeles, 323-965-1422

CALIFORNIA

Linda T. Sánchez (D-38th) 202-225-6676
2329 RHOB 8th Term/69% 98/99/96 Fax: 226-1012
lindasanchez.house.gov **twitter** RepLindaSanchez
CoS ....Lea Sulkala **LD** ....Melissa Kiedrowicz
Sch ....Juan Rangel **CD** ....Alex Nguyen
Bio: b. 1/28/69 Orange, CA; Catholic; JD Univ. of CA - Los
Angeles, 1995; Union Official, Attorney; m. Jim Sullivan
Comm.: Ways & Means
Dist. Offices: Cerritos, 562-860-5050

Ed Royce (R-39th) 202-225-4111
2310 RHOB 13th Term/58% 7/96/99 Fax: 226-0335
royce.house.gov **twitter** RepEdRoyce
CoS .... Amy Porter **LD** ....Peter Freeman
Sch ....Kate Barlow **CD** ....Saat Alety
Bio: b. 10/12/51 Los Angeles, CA; Catholic; BA CA St. Univ.
- Fullerton, 1977; Tax Manager; m. Marie
Comm.: Financial Services; Foreign Affairs (Chair)
Dist. Offices: Brea, 714-255-0101; Rowland Heights, 626-
964-5123

Lucille Roybal-Allard (D-40th) 202-225-1766
2083 RHOB 13th Term/72% 98/99/98 Fax: 226-0350
roybal-allard.house.gov **twitter** RepRoybalAllard
CoS ....Victor Castillo **LD** .... Joe Racalto
Sch ....Christine Ochoa **CD** ....Benjamin Soskin
Bio: b. 6/12/41 Boyle Heights, CA; Catholic; BA CA St. Univ.
- Los Angeles, 1965; Nonprofit Worker; m. Edward Allard III
Comm.: Appropriations
Dist. Offices: Commerce, 323-721-8790

Mark Takano (D-41st) 202-225-2305
1507 LHOB 3rd Term/62% 100/99/99 Fax: 225-7018
takano.house.gov **twitter** RepMarkTakano
CoS ....Richard McPike **LD** ....Yuri Beckelman
Sch .... Valeria Conti **CD** ....Josh Weisz
Bio: b. 12/10/60 Riverside, CA; Methodist; MFA Univ. of
CA - Riverside, 2010; Teacher; single
Comm.: Education & the Workforce; Science, Space &
Technology; Veterans' Affairs
Dist. Offices: Riverside, 951-222-0203

Ken Calvert (R-42nd) 202-225-1986
2205 RHOB 13th Term/60% 7/95/98 Fax: 225-2004
calvert.house.gov **twitter** KenCalvert
CoS ....Dave Kennett **LD** .... Rebecca Keightley
Sch .... Tricia Evans **CD** ....Jason Gagnon
Bio: b. 6/8/53 Corona, CA; Episcopal; BA San Diego St.
Univ., 1975; Real Estate Executive, Restaurant Executive; div.
Comm.: Appropriations
Dist. Offices: Corona, 951-277-0042

Maxine Waters (D-43rd) 202-225-2201
2221 RHOB 14th Term/75% 98/98/89 Fax: 225-7854
waters.house.gov **twitter** maxinewaters
CoS ....Twaun Samuel **LD** ....Jason Powell
Sch .... Dustin Brandenburg **CD** .... Vacant
Bio: b. 8/15/38 St. Louis, MO; Christian; BA CA St. Univ. -
Los Angeles, 1970; Public Official, City Council Aide; m.
Sidney Williams
Comm.: Financial Services (Rnk. Mem.)
Dist. Offices: Los Angeles, 323-757-8900

CALIFORNIA

Nanette Barragán *berra-GAHN*
(D-44th)   **202-225-8220**
1320 LHOB   1st Term/51%   Fax: 226-7290
barragan.house.gov   twitter RepBarragan
CoS ....Marsha Catron LD.................Javier Gamboa
Sch ...... Jonathan Cousimano CD .... Vacant
Bio: b. 9/15/76 San Pedro, CA; Catholic; JD USC, 2005;
Attorney; single
Comm.: Homeland Security; Natural Resources
Dist. Offices: South Gate, 323-563-9562

Mimi Walters (R-45th)   **202-225-5611**
215 CHOB   2nd Term/60%   8/97/91   Fax: 225-9177
walters.house.gov   twitter RepMimiWalters
CoS ....Sam Oh LD.............Casey Fitzpatrick
Sch ....Cody Lalibert CD .... Abigail Sigler
Bio: b. 5/14/62 Pasadena, CA; Catholic; BA Univ. of CA - Los
Angeles, 1984; Investment Bank Executive; m. David
Comm.: Energy & Commerce
Dist. Offices: Irvine, 949-263-8703

Lou Correa (D-46th)   **202-225-2965**
1039 LHOB   1st Term/70%   Fax: 225-5859
correa.house.gov   twitter RepLouCorrea
CoS ....Laurie Saroff LD...........Alejandro Renteria
Sch ....Julia Kermott CD .... Andrew Scibetta
Bio: b. 1/24/58 Los Angeles, CA; Catholic; MBA/JD UCLA,
1985; Attorney, Broker; m. Esther
Comm.: Homeland Security; Veterans' Affairs
Dist. Offices: Santa Ana, 202-738-6726

Alan Lowenthal (D-47th)   **202-225-7924**
125 CHOB   3rd Term/62%   96/99/98 Fax: 225-7926
lowenthal.house.gov   twitter RepLowenthal
CoS ....Tim Hysom LD.................Rachel Gentile
Sch ....Emily Strombom CD ....Keith Higginbotham
Bio: b. 3/8/41 Manhattan, NY; Jewish; PhD OH St. Univ.,
1967; College Professor, Psychologist; m. Deborah Malumed
Comm.: Natural Resources; Transportation & Infrastructure
Dist. Offices: Long Beach, 562-436-3828

Dana Rohrabacher (R-48th)
   ROAR-ah-BAH-ker
2300 RHOB   15th Term/59% 6/96/92   Fax: 225-0145
rohrabacher.house.gov   twitter DanaRohrabacher
CoS ....Rick Dykema LD................ Jeff Vanderslice
Sch ....Justin Ahn CD ....Ken Grubbs
Bio: b. 6/21/47 Coronado, CA; Christian; MA Univ. of Southern
CA, 1971; Speechwriter, Newspaper Reporter; m. Rhonda
Comm.: Foreign Affairs; Science, Space & Technology
Dist. Offices: Huntington Beach, 714-960-6483

Darrell Issa (R-49th) *EYE-sah*   **202-225-3906**
2269 RHOB   9th Term/51%   6/96/93   Fax: 225-3303
issa.house.gov   twitter DarrellIssa
CoS .... Veronica Wong LD................ Tyler Grimm
Sch ....Katie Weiss CD ....Calvin Moore
Bio: b. 11/1/53 Cleveland, OH; Antioch Orthodox Christian;
BA Siena Heights Col., 1976; USA, 1970-72, 1976-80; USAR,
1980-88; Car Alarm Company Owner; m. Kathy
Comm.: Foreign Affairs; Judiciary; Oversight & Government Reform
Dist. Offices: Vista, 760-599-5000

CALIFORNIA

Duncan Hunter (R-50th)   **202-225-5672**
2429 RHOB   5th Term/64%   8/98/97   Fax: 225-0235
hunter.house.gov   twitter Rep_Hunter
CoS .... Joe Kasper **LD** .... Reed Linsk
Sch ....Liz Argo **CD** ....Joe Kasper
Bio: b. 12/7/76 San Diego, CA; Baptist; BS San Diego St. Univ., 2001; USMC, 2002-05; USMCR, 2005-08; Business Analyst, Residential Real Estate Developer; m. Margaret
Comm.: Armed Services; Education & the Workforce; Transportation & Infrastructure
Dist. Offices: El Cajon, 619-448-5201; Temecula, 951-695-5108

Juan C. Vargas (D-51st)   **202-225-8045**
1605 LHOB   3rd Term/68%   87/96/99   Fax: 225-9073
vargas.house.gov   twitter RepJuanVargas
CoS .... Tim Walsh **LD** ....Scott Hinkle
Sch ....Christina Reyes **Press**........ Dayanara Ramirez
Bio: b. 3/7/61 National City, CA; Catholic; JD Harvard Univ., 1991; Missionary, Attorney; m. Adrienne
Comm.: Financial Services
Dist. Offices: Chula Vista, 619-422-5963; El Centro, 760-355-8800

Scott Peters (D-52nd)   **202-225-0508**
1122 LHOB   3rd Term/57%   66/88/99   Fax: 225-2558
scottpeters.house.gov   twitter repscottpeters
CoS .... Michelle Dorothy **LD** .... Daniel Zawitoski
Sch ....Baillee Brown **CD** ....Jacob Peters
Bio: b. 6/17/58 Springfield, OH; Lutheran; JD NYU, 1984; Attorney; m. Lynn Gorguze
Comm.: Energy & Commerce; Veterans' Affairs
Dist. Offices: San Diego, 858-455-5550

Susan A. Davis (D-53rd)   **202-225-2040**
1214 LHOB   9th Term/66%   98/96/98   Fax: 225-2948
susandavis.house.gov   twitter RepSusanDavis
CoS ....Lisa Sherman **LD** .... Matthew Weiner
Sch ....Cynthia Patton **Press**................Aaron Hunter
Bio: b. 4/13/44 Cambridge, MA; Jewish; MA Univ. of NC, 1968; Leadership Program Director, Social Worker; m. Steve
Comm.: Armed Services; Education & the Workforce
Dist. Offices: San Diego, 619-280-5353

COLORADO
colorado.gov

Pop.: 5,456,574   **Rank:** 22nd
Caucasian: 88%
African-Am.: 5%
Nat. Am.: 2%   **Asian:** 3%
Other: 3%   **Hisp.:** 21%
Reg. Voters: 3,299,036
Dem.: 31%   **Rep.:** 33%
Other: 36%
Land Area: 103,642 sq. mi.
Rank: 8th

Number of US House Seats: 4 Rep./3 Dem.

State Legislature
leg.colorado.gov
Senate: 18R/17D   House: 37D/28R
Session: 01/11/17– 5/10/2017

Colorado

Gov. John W. Hickenlooper (D)   303-866-2471
Next Election: 2018 2nd Term/49%   Fax: 303-866-2003
twitter hickforco
Bio: b. 2/7/52 Narberth, PA; Quaker; MS Wesleyan Univ., 1980; Geologist, Business Owner; div.

136 State Capitol, Denver, CO 80203-1792

SENATE

Michael Bennet (D)   202-224-5852
SR-261   3rd Term/49%   93/89/100 Fax: 228-5097
bennet.senate.gov   twitter SenBennetCo
CoS .... Jonathan Davidson **LD** .... Brian Appel
Sch .... Kristin Mollet **CD** .... Shannon Beckham
Bio: b. 11/28/64 New Delhi, India; Not Stated; JD Yale Univ.,1993; Attorney, Public Official; m. Susan Daggett
Comm.: Agriculture, Nutrition & Forestry; Finance; Health, Education, Labor & Pensions
Dist. Offices: Denver, 303-455-7600; Durango, 970-259-1710; Colorado Springs, 719-328-1100; Ft. Collins, 970-224-2200; Grand Junction, 970-241-6631; Pueblo, 719-542-7550; Alamosa, 719-587-0096

Cory Gardner (R)   202-224-5941
SR-354   1st Term/48%   55/85/97   Fax: 224-6524
gardner.senate.gov   twitter sencorygardner
CoS .... Natalie Rogers **LD** .... Curtis Swager
Sch .... Amy Barrera **CD** .... Alex Siciliano
Bio: b. 8/22/74 Yuma, CO; Lutheran - Missouri Synod; JD Univ. of CO, 2001; Attorney, Congressional Aide; m. Jaime
Comm.: Budget; Commerce, Science & Transportation; Energy & Natural Resources
Dist. Offices: Denver, 303-391-5777; Grand Junction, 970-245-9553; Greeley, 970-352-5546; Yuma, 970-848-3095; Pueblo, 719-543-1324; Colorado Springs, 719-632-6706; Ft. Collins, 970-484-3502; Durango, 970-259-1231

HOUSE

Diana DeGette (D-1st) de-GET   **202-225-4431**
2111 RHOB   11th Term/68%   100/99/98 Fax: 225-5657
degette.house.gov   twitter RepDianaDeGette
CoS .... Lisa Cohen **LD** .... Eleanor Bastian
Sch .... Diana Gambrel **CD** .... Lynne Weil
Bio: b. 7/29/57 Tachikawa AFB, Japan; Presbyterian; JD NYU, 1982; Attorney, State Public Defender; m. Lino Lipinsky
Comm.: Energy & Commerce
Dist. Offices: Denver, 303-844-4988

Jared Polis (D-2nd)   202-225-2161
1727 LHOB   5th Term/57%   92/97/98   Fax: 226-7840
polis.house.gov   twitter RepJaredPolis
CoS .... Eve Lieberman **LD** .... Hilary Gawrilow
Sch .... Lona Watts **CD** .... Jessica Bralish
Bio: b. 5/12/75 Boulder, CO; Jewish; AB Princeton Univ., 1996; Internet Entrepreneur, Venture Capitalist; dp Marlon Reis
Comm.: Education & the Workforce; Ethics; Rules
Dist. Offices: Ft. Collins, 970-226-1239; Boulder, 303-484-9596; Frisco, 970-409-7301

Colorado

Scott Tipton (R-3rd)   **202-225-4761**
218 CHOB   4th Term/55%   7/98/99   Fax: 226-9669
tipton.house.gov   twitter reptipton
CoS ....Joshua Green LD ....Dustin Sherer
Sch ....Madeline Grant CD ....Liz Payne
Bio: b. 11/9/56 Espanola, NM; Anglican; BA Ft. Lewis Col., 1978; Pottery Company Owner; m. Jean
Comm.: Financial Services; Natural Resources
Dist. Offices: Grand Junction, 970-241-2499; Alamosa, 719-587-5105; Pueblo, 719-542-1073; Durango, 970-259-1490; Steamboat Springs, 970-640-9718

Ken Buck (R-4th)   **202-225-4676**
1130 LHOB   2nd Term/64%   11/98/99   Fax: 225-5870
buck.house.gov   twitter RepKenBuck
CoS ....Ritika Robertson LD .... Garrett Bess
Sch ....Carly Wortham CD ....Kyle Huwa
Bio: b. 2/16/59 Ossining, NY; Christian; JD Univ. of WY, 1985; Business Advisor, Federal Prosecutor, Congressional Aide, Attorney; m. Perry
Comm.: Judiciary; Rules
Dist. Offices: Greeley, 970-702-2136; Castle Rock, 720-639-9165; Sterling, 970-762-0109

Doug Lamborn (R-5th)   **202-225-4422**
2402 RHOB   6th Term/62%   6/99/97   Fax: 226-2638
lamborn.house.gov   twitter RepDLamborn
CoS ....Adam Magary LD ....James Thomas
Sch .... Alysa Davis CD ....Jarred Rego
Bio: b. 5/24/54 Leavenworth, KS; Christian; JD Univ. of KS, 1985; Attorney; m. Jeanie
Comm.: Armed Services; Natural Resources
Dist. Offices: Colorado Springs, 719-520-0055

Mike Coffman (R-6th)   **202-225-7882**
2443 RHOB   5th Term/52%   7/95/99   Fax: 226-4623
coffman.house.gov   twitter RepMikeCoffman
CoS ....Ben Stein LD ....Jeremy Lippert
Sch ....Michelle Patrick CD ....Daniel Bucheli
Bio: b. 3/19/55 Ft. Leonard Wood, MO; Methodist; BA Univ. of CO, 1979; USA,72-74;USAR,75-79;USMC,79-83;USMCR,83-94,05-06; Property Management Company Owner, Public Official; m. Cynthia
Comm.: Armed Services; Veterans' Affairs
Dist. Offices: Aurora, 720-748-7514

Ed Perlmutter (D-7th)   **202-225-2645**
1410 LHOB   6th Term/55%   93/95/97   Fax: 225-5278
perlmutter.house.gov   twitter RepPerlmutter
CoS .... Danielle LD .... Noah Marine
            Radovich-Piper
CO .... Alison Inderfurth CD ....Ashley Verville
Bio: b. 5/1/53 Denver, CO; Protestant; JD Univ. of CO, 1978; Attorney; m. Nancy
Comm.: Financial Services; Science, Space & Technology
Dist. Offices: Lakewood, 303-274-7944

CONNECTICUT
ct.gov

Pop.: 3,590,886   **Rank:** 29th
Caucasian: 81%
African-Am.: 12%
Nat. Am.: 1%   **Asian:** 5%
Other: 2%   **Hisp.:** 15%
Reg. Voters: 2,187,349
Dem.: 37%   **Rep.:** 20%
Other: 43%
Land Area: 4,842 sq. mi.
Rank: 48th

Number of US House Seats: 5 Dem.

State Legislature
cga.ct.gov
Senate: 17R/17D/2Vac   House: 78D/72R/1Vac
Session: 01/04/17 – 6/7/2017

Gov. Dannel P. Malloy (D)   860-566-4840
Next Election: 2018   2nd Term/51%   Fax: 860-524-7395
twitter govmalloyoffice
Bio: b. 7/21/55 Stamford, CT; Catholic; JD Boston Col., 1980;
Attorney; m. Cathy

210 Capitol Avenue, Hartford, CT 06106
Washington Office: 202-403-8654

SENATE

Richard Blumenthal (D)   202-224-2823
SH-706   2nd Term/63%   83/96/99   Fax: 224-9673
blumenthal.senate.gov   **twitter** SenBlumenthal
CoS ....Laurie Rubiner **LD** ....Joel Kelsey
Sch ....Dana Sandman **Press**..............Kayla Johnson
Bio: b. 2/13/46 Brooklyn, NY; Jewish; JD Yale Univ., 1973;
USMCR, 1970-76; Attorney, Public Official; m. Cynthia
Comm.: Armed Services; Commerce, Science & Transportation; Judiciary; Veterans' Affairs; Special Aging
Dist. Offices: Hartford, 860-258-6940; Bridgeport, 203-330-0598

Christopher S. Murphy (D)   202-224-4041
SH-136   1st Term/55%   90/99/99   Fax: 224-9750
murphy.senate.gov   **twitter** senmurphyoffice
CoS ....Allison Herwitt **Dep CoS**..........David Bonine
Sch ....Maya Ashwal **CD** ....Chris Harris
Bio: b. 8/3/73 White Plains, NY; Protestant; JD Univ. of CT,
2002; Attorney, Legislative Aide; m. Cathy Holahan
Comm.: Appropriations; Foreign Relations; Health, Education, Labor & Pensions
Dist. Offices: Hartford, 860-549-8463

HOUSE

John B. Larson (D-1st)   202-225-2265
1501 LHOB   10th Term/64%   88/96/96   Fax: 225-1031
larson.house.gov   **twitter** repjohnlarson
CoS ....David Sitcovsky **LD** ....Scott Stephanou
Sch ....Owen Dodd **Press**..............Mary Yatrousis
Bio: b. 7/22/48 Hartford, CT; Catholic; BS Central CT St.
Univ., 1971; Teacher, Insurance Company Owner; m. Leslie
Comm.: Ways & Means
Dist. Offices: Hartford, 860-278-8888

CONNECTICUT

Joe Courtney (D-2nd)   **202-225-2076**
2348 RHOB   6th Term/63%   89/97/99   Fax: 225-4977
courtney.house.gov   twitter repjoecourtney
CoS ....Neil McKiernan **LD**...............Alexa Combelic
Sch .... Kathleen Corcoran **CD** .... Tim Brown
Bio: b. 4/6/53 Hartford, CT; Catholic; JD Univ. of CT, 1978;
Attorney, Public Defender; m. Audrey
Comm.: Armed Services; Education & the Workforce
Dist. Offices: Norwich, 860-886-0139; Enfield, 860-741-6011

Rosa DeLauro (D-3rd)   **202-225-3661**
2413 RHOB   14th Term/68%   92/98/93   Fax: 225-4890
delauro.house.gov   twitter rosadelauro
CoS ....Beverly Pheto **LD** ....Eric Anthony
Sch ....Ryann Kinney **CD** ....Ron Boehmer
Bio: b. 3/2/43 New Haven, CT; Catholic; MA Columbia Univ.,
1966; Political Activist, Congressional & Mayoral Aide; m.
Stanley Greenberg
Comm.: Appropriations
Dist. Offices: New Haven, 203-562-3718

Jim Himes (D-4th)   **202-225-5541**
1227 LHOB   5th Term/60%   87/95/99   Fax: 225-9629
himes.house.gov   twitter jahimes
CoS .... Mark Henson **Dep CoS**............Rachel Kelly
Sch ....Cara Pavlock **CD** ....Patrick Malone
Bio: b. 7/5/66 Lima, Peru; Presbyterian; MPhil Oxford Univ.,
1990; Housing Nonprofit Executive, Banker; m. Mary
Comm.: Financial Services; Select Intelligence
Dist. Offices: Bridgeport, 866-453-0028; Stamford, 203-
353-9400

Elizabeth Esty (D-5th)   **202-225-4476**
221 CHOB   3rd Term/57%   87/96/99   Fax: 225-5933
esty.house.gov   twitter RepEsty
CoS .... Tim Daly **LD**..................Danielle Most
Sch .... Hilary Badger **CD** ....Craig Frucht
Bio: b. 8/25/59 Oak Park, IL; Congregationalist; JD Yale Univ.,
1985; Attorney; m. Dan
Comm.: Science, Space & Technology; Transportation &
Infrastructure; Veterans' Affairs
Dist. Offices: New Britain, 860-223-8412

DELAWARE
delaware.gov

Wilmington.
• Newark

Pop.: 945,934   **Rank:** 45th
Caucasian: 70%   **African-Am.:** 22%   **Nat. Am.:** 1%   **Asian:** 4%
Other: 3%   **Hisp.:** 9%
Reg. Voters: 690,507
Dem.: 47%   **Rep.:** 28%   **Other:** 25%
Land Area: 1,949 sq. mi.   **Rank:** 49th

Number of US House Seats: 1 Dem.

Dover ★

1

State Legislature
legis.delaware.gov
Senate: 10R/10D/1Vac   House: 25D/16R
Session: 01/10/17 – 6/30/2017

Delaware

Gov. John Carney (D) **302-744-4101**
Next Election 2020   1st Term/58%   Fax: 302-739-2775
twitter johncarneyde
Bio: b. 5/20/56; Wilmington, DE; Roman Catholic; MPA Univ. of DE, 1987; Renewable Energy Company Executive; Gubernatorial and Congressional District Aide; m. Tracey Quillen

150 Martin Luther King Jr. Blvd. South, 2nd Floor, Dover, DE 19901
Washington Office: 202-624-7724

SENATE

Thomas R. Carper (D) **202-224-2441**
SH-513   3rd Term/66%   93/90/95   Fax: 228-2190
carper.senate.gov   twitter senatorcarper
CoS ....Bill Ghent **LD** ....Emily Spain
Sch ....Bryan Mack **CD** ....Meghan Pennington
Bio: b. 1/23/47 Beckley, WV; Presbyterian; MBA Univ. of DE, 1975; USN, 1968-73; USNR, 1973-91; Public Official; m. Martha
Comm.: Environment & Public Works; Finance; Homeland Security & Governmental Affairs
Dist. Offices: Wilmington, 302-573-6291; Dover, 302-674-3308; Georgetown, 302-856-7690

Chris Coons (D) **202-224-5042**
SR-127A   2nd Term/56%   93/96/96   Fax: 228-3075
coons.senate.gov   twitter sencoonsoffice
CoS .... Adam Bramwell **Dep CoS**......Jonathan Stahler
Sch .... Megan O'Neill **CD** ....Sean Coit
Bio: b. 9/9/63 Greenwich, CT; Presbyterian; JD Yale Univ., 1992; Attorney; m. Annie Lingenfelter
Comm.: Appropriations; Foreign Relations; Judiciary; Small Business & Entrepreneurship; Select Ethics (Vice Chair)
Dist. Offices: Wilmington, 302-573-6345; Dover, 302-736-5601

HOUSE

Lisa Blunt Rochester (D-At Large) **202-225-4165**
1123 LHOB   1st Term/56%   Fax: 225-2291
bluntrochester.house.gov   twitter RepBRochester
CoS ....Minh Ta **LD** .... Elizabeth Connolly
Sch ....Kalila Hines **CD** ....Courtney McGregor
Bio: b. 2/10/62 Philadelphia; Christian; MA Univ. of DE, 2002; CEO, Aide; wid.
Comm.: Agriculture; Education & the Workforce
Dist. Offices: Wilmington, 302-830-2330

Florida
myflorida.gov

Pop.: 20,271,272   **Rank:** 3rd
Caucasian: 78%   **African-Am.:** 17%
Nat. Am.: 1%   **Asian:** 3%   **Other:** 2%   **Hisp.:** 25%
Reg. Voters: 12,968,858
Dem.: 38%   **Rep.:** 35%   **Other:** 27%
Land Area: 53,625 sq. mi.   **Rank:** 26th

Number of US House Seats: 16 Rep./11 Dem.

State Legislature
leg.state.fl.us
Senate: 25R/15D   House: 79R/41D
Session: 03/07/17 – 5/5/2017

FLORIDA

Gov. Rick Scott (R)   **850-488-7146**
Next Election: 2018   2nd Term/48%   Fax: 850-487-0801
twitter flgovscott
Bio: b. 12/1/52 Bloomington, IL; Christian; JD Southern
Methodist Univ., 1978; USN, 1971-73; Businessman; m. Ann

The Capitol, 400 South Monroe Street,
Tallahassee, FL 32399-0001
Washington Office: 202-624-5885

SENATE

Bill Nelson (D)   **202-224-5274**
SH-716   3rd Term/55%   93/92/95   Fax: 228-2183
billnelson.senate.gov   twitter SenBillNelson
CoS .... Susie Perez Quinn   **LD** .... Carla McGarvey
Sch .... Maria Stratienko   **CD** .... Ryan Brown
Bio: b. 9/29/42 Miami, FL; Presbyterian; JD Univ. of VA,
1968; USAR, 1965-71; Attorney; m. Grace
Comm.: Armed Services; Commerce, Science & Transporta-
tion (Rnk. Mem.); Finance; Special Aging
Dist. Offices: Orlando, 407-872-7161; Tallahassee, 850-942-
8415; Tampa, 813-225-7040; Coral Gables, 305-536-5999;
Pensacola, 850-433-2603; Naples, 239-213-1521; Tallahas-
see, 850-599-9100

Marco Rubio (R)   **202-224-3041**
SR-284   2nd Term/52%   50/90/77   Fax: 228-0285
rubio.senate.gov   twitter SenRubioPress
CoS .... Clint Reed   **LD** .... Sara Decker
Sch .... Bridget Spurlock   **CD** .... Alex Burgos
Bio: b. 5/28/71 Miami, FL; Catholic; JD Univ. of Miami,
1996; Attorney; m. Jeanette
Comm.: Appropriations; Foreign Relations; Small Business &
Entrepreneurship; Select Intelligence; Special Aging
Dist. Offices: Orlando, 407-254-2573; Doral, 305-418-8553;
Tampa, 813-287-5035; Jacksonville, 904-398-8586

HOUSE

Matt Gaetz (R-1st) *GATES*   **202-225-4136**
507 CHOB   1st Term/69%   Fax: 225-3414
gaetz.house.gov   twitter mattgaetz
CoS .... Amanda Logan   **LD** ...... Heather Ham-Warren
Sch .... Kendall Kelley   **CD** .... Vacant
Bio: b. 5/7/82 Hollywood, FL; Baptist; JD Col. of William &
Mary, 2007; Attorney; single
Comm.: Armed Services; Budget; Judiciary
Dist. Offices: Pensacola, 850-479-1183

Neal Dunn (R-2nd)   **202-225-5235**
423 CHOB   1st Term/67%   Fax: 225-5615
dunn.house.gov   twitter DrNealDunnFL2
CoS .... Brian Schubert   **LD** .... Evan Lee
Sch .... Danielle Houser   **Press** .... Shelby Hodgkins
Bio: b. 2/16/53 New Haven, CT; Catholic; MD George
Washington Univ.; USAR 1975-79; USA 1979-90; Urolo-
gist, Surgeon; m. Leah
Comm.: Agriculture; Science, Space & Technology; Veter-
ans' Affairs
Dist. Offices: Panama City, 850-785-0812; Tallahassee,
850-891-8610

Ted Yoho (R-3rd)   **202-225-5744**
511 CHOB   3rd Term/57%   8/97/99   Fax: 225-3973
yoho.house.gov   twitter RepTedYoho
CoS .... Larry Calhoun   **LD** .... James Walsh
Sch .... Emily Scheinost   **CD** .... Brian Kaveney
Bio: b. 4/13/55 Minneapolis, MN; Catholic; DVM Univ. of
FL, 1983; Veterinarian; m. Carolyn
Comm.: Agriculture; Foreign Affairs
Dist. Offices: Gainesville, 352-505-0838; Orange Park,
904-276-9626

FLORIDA

John Rutherford (R-4th)　　　　**202-225-2501**
230 CHOB　　1st Term/70%　　　　Fax: 225-2504
rutherford.house.gov　　　　**twitter** jrutherfordfl
CoS .... Kelly Simpson　**LD** ....Jenifer Nowrocki
Sch .... Carole Anne Spohn　**CD** .... Taryn Fenske
Bio: b. 9/2/52 Omaha, NE; Catholic; BS FSU, 1974; Police Officer; m. Patricia
Comm.: Homeland Security; Veterans' Affairs
Dist. Offices: Jacksonville, 904-831-5205

Al Lawson, Jr. (D-5th)　　　　**202-225-0123**
1337 LHOB　　1st Term/64%　　　　Fax: 225-2256
lawson.house.gov　　　　**twitter** RepAlLawsonJr
CoS .... Tola Thompson　**Dep CoS** .... Vacant
Sch ....Vincent Evans　**Press**.......................... Vacant
Bio: b. 9/23/48 Midway, FL; Episcopal; MPA FL St. Univ., 1973; Insurance Company Owner; m. Delores
Comm.: Agriculture; Small Business
Dist. Offices: Tallahassee, 904-354-1652; Jacksonville, 904-385-4595

Ron DeSantis (R-6th)　　　　**202-225-2706**
1524 LHOB　　3rd Term/59%　　7/98/97　　Fax: 226-6299
desantis.house.gov　　　　**twitter** RepDeSantis
CoS .... Dustin Carmack　**LD** ....John Maniscalco
Sch ....Mimi Rothfus　**CD** ....Elizabeth Fusick
Bio: b. 9/14/78 Jacksonville, FL; Catholic; JD Harvard Univ., 2005; USN, 2004-10; USNR, 2010-present; Attorney, Military Prosecutor; m. Casey Black DeSantis
Comm.: Foreign Affairs; Judiciary; Oversight & Government Reform
Dist. Offices: St. Augustine, 904-827-1101; Port Orange, 386-756-9798

Stephanie Murphy (D-7th)　　　　**202-225-4035**
1237 LHOB　　1st Term/51%　　　　Fax: 226-0821
stephaniemurphy.house.gov　　　　**twitter** RepStephMurphy
CoS ....Brad Howard　**LD** .... John Laufer
Sch .... Alli Everton　**Press**............ Roberto Valdez
Bio: b. 9/16/78 Ho Chi Minh City, Viet Nam; Christian; MSFS Georgetown, 2004; Security Specialist, Consultant; m. Sean
Comm.: Armed Services; Small Business
Dist. Offices: Orlando, 888-205-5421

Bill Posey (R-8th)　　　　**202-225-3671**
2150 RHOB　　5th Term/63%　　9/97/99　　Fax: 225-3516
posey.house.gov　　　　**twitter** congbillposey
CoS .... Marcus Brubaker　**LD** .... Patrick Deitz
Sch ....Darren Gaddis　**CD** ....George Cecala
Bio: b. 12/18/47 Washington, DC; Methodist; AA Brevard Jr. Col., 1969; Realtor, Insurance Claims Adjuster; m. Katie
Comm.: Financial Services; Science, Space & Technology
Dist. Offices: Melbourne, 321-632-1776

Darren Soto (D-9th)　　　　**202-225-9889**
1429 LHOB　　1st Term/57%　　　　Fax: 225-9742
soto.house.gov　　　　**twitter** USRepSoto
CoS .... Christine Biron　**LD** ....Mike Nichola
Sch .... Liana Guerra　**CD** .... Iza Montalvo
Bio: b. 2/25/78 Ringwood, NJ; Christian; JD George Washington Univ., 2004; Attorney; m. Amanda
Comm.: Agriculture; Natural Resources
Dist. Offices: Kissimmee, 407-452-1171

Val B. Demings (D-10th)   **202-225-2176**
238 CHOB   1st Term/65%   Fax: 225-0999
demings.house.gov   twitter RepValDemings
CoS ....Wendy Anderson **LD** ....Aimee
Collins-Mandeville
Sch ....Wendy Featherson **CD** ....Caroline Rowland
Bio: b. 3/12/57 Jacksonville, FL; Christian; MA Webster University, 1996; Law Enforcement Officer, Social Worker; m. Jerry
Comm.: Homeland Security; Oversight & Government Reform
Dist. Offices: Orlando, 321-388-9808

Daniel Webster (R-11th)   **202-225-1002**
1210 LHOB   4th Term/65%   10/98/92   Fax: 226-6559
webster.house.gov   twitter repwebster
CoS ....Jaryn Emhof **LD** ....Steven Koncar
Sch ....Natalie Knight **CD** ....Jaryn Emhof
Bio: b. 4/27/49 Charleston, WV; Baptist; BEE GA Tech, 1971;
Air Conditioning & Heating Company Owner; m. Sandy
Comm.: Natural Resources; Science, Space & Technology;
Transportation & Infrastructure
Dist. Offices: Minneola, 352-383-3552; The Villages; Inverness; Brooksville

Gus Bilirakis (R-12th) *bil-uh-RACK-iss* **202-225-5755**
2112 RHOB   6th Term/69%   7/98/99   Fax: 225-4085
bilirakis.house.gov   twitter RepGusBilirakis
CoS ....Liz Hittos **LD** ....Thomas Power
Sch ....Samantha Gottshall **Press**.......... Elena Hernandez
Bio: b. 2/8/63 Gainesville, FL; Greek Orthodox; JD Stetson
Univ., 1989; Attorney, College Instructor; m. Eva
Comm.: Energy & Commerce; Veterans' Affairs
Dist. Offices: New Port Richey, 727-232-2921; Tarpon Springs,
727-940-5860

Charlie Crist (D-13th)   **202-225-5961**
427 CHOB   1st Term/52%   Fax: 225-9764
crist.house.gov   twitter RepCharlieCrist
CoS .... Austin Durrer **LD** ....Christopher Fisher
Sch ....Jonathan Pekkala **CD** ....Erin Moffet
Bio: b. 7/24/56 Altoona, PA; Methodist; JD Samford University
1981; Attorney, Public Official; sep.
Comm.: Financial Services; Science, Space & Technology
Dist. Offices: St. Petersburg, 888-226-0346

Kathy Castor (D-14th)   **202-225-3376**
2052 RHOB   6th Term/62%   100/98/96   Fax: 225-5652
castor.house.gov   twitter USRepKCastor
CoS ....Clay Phillips **LD** .... Elizabeth Brown
Sch ....Lara Hopkins **Press**..............Steven Angotti
Bio: b. 8/20/66 Miami, FL; Presbyterian; JD FL St. Univ.,
1991; Attorney; m. Bill Lewis
Comm.: Energy & Commerce
Dist. Offices: Tampa, 813-871-2817

Dennis A. Ross (R-15th)   **202-225-1252**
436 CHOB   4th Term/57%   10/99/97   Fax: 226-0585
dennisross.house.gov   twitter repdennisross
CoS ....Anthony Foti **Dep CoS**..............Kyle Glenn
Sch ....Joni Shockey **Press**................Joni Shockey
Bio: b. 10/18/59 Lakeland, FL; Presbyterian; JD Samford Univ.,
1987; Attorney, State Legislative Aide; m. Cindy
Comm.: Financial Services; Oversight & Government Reform
Dist. Offices: Lakeland, 863-644-8215; Plant City, 813-752-4790

FLORIDA

Vern Buchanan (R-16th)　　202-225-5015
2104 RHOB　6th Term/60%　11/91/92　Fax: 226-0828
buchanan.house.gov　　twitter vernbuchanan
CoS .... Dave Karvelas　LD .... Sean Brady
Sch .... Dylan Allen　Press .... Gretchen Andersen
Bio: b. 5/8/51 Detroit, MI; Baptist; MBA Univ. of Detroit, 1986; MIANG, 1970-76; Car Dealership Owner, Copy & Printing Company Owner; m. Sandy
Comm.: Ways & Means
Dist. Offices: Sarasota, 941-951-6643; Bradenton, 941-747-9081

Tom Rooney (R-17th)　　202-225-5792
2160 RHOB　5th Term/62%　6/96/91　Fax: 225-3132
rooney.house.gov　　twitter TomRooney
CoS .... Pete Giambastiani　LD .... Jessica Moore
Sch .... Michelle Reinshuttle　CD .... Meghan Rodgers
Bio: b. 11/21/70 Philadelphia, PA; Catholic; JD Univ. of Miami, 1999; USA, 2000-04; College Instructor, Attorney; m. Tara
Comm.: Appropriations; Select Intelligence
Dist. Offices: Punta Gorda, 941-575-9101; Riverview, 813-677-8646; Sebring, 863-402-9082; Okeechobee, 863-402-9082

Brian Mast (R-18th)　　202-225-3026
2182 RHOB　1st Term/54%　　Fax: 225-8398
mast.house.gov　　twitter BrianMastFL
CoS .... James Langenderfer　LD .... Barry Smith
Sch .... Caitlin McBride　CD .... Brad Stewart
Bio: b. 7/10/80 Grand Rapids, MI; Christian; ALB Harvard, 2016; USAR, 2000-12; Military Officer, Commentator; m. Brianna
Comm.: Foreign Affairs; Transportation & Infrastructure
Dist. Offices: Port St. Lucie, 772-536-2877; Stuart, 772-781-3266

Francis Rooney (R-19th)　　202-225-2536
120 CHOB　1st Term/66%　　Fax: 226-0439
francisrooney.house.gov　　twitter RepRooney
CoS .... Jessica Carter　LD .... Corey Schrodt
Sch .... Janae Cardinali　CD .... Chris Berardi
Bio: b. 12/4/53 Tulsa, Ok; Catholic; JD Georgetown, 1978; Business Owner, Ambassador; m. Kathleen
Comm.: Education & the Workforce; Foreign Affairs; Joint Economic
Dist. Offices: Cape Coral, 239-599-6033; Naples, 239-252-6225

Alcee L. Hastings (D-20th)　　202-225-1313
2353 RHOB　13th Term/80%　92/97/72　Fax: 225-1171
alceehastings.house.gov　　twitter rephastingsfl
CoS .... Lale Morrison　LD .... Tom Carnes
Sch .... DeBorah Posey　Press .... Evan Polisar
Bio: b. 9/5/36 Altamonte Springs, FL; African Methodist Episcopal; JD FL A&M Univ., 1963; Attorney, Judge; div.
Comm.: Rules
Dist. Offices: Ft. Lauderdale, 954-733-2800; Mangonia Park, 561-676-7911

Lois Frankel (D-21st)　　202-225-9890
1037 LHOB　3rd Term/63%　98/98/98　Fax: 226-3944
frankel.house.gov　　twitter reploisfrankel
CoS .... James Cho　LD .... Kelsey Moran
Sch .... Kate Regan　Press ... Rachel Huxley-Cohen
Bio: b. 5/16/48 Manhattan, NY; Jewish; JD Georgetown Univ., 1973; Attorney; div.
Comm.: Foreign Affairs; Transportation & Infrastructure
Dist. Offices: Boca Raton, 561-998-9045

FLORIDA

Ted Deutch (D-22nd) *DOYTCH*   **202-225-3001**
2447 RHOB   5th Term/59%   96/98/97   Fax: 225-5974
teddeutch.house.gov   twitter RepTedDeutch
CoS .... Joshua Rogin LD .... Joshua Lipman
Sch .... Alex Rocha CD .... Jason Attermann
Bio: b. 5/7/66 Bethlehem, PA; Jewish; JD Univ. of MI, 1990;
Attorney; m. Jill
Comm.: Ethics (Rnk. Mem.); Foreign Affairs; Judiciary
Dist. Offices: Boca Raton, 561-470-5440; Coral Springs,
954-255-8336; Margate, 954-972-6454

Debbie Wasserman Schultz (D-23rd)   **202-225-7931**
1114 LHOB   7th Term/55%   94/99/94   Fax: 226-2052
wassermanschultz.house.gov   twitter RepDWStweets
CoS .... Tracie Pough LD .... Sarah Farhadian
Sch .... Vacant CD .... David Damron
Bio: b. 9/27/66 Queens, NY; Jewish; MA Univ. of FL, 1990;
Public Official, College Instructor, State Legislative Aide;
m. Steve Schultz
Comm.: Appropriations; Budget
Dist. Offices: Pembroke Pines, 954-437-3936; Aventura,
305-936-5724

Frederica S. Wilson (D-24th)   **202-225-4506**
2445 RHOB   4th Term/Unc.   100/99/88 Fax: 226-0777
wilson.house.gov   twitter RepWilson
CoS .... Kim Bowman Sr LA .... David Simon
Sch .... Vacant CD .... Joyce Jones
Bio: b. 11/5/42 Miami, FL; Episcopal; MEd Univ. of Miami,
1972; Mentorship Program Founder, Principal, Teacher; wid.
Comm.: Education & the Workforce; Transportation &
Infrastructure
Dist. Offices: Miami Gardens, 305-690-5905; West Park,
954-989-2688

Mario Diaz-Balart (R-25th)   **202-225-4211**
440 CHOB   8th Term/62%   11/91/97   Fax: 225-8576
mariodiazbalart.house.gov   twitter MarioDB
CoS .... Cesar Gonzalez LD .... Miguel Mendoza
Sch .... Sarah Hodgkins CD .... Katrina Valdes
Bio: b. 9/25/61 Ft. Lauderdale, FL; Catholic; Attended Univ.
of S. FL, 1979-82; Public Official, Marketing Firm Execu-
tive; m. Tia
Comm.: Appropriations; Budget
Dist. Offices: Doral, 305-470-8555; Naples, 239-348-1620

Carlos Curbelo (R-26th)   **202-225-2778**
1404 LHOB   2nd Term/53%   20/76/97   Fax: 226-0346
curbelo.house.gov   twitter RepCurbelo
CoS .... Roy Schultheis LD .... Adam Wolf
Sch .... Alex Cisneros CD .... Joanna Rodriguez
Bio: b. 3/1/80 Miami, FL; Catholic; MPA Univ. of Miami,
2011; Public Affairs Firm Owner, Congressional State Direc-
tor; m. Cecilia Lowell
Comm.: Ways & Means
Dist. Offices: Miami, 305-222-0160; Key West, 305-292-4485;
Florida City, 305-247-1234

Ileana Ros-Lehtinen (R-27th)
il-ee-AH-na ross-LAY-tin-nen   **202-225-3931**
2206 RHOB   15th Term/55%   19/79/98   Fax: 225-5620
ros-lehtinen.house.gov   twitter RosLehtinen
CoS .... Maytee Sanz LD .... Gabriella Boffelli
Dep CoS .... Christine CD .... Keith Fernandez
             Del Portillo
Bio: b. 7/15/52 Havana, Cuba; Episcopal; PhD Univ. of
Miami, 2004; Teacher, Private School Administrator; m.
Dexter Lehtinen
Comm.: Foreign Affairs; Select Intelligence
Dist. Offices: Miami, 305-668-2285

GEORGIA
georgia.gov

Pop.: 10,214,860　**Rank:** 8th
Caucasian: 62%　**African-Am.:** 32%
Nat. Am.: 1%　**Asian:** 4%
Other: 2%　**Hisp.:** 9%
Reg. Voters: 5,430,571
Party registration not required
Land Area: 57,513 sq. mi.　**Rank:** 21st

Number of US House Seats:
9 Rep./4 Dem./1 Vac.

State Legislature
legis.state.ga.us
Senate: 38R/18D　House: 118R/62D
Session: 01/09/17 – 3/24/2017

Gov. Nathan Deal (R)　　**404-656-1776**
Next Election: 2018　2nd Term/53%　Fax: 404-657-7332
twitter governordeal
Bio: b. 8/25/42 Millen, GA; Baptist; JD Mercer Univ., 1966;
USA, 1966-68; Attorney, Judge; m. Sandra

203 State Capitol, Atlanta, GA 30334
Washington Office: 202-652-2299

SENATE

Johnny Isakson (R)　　　**202-224-3643**
SR-131　　3rd Term/55%　48/85/98　Fax: 228-0724
isakson.senate.gov　　　　**twitter** SenatorIsakson
CoS ....Joan Kirchner　**LD** ....Jay Sulzmann
Sch ....Stefanie Mohler　**CD** ....Amanda Maddox
Bio: b. 12/28/44 Atlanta, GA; Methodist; BBA Univ. of GA,
1966; GAANG, 1966-72; Real Estate Executive; m. Dianne
Comm.: Finance; Foreign Relations; Health, Education, Labor
& Pensions; Veterans' Affairs (Chair); Select Ethics (Chair)
Dist. Offices: Atlanta, 770-661-0999

David Perdue (R)　　　**202-224-3521**
SR-383　　1st Term/53%　50/96/95　Fax: 228-1031
perdue.senate.gov　　　　**twitter** sendavidperdue
CoS ....Derrick Dickey　**LD** .....................P.J. Waldrop
Sch ....Gabriele Forsyth　**CD** ....Megan Whittemore
Bio: b. 12/10/49 Macon, GA; Methodist; MS GA Tech, 1976;
Business Owner, Management Consultant; m. Bonnie
Comm.: Agriculture, Nutrition & Forestry; Armed Services;
Banking, Housing, & Urban Affairs; Budget
Dist. Offices: Atlanta, 404-865-0087

HOUSE

Earl L. "Buddy" Carter (R-1st)　　**202-225-5831**
432 CHOB　2nd Term/Unc.　8/99/97　Fax: 226-2269
buddycarter.house.gov　　　　**twitter** RepBuddyCarter
CoS ....Chris Crawford　**LD** ....Jordan See
Sch ....Brooke Miller　**CD** ....Mary Carpenter
Bio: b. 9/6/57 Port Wentworth, GA; Methodist; BS Univ. of
GA, 1980; Pharmacy Owner, Pharmacist; m. Amy
Comm.: Energy & Commerce
Dist. Offices: Brunswick, 912-265-9010; Savannah, 912-
352-0101

GEORGIA

Sanford D. Bishop, Jr. (D-2nd)   **202-225-3631**
2407 RHOB   13th Term/60%   73/83/98   Fax: 225-2203
bishop.house.gov   𝕥𝕨𝕚𝕥𝕥𝕖𝕣 sanfordbishop
CoS .... Michael Reed   **LD** .... Jonathan Halpern
Sch .... Whitney Woods   **CD** .... Jonathan Black
Bio: b. 2/4/47 Mobile, AL; Baptist; JD Emory Univ., 1971;
USA, 1971; Attorney; m. Vivian
Comm.: Appropriations
Dist. Offices: Albany, 229-439-8067; Columbus, 706-320-
9477; Macon, 478-803-2631

Drew Ferguson (R-3rd)   **202-225-5901**
1032 LHOB   1st Term/68%   Fax: 225-2515
ferguson.house.gov   𝕥𝕨𝕚𝕥𝕥𝕖𝕣 RepDrewFerguson
CoS .... Bobby Saparow   **LD** .... Mary Dee Beal
Sch .... Jenna Heard   **CD** .... Amy Timmerman
Bio: b. 11/15/66 Langdale, AL; Non-demoniational Christian;
DMD Medical College of GA, 1992; Dentist; m. Elizabeth
Comm.: Budget; Education & the Workforce; Transportation
& Infrastructure
Dist. Offices: Newnan, 770-683-2033

Hank Johnson (D-4th)   **202-225-1605**
2240 RHOB   6th Term/76%   100/98/97   Fax: 226-0691
hankjohnson.house.gov   𝕥𝕨𝕚𝕥𝕥𝕖𝕣 RepHankJohnson
CoS .... Arthur Sidney   **LD** .... Arya Hariharan
Sch ...... Alem Tewoldeberhan   **CD** .... Andy Phelan
Bio: b. 10/2/54 Washington, DC; Buddhist; JD TX Southern
Univ., 1979; Attorney, County Judge; m. Mereda
Comm.: Judiciary; Transportation & Infrastructure
Dist. Offices: Decatur, 770-987-2291

John Lewis (D-5th)   **202-225-3801**
343 CHOB   16th Term/86%   100/99/94   Fax: 225-0351
johnlewis.house.gov   𝕥𝕨𝕚𝕥𝕥𝕖𝕣 RepJohnLewis
CoS .... Michael Collins   **LD** .... Jamila Thompson
Sch .... David Bowman   **CD** .... Brenda Jones
Bio: b. 2/21/40 Troy, AL; Baptist; BA Fisk Univ., 1963; Civil
Rights Activist; wid.
Comm.: Ways & Means
Dist. Offices: Atlanta, 404-659-0116

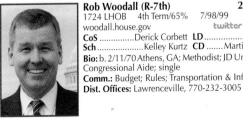

Vacant (6th)   **202-225-4501**
1211 LHOB   Fax: 225-4656
*Rep. Tom Price (R) resigned February 10, 2017. A special
election has been scheduled for April 18, 2017.*

OPEN
SEAT

Rob Woodall (R-7th)   **202-225-4272**
1724 LHOB   4th Term/65%   7/98/99   Fax: 225-4696
woodall.house.gov   𝕥𝕨𝕚𝕥𝕥𝕖𝕣 reprobwoodall
CoS .... Derick Corbett   **LD** .... Janet Rossi
Sch .... Kelley Kurtz   **CD** .... Martin Wattenbarger
Bio: b. 2/11/70 Athens, GA; Methodist; JD Univ. of GA, 1997;
Congressional Aide; single
Comm.: Budget; Rules; Transportation & Infrastructure
Dist. Offices: Lawrenceville, 770-232-3005

Georgia

Austin Scott (R-8th)　　　**202-225-6531**
2417 RHOB　4th Term/60%　9/99/98　Fax: 225-3013
austinscott.house.gov　　　twitter AustinScottGA08
CoS .... Joby Young **LD** .... Cameron Bishop
Sch ....Haley Dorval **CD** .... Ryann DuRant
Bio: b. 12/10/69 Augusta, GA; Baptist; BBA Univ. of GA,
1993; Insurance Agency Owner; m. Vivien
Comm.: Agriculture; Armed Services
Dist. Offices: Warner Robins, 478-971-1776; Tifton, 229-396-5175

Doug Collins (R-9th)　　　**202-225-9893**
1504 LHOB　3rd Term/Unc.　9/99/98　Fax: 226-1224
dougcollins.house.gov　　twitter RepDougCollins
CoS .... Brendan Belair **LD** ....Sally Rose Larson
Sch .... Erin Wall **CD** .... Jessica Andrews
Bio: b. 8/16/66 Gainesville, GA; Baptist; JD John Marshall
Law School, 2008; USNR, 1994-96; USAFR, 2002-present;
Attorney, Minister; m. Lisa
Comm.: Judiciary; Rules
Dist. Offices: Gainesville, 770-297-3388

Jody B. Hice (R-10th)　　　**202-225-4101**
324 CHOB　2nd Term/Unc.　7/98/98　Fax: 226-0776
hice.house.gov　　　twitter congressmanhice
CoS ....David Sours **Dep CoS**.......... Jessica Hayes
Sch .... Taylor Ford **Press**...Nadgey Louis-Charles
Bio: b. 4/22/60 Atlanta, GA; Southern Baptist; DMin Luther
Rice Univ., 1988; Pastor, Radio Host; m. Dee Dee
Comm.: Natural Resources; Oversight & Government Reform
Dist. Offices: Monroe, 770-207-1776; Milledgeville, 478-457-0007; Thomson, 770 207-1776

Barry Loudermilk (R-11th)　　　**202-225-2931**
329 CHOB　2nd Term/67%　9/98/97　Fax: 225-2944
loudermilk.house.gov　　　twitter reploudermilk
CoS ....Rob Adkerson **LD** ....Colin Carr
Sch ....Ellen James **CD** ....Shawna Mercer
Bio: b. 12/22/63 Riverdale, GA; Baptist; BS Wayland Baptist
Univ., 1999; USAF, 1984-92; Information Technology Executive; m. Desiree
Comm.: Financial Services; House Administration; Science,
Space & Technology; Joint Library
Dist. Offices: Woodstock, 770-429-1776; Cartersville, 770-429-1776; Atlanta, 770-429-1776

Rick W. Allen (R-12th)　　　**202-225-2823**
426 CHOB　2nd Term/62%　7/99/98　Fax: 225-3377
allen.house.gov　　　twitter RepRickAllen
CoS ....Tim Baker **LD** .... Katie Hunter
Sch ....Heath Wheat **CD** .... Madison Porter
Bio: b. 11/11/51 Augusta, GA; Methodist; BS Auburn Univ.,
1973; Construction Company Owner; m. Robin
Comm.: Agriculture; Education & the Workforce
Dist. Offices: Augusta, 706-228-1980; Dublin, 478-272-4030;
Statesboro, 912-243-9452; Vidalia, 912-403-3311

David Scott (D-13th)　　　**202-225-2939**
225 CHOB　8th Term/Unc.　78/91/93　Fax: 225-4628
davidscott.house.gov　　　twitter RepDavidScott
CoS ....Gary Woodward **LD** ....Ashley Smith
Sch ....Breanna Swims **Press**.......... Gary Woodward
Bio: b. 6/27/45 Aynor, SC; Baptist; MBA Univ. of PA, 1969; Advertising Agency Owner, Recruiting Firm Executive; m. Alfredia
Comm.: Agriculture; Financial Services
Dist. Offices: Jonesboro, 770-210-5073; Smyrna, 770-432-5405

GEORGIA

Tom Graves (R-14th)   **202-225-5211**
2078 RHOB   5th Term/Unc.   10/98/98   Fax: 225-8272
tomgraves.house.gov   twitter RepTomGraves
CoS .... John Donnelly   **LD** .... Jason Murphy
Sch .... Morgan Joyce   **CD** .... Garrett Hawkins
Bio: b. 2/3/70 St. Petersburg, FL; Southern Baptist; BBA Univ. of GA, 1993; Commercial Property Developer, Landscape Company Owner; m. Julie
Comm.: Appropriations
Dist. Offices: Dalton, 706-226-5320; Rome, 706-290-1776

HAWAII   2
hawaii.gov

Pop.: 1,431,603   **Rank:** 40th
Caucasian: 27%   **African-Am.:** 3%
Nat. Am.: 1%   **Asian:** 37%   **Other:** 33%
Hisp.: 10%
Reg. Voters: 726,940   *Party registration not required*
Land Area: 6,423 sq. mi.   **Rank:** 47th

Number of US House Seats: 2 Dem.

State Legislature
capitol.hawaii.gov
Senate: 25D   House: 45D/6R
Session: 01/18/17 – 5/4/2017

(map of Hawaii with labels: Honolulu, Mauna Loa, Kahului, Kailua, Hilo)

Gov. David Ige (D)   **808-586-0034**
Next Election: 2018   1st Term/49%   Fax: 808-586-0006
twitter govhawaii
Bio: b. 1/15/57 Pearl City, HI; Buddhist; MBA Univ. of HI, 1985; Electrical Engineer; m. Dawn

State Capitol, Executive Chambers, Honolulu, HI 96813

SENATE

Brian Schatz (D)   **202-224-3934**
SH-722   2nd Term/74%   90/99/100   Fax: 228-1153
schatz.senate.gov   twitter SenBrianSchatz
CoS .... Andrew Winer   **LD** .... Arun Revana
Sch .... Diane Miyasato   **CD** .... Michael Inacay
Bio: b. 10/20/72 Ann Arbor, MI; Jewish; BA Pomona Col., 1994; Teacher; m. Linda
Comm.: Appropriations; Banking, Housing, & Urban Affairs; Commerce, Science & Transportation; Indian Affairs; Select Ethics
Dist. Offices: Honolulu, 808-523-2061

Mazie K. Hirono (D)   **202-224-6361**
SH-730   1st Term/63%   90/100/100   Fax: 224-2126
hirono.senate.gov   twitter maziehirono
CoS .... Betsy Lin   **LD** .... Jeremy Horan
Sch .... Anthony Lopez   **CD** .... Will Dempster
Bio: b. 11/3/47 Fukushima, Japan; Buddhist; JD Georgetown Univ., 1978; Legislative Aide, Attorney; m. Leighton Kim Oshima
Comm.: Armed Services; Energy & Natural Resources; Judiciary; Small Business & Entrepreneurship; Veterans' Affairs
Dist. Offices: Honolulu, 808-522-8970

Hawaii

HOUSE

Colleen Hanabusa (D-1st)　　　　**202-225-2726**
422 CHOB　　4th Term/72%　100/100/100　Fax: 225-0688
hanabusa.house.gov　　　　　　　　twitter rephanabusa
CoS .... Michael Formby　LD .... Elizabeth Songvilay
Sch .... Ian Terayama　CD .... Vacant
Bio: b. 5/4/51 Honolulu, HI; Buddhist; JD Univ. of HI, 1977;
Attorney; m. John F. Souza
Comm.: Armed Services; Natural Resources; Science, Space
& Technology
Dist. Offices: Honolulu, 808-541-2570

Tulsi Gabbard (D-2nd)　　　　　**202-225-4906**
1433 LHOB　　3rd Term/81%　92/96/99　Fax: 225-4987
gabbard.house.gov　　　　　　　　twitter tulsipress
CoS .... Kainoa Penaroza　LD .... Jamie Morgan
Sch .... Lauren McIlvaine　**Press** .... Emily Latimer
Bio: b. 4/12/81 Leloaloa, AS; Hindu; BA HI Pacific Univ.,
2009; HING, 2003-present; Business Owner, Congressional
Aide; m. Abraham Williams
Comm.: Armed Services; Foreign Affairs
Dist. Offices: Honolulu, 808-541-1986

IDAHO
idaho.gov

Pop.: 1,654,930　**Rank:** 39th
Caucasian: 93%　**African-Am.:** 1%　**Nat. Am.:** 2%　**Asian:**
2%　**Other:** 3%　**Hisp.:** 12%
Reg. Voters: 854,402　*Party registration not required*
Land Area: 82,643 sq. mi.　**Rank:** 11th

Number of US House Seats: 2 Rep.

State Legislature
legislature.idaho.gov
Senate: 29R/6D　House: 59R/11D
Session: 01/09/17 – 3/31/2017

Gov. C.L. "Butch" Otter (R)　　**208-334-2100**
Next Election: 2018　3rd Term/54%　Fax: 208-334-3454
twitter butchotter
Bio: b. 5/3/42 Caldwell, ID; Roman Catholic; BA Col. of ID,
1967; IDARNG, 1968-73; Businessman; m. Lori

State Capitol, 700 West Jefferson Street, Boise, ID 83702

SENATE

Michael D. Crapo (R) *CRAY-poe*　　**202-224-6142**
SD-239　　4th Term/66%　48/95/98　Fax: 228-1375
crapo.senate.gov　　　　　　　　twitter mikecrapo
CoS .... Susan Wheeler　LD .... Ken Flanz
Sch .... Kathleen Amacio　**Press** .... Robert Summer
Bio: b. 5/20/51 Idaho Falls, ID; Mormon; JD Harvard Univ.,
1977; Attorney; m. Susan
Comm.: Banking, Housing & Urban Affairs (Chair); Budget;
Finance; Judiciary; Indian Affairs; Joint Taxation
Dist. Offices: Boise, 208-334-1776; Pocatello, 208-236-6775;
Coeur d'Alene, 208-664-5490; Twin Falls, 208-734-2515

IDAHO

Jim Risch (R)   **202-224-2752**
SR-483   2nd Term/65%   45/95/99   Fax: 224-2573
risch.senate.gov   **twitter** SenatorRisch
CoS .... John Sandy   **LD** .... Darren Parker
Sch .... Rachel Burkett   **CD** .... Kaylin Minton
Bio: b. 5/3/43 Milwaukee, WI; Catholic; JD Univ. of ID, 1968; Attorney, Rancher; m. Vicki
Comm.: Energy & Natural Resources; Foreign Relations; Small Business & Entrepreneurship (Chair); Select Ethics; Select Intelligence
Dist. Offices: Boise, 208-342-7985; Coeur d'Alene, 208-667-6130; Idaho Falls, 208-523-5541; Lewiston, 208-743-0792; Lewiston, 208-743-1492; Idaho Falls, 208-522-9779

HOUSE

Raúl R. Labrador (R-1st)   **202-225-6611**
1523 LHOB   4th Term/67%   12/96/97   Fax: 225-3029
labrador.house.gov   **twitter** Raul_Labrador
CoS .... Mike Cunnington   **LD** .... Aaron Calkins
Sch .... Estephania Gongora   **Press** .... Dan Popkey
Bio: b. 12/8/67 Carolina, PR; Mormon; JD Univ. of WA, 1995; Attorney; m. Rebecca
Comm.: Judiciary; Natural Resources
Dist. Offices: Meridian, 208-888-3188; Lewiston, 208-743-1388; Coeur d'Alene, 208-667-0127

Mike Simpson (R-2nd)   **202-225-5531**
2084 RHOB   10th Term/63%   8/93/96   Fax: 225-8216
simpson.house.gov   **twitter** CongMikeSimpson
CoS .... Lindsay Slater   **LD** .... Sarah Cannon
Sch .... Emilee Henshaw   **CD** .... Nikki Wallace
Bio: b. 9/8/50 Burley, ID; Mormon; DMD Washington Univ., 1977; Dentist; m. Kathy
Comm.: Appropriations
Dist. Offices: Boise, 208-334-1953; Idaho Falls, 208-523-6701; Twin Falls, 208-734-7219; Pocatello, 208-233-2222; Pocatello, 208-236-6817; Twin Falls, 208-734-6780

ILLINOIS
illinois.gov

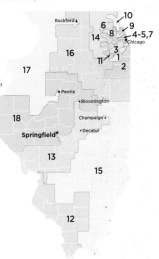

Pop.: 1,285,9995   **Rank:** 5th
Caucasian: 77%   **African-Am.:** 15%
Nat. Am.: 1%   **Asian:** 6%   **Other:** 2%
Hisp.: 17%
Reg. Voters: 8,045,141
Party registration not required
Land Area: 55,519 sq. mi.
Rank: 24th

Number of US House Seats:
11 Dem./7 Rep.

State Legislature
ilga.gov
Senate: 37D/22R   House: 67D/51R
Session: 01/11/17 – 5/31/2017

Gov. Bruce Rauner (R)   **217-782-0244**
Next Election: 2018   1st Term/50%   Fax: 217-524-4049
twitter govrauner
Bio: b. 2/18/57 Chicago, IL; Episcopal; MBA Harvard Univ., 1981; Private Equity Executive; m. Diana

207 State House, Springfield, IL 62706
Washington Office: 202-624-7760

ILLINOIS

SENATE

Richard J. Durbin (D)   **202-224-2152**
SH-711   4th Term/54%   90/100/95   Fax: 228-0400
durbin.senate.gov   **twitter** SenatorDurbin
CoS .... Pat Souders   **LD** .... Corey Tellez
Sch .... Claire Reuschel   **CD** .... Ben Marter
Bio: b. 11/21/44 East St. Louis, IL; Catholic; JD Georgetown
Univ., 1969; Attorney; m. Loretta
Comm.: Appropriations; Judiciary; Rules & Administration;
Minority Whip
Dist. Offices: Chicago, 312-353-4952; Springfield, 217-492-
4062; Carbondale, 618-351-1122; Rock Island, 309-786-5173

Tammy Duckworth (D)   **202-224-2854**
SH-524   1st Term/54%   Fax: 228-4611
duckworth.senate.gov   **twitter** SenDuckworth
CoS .... Kaitlin Fahey   **LD** .... Kalina Bakalov
Sch .... Kelsey Becker   **CD** .... Ben Garmisa
Bio: b. 3/12/68 Bangkok, Thailand; Not Stated; MA George
Washington Univ., 1992; USAR, 1991-96; ILNG, 1996-2014;
State Veterans Affairs Director; m. Bryan Bowlsbey
Comm.: Commerce, Science & Transportation; Environment
& Public Works; Small Business & Entrepreneurship
Dist. Offices: Chicago, 312-886-3506, Springfield, TBA

HOUSE

Bobby L. Rush (D-1st)   **202-225-4372**
2188 RHOB   13th Term/73%   97/97/67   Fax: 226-0333
rush.house.gov   **twitter** RepBobbyRush
CoS .... Yardly Pollas   **LD** .... Nishith Pandya
AD .... N. Lenette Myers   **CD** .... Debra Johnson
Bio: b. 11/23/46 Albany, GA; Protestant; MA McCormick
Theological Seminary, 1998; USA, 1963-68; Insurance Broker,
Political Activist; m. Carolyn
Comm.: Energy & Commerce
Dist. Offices: Chicago, 773-779-2400

Robin Kelly (D-2nd)   **202-225-0773**
1239 LHOB   3rd Term/80%   100/98/93   Fax: 225-4583
robinkelly.house.gov   **twitter** RepRobinKelly
CoS .... Brandon Webb   **LD** .... Zach Ostro
Sch .... Tony Presta   **CD** .... James Lewis
Bio: b. 4/30/56 Manhattan, NY; Non-Denominational
Christian; PhD Northern IL Univ., 2004; Public Official; m.
Nathaniel Horn
Comm.: Foreign Affairs; Oversight & Government Reform
Dist. Offices: Matteson, 708-679-2001

Daniel Lipinski (D-3rd)   **202-225-5701**
2346 RHOB   7th Term/Unc.   74/87/95   Fax: 225-1012
lipinski.house.gov   **twitter** replipinski
CoS .... Eric Lausten   **LD** .... Sofya Leonova
AA .... Jennifer Sypolt   **CD** .... Isaac Sancken
Bio: b. 7/15/66 Chicago, IL; Catholic; PhD Duke Univ., 1998;
Professor, Congressional & Campaign Aide; m. Judy
Comm.: Science, Space & Technology; Transportation &
Infrastructure
Dist. Offices: Chicago, 773-948-6223; Oak Lawn, 708-424-
0853; Lockport, 815-838-1990; Orland Park, 708-403-4379

Luis V. Gutiérrez (D-4th)   **202-225-8203**
2408 RHOB   13th Term/Unc.   96/99/84   Fax: 225-7810
gutierrez.house.gov   **twitter** repgutierrez
CoS .... Susan Collins   **LD** ...... AnneRose Menachery
Sch .... Julissa Santoy   **CD** .... Douglas Rivlin
Bio: b. 12/10/53 Chicago, IL; Catholic; BA Northeastern IL
Univ., 1975; Teacher, Social Worker, Mayoral Aide; m. Soraida
Comm.: Judiciary
Dist. Offices: Chicago, 773-342-0774

ILLINOIS

Mike Quigley (D-5th)　　　　　**202-225-4061**
2458 RHOB　　5th Term/68%　　92/97/98　　Fax: 225-5603
quigley.house.gov　　　　　**twitter** RepMikeQuigley
CoS ....Juan Hinojosa **LD** ....Doug Lee
Sch .... Haley Fulford **CD** ....Tara Vales
Bio: b. 10/17/58 Indianapolis, IN; Christian; JD Loyola Univ. (Chicago), 1989; Attorney, College Instructor, Legislative Aide; m. Barbara
Comm.: Appropriations; Select Intelligence
Dist. Offices: Chicago, 773-267-5926

Peter Roskam (R-6th)　　　　　**202-225-4561**
2246 RHOB　　6th Term/59%　　10/95/96　　Fax: 225-1166
roskam.house.gov　　　　　**twitter** PeterRoskam
CoS ....David Mork **LD** .... Aaron Krejci
Sch ....Amanda Grey **CD** ....David Pasch
Bio: b. 9/13/61 Hinsdale, IL; Anglican; JD IL Tech., 1989; Attorney, Nonprofit Executive, Congressional Aide; m. Elizabeth
Comm.: Ways & Means
Dist. Offices: West Chicago, 630-232-0006

Danny K. Davis (D-7th)　　　　　**202-225-5006**
2159 RHOB　　11th Term/84%　　98/100/94　　Fax: 225-5641
davis.house.gov　　　　　**twitter** RepDannyDavis
CoS ....Yul Edwards **LD** .... Jill Hunter-Williams
Sch ....Jenell Brown **CD** ....Ira Cohen
Bio: b. 9/6/41 Parkdale, AR; Baptist; PhD Union Inst., 1977; Health Care Association Executive, Teacher; m. Vera
Comm.: Ways & Means
Dist. Offices: Chicago, 773-533-7520

Raja Krishnamoorthi (D-8th)
　RA-zhah krish-na-MUR-thee　　　**202-225-3711**
515 CHOB　　1st Term/58%　　　　Fax: 225-7830
krishnamoorthi.house.gov　　**twitter** CongressmanRaja
CoS .... Mark Schauerte **LD** ....Sam Margante
Sch .... Lisa Walker **CD** .... Wilson Baldwin
Bio: b. 7/19/73 New Delhi, India; Hindu; JD Harvard 2000; Executive; m. Priya
Comm.: Education & the Workforce; Oversight & Government Reform
Dist. Offices: Schaumburg, 847-413-1959

Jan Schakowsky (D-9th) *shuh-KOW-ski* **202-225-2111**
2367 RHOB　　10th Term/66%　　94/100/94　　Fax: 226-6890
schakowsky.house.gov　　　　　**twitter** janschakowsky
CoS ....Cathy Hurwit **LD** ....Matt Hayward
Sch .... Kim Muzeroll **Press**... Jeronimo Anaya Ortiz
Bio: b. 5/26/44 Chicago, IL; Jewish; BS Univ. of IL, 1965; Senior Citizens Group Director, Consumer Advocate, Teacher; m. Robert Creamer
Comm.: Budget; Energy & Commerce
Dist. Offices: Chicago, 773-506-7100; Evanston, 847-328-3409; Glenview, 847-328-3409

Brad Schneider (D-10th)　　　　**202-225-4835**
1432 LHOB　　2nd Term/52%　　　　Fax: 225-0837
schneider.house.gov　　　　　**twitter** RepSchneider
CoS ....Ashley Jones **LD** ....Jessica Schwartz
Sch .... Gabrielle Hart **CD** .... Steven Kirsch
Bio: b. 8/20/61 Denver, CO; Jewish; JD Northwestern Univ., 1988; Management Consultant, Industrial Engineer; m. Julie Dann
Comm.: Foreign Affairs; Judiciary; Small Business
Dist. Offices: Lincolnshire, 847-383-4870

Bill Foster (D-11th)   **202-225-3515**
1224 LHOB   5th Term/60%   91/96/99   Fax: 225-9420
foster.house.gov   twitter RepBillFoster
CoS .... Adam Elias **LD** .... Scott Shewcraft
Sch .... Diana Konate **CD** .... Mary Werden
Bio: b. 10/7/55 Madison, WI; Not Stated; PhD Harvard Univ.,
1983; Physicist, Business Owner; m. Aesook Byon
Comm.: Financial Services; Science, Space & Technology
Dist. Offices: Aurora, 630-585-7672; Joliet, 815-280-5876;
Granite City, 618-233-8026

Mike Bost (R-12th) *BOST (like "cost")*   **202-225-5661**
1440 LHOB   2nd Term/54%   9/95/91   Fax: 225-0285
bost.house.gov   twitter RepBost
CoS .... Matt McCullough **LD** .... Mark Ratto
Sch .... Kristen Lebryk **Press** .... George O'Connor
Bio: b. 12/30/60 Murphysboro, IL; Southern Baptist; HS Diplo-
ma; USMC, 1979-82; Beauty Salon Owner, Firefighter; m. Tracy
Comm.: Agriculture; Transportation & Infrastructure; Vet-
erans' Affairs
Dist. Offices: Belleville, 618-233-8026; Carbondale, 618-
457-5787; Mt. Vernon, 618-513-5294; Alton, 618-233-8026;
Glen Carbon, 618-205-8660

Rodney Davis (R-13th)   **202-225-2371**
1740 LHOB   3rd Term/60%   6/94/98   Fax: 226-0791
rodneydavis.house.gov   twitter RodneyDavis
CoS .... Jen Daulby **LD** .... Miles Chiotte
Sch ....Brittany Randall **CD** .... Ashley Phelps
Bio: b. 1/5/70 Des Moines, IA; Catholic; BA Millikin Univ.,
1992; Congressional Aide; m. Shannon
Comm.: Agriculture; House Administration; Transportation
& Infrastructure; Joint Printing
Dist. Offices: Champaign, 217-403-4690; Decatur, 217-791-
6224; Normal, 309-252-8834; Taylorville, 217-824-5117

Randy Hultgren (R-14th)   **202-225-2976**
2455 RHOB   4th Term/60%   8/98/98   Fax: 225-0697
hultgren.house.gov   twitter RepHultgren
CoS ....Katherine McGuire **Dep CoS** .... Doug Thomas
Sch ....Katie Hunt **CD** .....Jameson Cunningham
Bio: b. 3/1/66 Park Ridge, IL; Protestant; JD IL Inst. of Tech.,
1993; Securities Company Executive, Attorney; m. Christy
Comm.: Financial Services; Science, Space & Technology
Dist. Offices: Campton Hills, 630-584-2734

John Shimkus (R-15th)   **202-225-5271**
2217 RHOB   11th Term/Unc.   7/96/99   Fax: 225-5880
shimkus.house.gov   twitter RepShimkus
CoS ....Craig Roberts **Dep CoS** .... Greta Joynes
Sch ....Molly Harris **CD** .... Jordan Haverly
Bio: b. 2/21/58 East St. Louis, IL; Lutheran; MBA Southern
IL Univ. - Edwardsville, 1997; USA, 1980-86; USAR, 1986-
2008; Teacher; m. Karen
Comm.: Energy & Commerce
Dist. Offices: Maryville, 618-288-7190; Effingham, 217-347-
7947; Harrisburg, 618-252-8271; Danville, 217-446-0664

Adam Kinzinger (R-16th)   **202-225-3635**
2245 RHOB   4th Term/Unc.   7/92/99   Fax: 225-3521
kinzinger.house.gov   twitter repkinzinger
CoS ....Austin Weatherford **LD** .... Josh Baggett
Sch .... Tamara Edwards **CD** .... Maura Gillespie
Bio: b. 2/27/78 Kankakee, IL; Protestant; BA IL St. Univ.,
2000; ILANG, 2001-03; WIANG, 2003-present; IT Services
Company Representative; single
Comm.: Energy & Commerce; Foreign Affairs
Dist. Offices: Ottawa, 815-431-9271

ILLINOIS

Cheri Bustos (D-17th)   **202-225-5905**
1009 LHOB   3rd Term/60%   89/94/99   Fax: None
bustos.house.gov   **twitter** RepCheri
CoS ....Jon Pyatt **LD**...............Trevor Reuschel
Sch ....Laura Piccioli **CD** ....Jared Smith
Bio: b. 10/17/61 East Moline, IL; Catholic; MA Univ. of IL - Springfield, 1985; Journalist, Communications Executive; m. Gerry
Comm.: Agriculture; Transportation & Infrastructure
Dist. Offices: Rock Island, 309-786-3406; Peoria, 309-966-1813; Rockford, 815-968-8011

Darin LaHood (R-18th)   **202-225-6201**
1424 LHOB   2nd Term/72%   7/97/99   Fax: 225-9249
lahood.house.gov   **twitter** replahood
CoS .... Steve Pfrang **LD**........Ashley Antoskiewicz
Sch ....Kelsey Gorman **CD** ..................J.D. Dalfonso
Bio: b. 7/5/68 Peoria, IL; Catholic; JD John Marshall Law School, 1997; Attorney, Prosecutor; m. Kristen
Comm.: Natural Resources; Science, Space & Technology; Joint Economic
Dist. Offices: Peoria, 309-671-7027; Springfield, 217-670-1653; Jacksonville, 217-245-1431

INDIANA
in.gov

Pop.: 6,619,680   **Rank:** 16th
Caucasian: 86%   **African-Am.:** 10%
Nat. Am.: 0%   **Asian:** 2%   **Other:** 2%
Hisp.: 7%
Reg. Voters: 4,829,243
Party registration not required
Land Area: 35,826 sq. mi.   **Rank:** 38th

Number of US House Seats: 7 Rep./2 Dem.

State Legislature
state.in.us
Senate: 41R/9D   House: 70R/30D
Session: 01/03/17 – 4/29/2017

Gov. Eric Holcomb (R)   **317-232-4567**
Next Election 2020   1st Term/51%   Fax: 317-232-3443
twitter govholcomb
Bio: b. 5/2/68; Vincennes, IN; Christian; BA Hanover College, 1990; USANG; Gubernatorial Aide; Congressional Aide; Campaign Aide; m. Janet

State House, Room 206, Indianapolis, IN 46204-2797
Washington Office: 202-624-1474

SENATE

Joe Donnelly (D)   **202-224-4814**
SH-720   1st Term/50%   77/57/99   Fax: 224-5011
donnelly.senate.gov   **twitter** SenDonnelly
CoS ....Joel Elliott **LD** ....Andrew Lattanner
Sch ....Lynn Demos **CD** ....Sarah Rothschild
Bio: b. 9/29/55 Queens, NY; Catholic; JD Univ. of Notre Dame, 1981; Attorney, Office Products Company Owner; m. Jill
Comm.: Agriculture, Nutrition & Forestry; Armed Services; Banking, Housing, & Urban Affairs; Special Aging
Dist. Offices: Indianapolis, 317-226-5555; South Bend, 574-288-2780; Evansville, 812-425-5862; Ft. Wayne, 260-420-4955

INDIANA

Todd Young (R)   **202-224-5623**
SR-B33   1st Term/52%   Fax: 228-1820
young.senate.gov   twitter SenToddYoung
CoS .... John Connell **LD** .... Adam Hechavarria
Sch .... Clay Helton **CD** .... Cassie Smedile
Bio: b. 8/24/72 Lancaster, PA; Christian; JD IN Univ. - Indianapolis, 2006; USMC, 1995-2000; Think Tank Aide, Congressional Aide, Attorney; m. Jenny
Comm.: Commerce, Science & Transportation; Foreign Relations; Health, Education, Labor & Pensions; Small Business & Entrepreneurship
Dist. Offices: Indianapolis, 317-226-6700; New Albany, 812-542-4820; Evansville, TBA; Fort Wayne, TBA

HOUSE

Peter J. Visclosky (D-1st)   **202-225-2461**
2328 RHOB   17th Term/82%   98/98/99   Fax: 225-2493
visclosky.house.gov   twitter repvisclosky
CoS .... Mark Lopez **LD** .... Emma Norvell
EA .... Korry Baack **CD** .... Kevin Spicer
Bio: b. 8/13/49 Gary, IN; Catholic; LLM Georgetown Univ., 1982; Attorney, Congressional Aide; m. Joanne Royce
Comm.: Appropriations
Dist. Offices: Merrillville, 219-795-1844

Jackie Walorski (R-2nd)   **202-225-3915**
419 CHOB   3rd Term/59%   9/98/100   Fax: 225-6798
walorski.house.gov   twitter RepWalorski
CoS .... Ben Falkowski **LD** .... Mike Dankler
Sch .... Faith Ammen **CD** .... Jack Morrissey
Bio: b. 8/17/63 South Bend, IN; Evangelical Christian; BA Taylor Univ., 1985; Development Director; m. Dean Swihart
Comm.: Ways & Means
Dist. Offices: Mishawaka, 574-204-2645; Rochester, 574-223-4373

Jim Banks (R-3rd)   **202-225-4436**
509 CHOB   1st Term/70%   Fax: 226-9870
banks.house.gov   twitter Jim_Banks
CoS .... Matt Lahr **LD** .... Brandt Anderson
Sch .... Elizabeth Bettis **Press** .... Anna Swick
Bio: b. 7/16/79 Columbia City, IN; Evangelical; MBA Grace Col., 2013; USNR, 2012-present; Commercial Realtor; m. Amanda
Comm.: Armed Services; Science, Space & Technology Veterans' Affairs
Dist. Offices: Fort Wayne, 260-702-4750

Todd Rokita (R-4th) *ro-KEE-ta*   **202-225-5037**
2439 RHOB   4th Term/65%   7/98/97   Fax: 226-0544
rokita.house.gov   twitter ToddRokita
CoS .... Mark Cruz **LD** .... Parker Reynolds
EA .... Jessica Williams **Press** .... Luke Bunting
Bio: b. 2/9/70 Chicago, IL; Catholic; JD IN Univ. - Indianapolis, 1995; Attorney, State Government Official; m. Kathy
Comm.: Budget; Education & the Workforce; Transportation & Infrastructure
Dist. Offices: Danville, 317-718-0404; Lafayette, 765-838-3930

Susan W. Brooks (R-5th)   **202-225-2276**
1030 LHOB   3rd Term/61%   7/96/99   Fax: 225-0016
susanwbrooks.house.gov   twitter SusanWBrooks
CoS .... Megan Savage **LD** .... Helen Dwight
Sch .... Jack Miles **CD** .... Kristen Johnson
Bio: b. 8/25/60 Auburn, IN; Catholic; JD IN Univ. - Indianapolis, 1985; Community College Administrator, Attorney; m. David
Comm.: Energy & Commerce; Ethics (Chair)
Dist. Offices: Carmel, 317-848-0201; Anderson, 765-640-5115

INDIANA

Luke Messer (R-6th)   202-225-3021
1230 LHOB   3rd Term/69%   6/98/98   Fax: 225-3382
messer.house.gov   **twitter** RepLukeMesser
CoS .... Douglas Menorca   **LD** .... Jason Grassie
Sch .... Amy Burke   **CD** .... Molly Gillaspie
Bio: b. 2/27/69 Evansville, IN; Presbyterian; JD Vanderbilt Univ., 1994; Nonprofit Executive, Congressional Aide; m. Jennifer
Comm.: Education & the Workforce; Financial Services
Dist. Offices: Muncie, 765-747-5566; Shelbyville, 317-421-0704

André Carson (D-7th)   202-225-4011
2135 RHOB   6th Term/60%   98/97/98   Fax: 225-5633
carson.house.gov   **twitter** repandrecarson
CoS .... Kim Rudolph   **LD** .... Nathan Bennett
Sch .... Cynthia Johnson   **CD** .... Jessica Gail
Bio: b. 10/16/74 Indianapolis, IN; Muslim; MS IN Wesleyan Univ., 2005; Marketing Specialist; sep. Mariama Shaheed-Carson
Comm.: Transportation & Infrastructure; Select Intelligence
Dist. Offices: Indianapolis, 317-283-6516

Larry Bucshon (R-8th) *boo-SHON*   202-225-4636
1005 LHOB   4th Term/64%   8/97/99   Fax: 225-3284
bucshon.house.gov   **twitter** RepLarryBucshon
CoS .... Teresa Buckley   **LD** .... Sarah Killeen
Sch .... Susey Davis   **CD** .... Nick McGee
Bio: b. 5/31/62 Taylorville, IL; Lutheran; MD Univ. of IL - Chicago, 1988; USNR, 1989-98; Surgeon; m. Kathryn
Comm.: Energy & Commerce
Dist. Offices: Evansville, 812-465-6484; Terre Haute, 812-232-0523

Trey Hollingsworth (R-9th)   202-225-5315
1641 LHOB   1st Term/54%   Fax: 226-6866
hollingsworth.house.gov   **twitter** RepTrey
CoS .... Rebecca Shaw   **LD** .... Connor Lentz
Sch .... Marjorie Daily   **CD** .... Rob Burgess
Bio: b. 9/12/83 Clinton, TN; Christian; MPP Georgetown 2014; Business Owner; m. Kelly
Comm.: Financial Services
Dist. Offices: Jeffersonville, ; Hammond, 219 852-0089; Jeffersonville, 812 284-2027

IOWA
iowa.gov

Pop.: 3,123,899
Rank: 30th
Caucasian: 92%
African-Am.: 4%
Nat. Am.: 1%   **Asian:** 2%
Other: 2%   **Hisp.:** 6%
Reg. Voters: 2,045,864
Dem.: 30%   **Rep.:** 32%
Other: 38%
Land Area: 55,857 sq. mi.   **Rank:** 23rd

Number of US House Seats: 3 Rep./1 Dem.

State Legislature
legis.iowa.gov
Senate: 29R/20D/1 Other   House: 59R/40D/1Vac
Session: 01/09/17 – 4/18/2017

IOWA

Gov. Terry E. Branstad (R) **515-281-5211**
Next Election: 2018 6th Term/59% Fax: 515-281-6611
twitter terrybranstad
Bio: b. 11/17/46 Leland, IA; Catholic; JD Drake Univ., 1974; USA, 1969-71; Attorney, Public Official, College President; m. Chris

State Capitol, 1007 East Grand Avenue, Des Moines, IA 50319
Washington Office: 202-624-5479

SENATE

Charles E. Grassley (R) **202-224-3744**
SH-135 7th Term/60% 60/87/100 Fax: 224-6020
grassley.senate.gov **twitter** ChuckGrassley
CoS ....Jill Kozeny **LD** ....Kurt Kovarik
Sch ....Jennifer Heins **Press**........ Beth Pellett Levine
Bio: b. 9/17/33 New Hartford, IA; Baptist; MA Univ. of Northern IA, 1956; Farmer; m. Barbara
Comm.: Agriculture, Nutrition & Forestry; Budget; Finance; Judiciary (Chair); Joint Taxation
Dist. Offices: Des Moines, 515-288-1145; Davenport, 563-322-4331; Cedar Rapids, 319-363-6832; Sioux City, 712-233-1860

Joni Ernst (R) **202-224-3254**
SR-111 1st Term/52% 53/95/100 Fax: 224-9369
ernst.senate.gov **twitter** SenJoniErnst
CoS ....Lisa Goeas **Dep CoS**............ Ryan Berger
Sch ....Josie Beecher **CD** ....Brook Hougesen
Bio: b. 7/1/70 Red Oak, IA; Lutheran; MPA Columbus Col., 1995; USAR, 1992-2001; IANG, 2001-15; Emergency Management Office Director, Job Training Coordinator; m. Gail
Comm.: Agriculture, Nutrition & Forestry; Armed Services; Environment & Public Works; Small Business & Entrepreneurship
Dist. Offices: Des Moines, 515-284-4574; Cedar Rapids, 319-365-4504; Davenport, 563-322-0677; Sioux City, 712-252-1550; Council Bluffs, 712-352-1167

HOUSE

Rod Blum (R-1st) *BLUM (like "plum")* **202-225-2911**
1108 LHOB 2nd Term/54% 8/94/99 Fax: None
blum.house.gov **twitter** RepRodBlum
CoS .... Paul Smith **LD** ....Kelsey Griswold
Sch ....Justin Bryant **Acting CD** ....Paul Smith
Bio: b. 4/26/55 Dubuque, IA; Episcopal; MBA Dubuque Univ., 1989; Business Owner, Software Developer; m. Karen
Comm.: Oversight & Government Reform; Small Business
Dist. Offices: Cedar Rapids, 319-364-2288; Dubuque, 563-557-7789; Cedar Falls, 319-266-6925

Dave Loebsack (D-2nd) **202-225-6576**
1527 LHOB 6th Term/54% 96/97/99 Fax: 226-0757
loebsack.house.gov **twitter** daveloebsack
CoS .... Eric Witte **LD** .... Ashley Shillingsburg
Sch .... Sam Ward **CD** ....Joe Hand
Bio: b. 12/23/52 Sioux City, IA; Methodist; PhD Univ. of CA - Davis, 1985; Professor; m. Teresa
Comm.: Energy & Commerce
Dist. Offices: Iowa City, 319-351-0789; Davenport, 563-323-5988

Iowa

David Young (R-3rd)　　　　　**202-225-5476**
240 CHOB　2nd Term/54%　7/96/100　Fax: 226-1329
davidyoung.house.gov　　　　**twitter** RepDavidYoung
CoS ....James Carstensen **LD** ....Jacob Olson
Sch ....Sierra Smith **CD** .... Taylor Mason
Bio: b. 5/11/68 Des Moines, IA; Lutheran; BA Drake Univ., 1991; Congressional Aide, Fundraiser; single
Comm.: Appropriations
Dist. Offices: Des Moines, 515-282-1909; Creston, 641-782-2495; Council Bluffs, 712-325-1404; Ft. Dodge, 515-573-2738

Steve King (R-4th)　　　　　**202-225-4426**
2210 RHOB　8th Term/62%　12/98/94　Fax: 225-3193
steveking.house.gov　　　　**twitter** SteveKingIA
CoS .... Sarah Stevens **LD** ....Jared Culver
Sch ....Hunter King **CD** .... Tori Beth Black
Bio: b. 5/28/49 Storm Lake, IA; Catholic; Attended NW MO St. Univ., 1967-70; Construction Company Owner; m. Marilyn
Comm.: Agriculture; Judiciary; Small Business
Dist. Offices: Sioux City, 712-224-4692; Spencer, 712-580-7754; Ames, 515-232-2885; Mason City, 641-201-1624; Council Bluffs, 712-352-1167

Kansas
kansas.gov

Pop.: 2,911,641
Rank: 34th
Caucasian: 87%
African-Am.: 6%
Nat. Am.: 1%　**Asian:** 3%
Other: 3%　**Hisp.:** 12%
Reg. Voters: 1,705,537
Dem.: 24%　**Rep.:** 45%　**Other:** 31%
Land Area: 81,759 sq. mi.　**Rank:** 13th

Number of US House Seats: 3 Rep./1. Vac.

State Legislature
kslegislature.org
Senate: 32R/8D　House: 97R/28D
Session: 01/12/17 – 5/15/2017

Gov. Sam Brownback (R)　　　　**785-296-3232**
Next Election: 2018　2nd Term/50%　Fax: 785-296-7973
twitter govsambrownback
Bio: b. 9/12/56 Garnett, KS; Catholic; JD Univ. of KS, 1982; College Instructor, Attorney; m. Mary

Capitol, 300 SW 10th Avenue, Suite 241S, Topeka, KS 66612-1590
Washington Office: 202-715-2923

SENATE

Pat Roberts (R)　　　　　**202-224-4774**
SH-109　4th Term/53%　54/95/96　Fax: 224-3514
roberts.senate.gov　　　　**twitter** senpatroberts
CoS ....Jackie Cottrell **LD** ....Amber Kirchhoefer
Sch ....Jensine Moyer **CD** ....Sarah Little
Bio: b. 4/20/36 Topeka, KS; Methodist; BA KS St. Univ., 1958; USMC, 1958-62; Journalist, Congressional Aide; m. Franki
Comm.: Agriculture, Nutrition & Forestry (Chair); Finance; Health, Education, Labor & Pensions; Rules & Administration; Select Ethics; Joint Library; Joint Printing
Dist. Offices: Overland Park, 913-451-9343; Topeka, 785-295-2745; Wichita, 316-263-0416; Dodge City, 620-227-2244

KANSAS

Jerry Moran (R)   **202-224-6521**
SD-521   2nd Term/62% 46/95/98 Fax: 228-6966
moran.senate.gov   twitter jerrymoran
CoS ....Brennan Britton **LD** ....William Ruder
Sch ....Emily Whitfield **CD** ....Katie Niederee
Bio: b. 5/29/54 Great Bend, KS; Christian; JD Univ. of KS,
1981; Attorney, Bank Officer; m. Robba
Comm.: Appropriations; Commerce, Science & Transportation; Environment & Public Works; Veterans' Affairs; Indian Affairs
Dist. Offices: Hays, 785-628-6401; Manhattan, 785-539-8973; Pittsburg, 620-232-2286; Wichita, 316-631-1410

HOUSE

Roger Marshall (R-1st)   **202-225-2715**
312 CHOB   1st Term/66%   Fax: 225-5124
marshall.house.gov   twitter RogerMarshallMD
CoS ....Brent Robertson **LD** ....Dalton Henry
Sch ....Katie Moore **CD** ....Eric Pahls
Bio: b. 8/9/60 El Dorado, KS; Non-demoniational Christian; MD Univ. of KS, 1987; USAR, 1984-91; Doctor; m. Laina
Comm.: Agriculture; Science, Space & Technology; Small Business
Dist. Offices: Salina, 785-714-0102

Lynn Jenkins (R-2nd)   **202-225-6601**
1526 LHOB   5th Term/61% 8/97/96 Fax: 225-7986
lynnjenkins.house.gov   twitter replynnjenkins
CoS ....Patrick Leopold **LD** .... Colin Brainard
Sch .....Jaclyn Schwinghamer **Press**.............Michael Byerly
Bio: b. 6/10/63 Topeka, KS; United Methodist; BS Weber St. Col., 1985; Accountant; div.
Comm.: Ways & Means
Dist. Offices: Topeka, 785-234-5966; Pittsburg, 620-231-5966; Independence, 620-231-5966

Kevin Yoder (R-3rd)   **202-225-2865**
2433 RHOB   4th Term/51% 7/98/99 Fax: 225-2807
yoder.house.gov   twitter RepKevinYoder
CoS ....Dave Natonski **LD** ....Joseph Eannello
Sch ....Cate Deurst **CD** ....CJ Grover
Bio: b. 1/8/76 Hutchinson, KS; Methodist; JD Univ. of KS, 2002; Attorney; m. Brooke
Comm.: Appropriations; Joint Library
Dist. Offices: Overland Park, 913-621-0832

OPEN SEAT

Vacant (4th)   **202-225-6216**
2452 RHOB
Rep. Mike Pompeo (R) resigned on January 23, 2017. A special election has been scheduled for April 11, 2017.

KENTUCKY
kentucky.gov

Pop.: 4,425,092   **Rank:** 26th
Caucasian: 88%   **African-Am.:** 8%   **Nat. Am.:** 0%   **Asian:** 1%
Other: 2%   **Hisp.:** 3%
Reg. Voters: 3,311,950
Dem.: 53%   **Rep.:** 39%   **Other:** 8%
Land Area: 39,486 sq. mi.   **Rank:** 37th

Number of US House Seats: 5 Rep./1 Dem.

State Legislature
lrc.state.ky.us
Senate: 27R/11D   House: 64R/36D
Session: 01/03/17 – 3/30/2017

Gov. Matt Bevin (R)   **502-564-2611**
Next Election: 2019 1st Term/53%   Fax: 502-564-2517
twitter GovMattBevin

Bio: b. 1/9/67 Shelburne, NH; Christian; BA Washington &
Lee Univ., 1989; USA, 1989-1993; Businessman; m. Glenna

700 Capitol Avenue, Suite 100, Frankfort, KY 40601
Washington Office: 202-220-1350

SENATE

Mitch McConnell (R)   **202-224-2541**
SR-317   6th Term/56%   67/77/100   Fax: 224-2499
mcconnell.senate.gov   **twitter** McConnellPress
CoS .... Sharon Soderstrom **LD** .... Phil Maxson
Sch .... Rebecca Fleeson **CD** .... David Popp
Bio: b. 2/20/42 Sheffield, AL; Baptist; JD Univ. of KY, 1967;
Attorney, Congressional Aide; m. Elaine Chao
Comm.: Agriculture, Nutrition & Forestry; Appropriations;
Rules & Administration; Majority Leader
Dist. Offices: Louisville, 502-582-6304; Lexington, 859-
224-8286; London, 606-864-2026; Paducah, 270-442-4554;
Louisville, 502-582-5341; Owensboro, 270-689-9085

Rand Paul (R)   **202-224-4343**
SR-167   2nd Term/57%   62/74/97   Fax: none
paul.senate.gov   **twitter** RandPaul
CoS .... William Henderson **LD** .... Vacant
Sch .... Drake Henley **CD** .... Sergio Gor
Bio: b. 1/7/63 Pittsburgh, PA; Presbyterian; MD Duke Univ.,
1988; Ophthalmologist; m. Kelley
Comm.: Foreign Relations; Health, Education, Labor & Pen-
sions; Homeland Security & Governmental Affairs; Small
Business & Entrepreneurship
Dist. Offices: Bowling Green, 270-782-8303; Crescent Springs,
859-426-0165; Hopkinsville, 270-885-1212; Lexington,
859-219-2239

HOUSE

James R. Comer (R-1st)   202-225-3115
1513 LHOB   2nd Term/73%   20/100/100   Fax: 225-3547
comer.house.gov   twitter KYComer
CoS ....Caroline Cash   **LD** ....Jim Goldenstein
Sch ....Kaity Wolfe   **Press**..........Michael Gossum
Bio: b. 8/19/72 Carthage, TN; Baptist; BS Western KY Univ.,
1993; Cattle Farmer, Businessman; m. Tamara Jo
Comm.: Agriculture; Oversight & Government Reform;
Small Business
Dist. Offices: Tompkinsville, 270-487-9509; Paducah, 270-
408-1865

Brett Guthrie (R-2nd)   202-225-3501
2434 RHOB   5th Term/Unc.   9/99/98   Fax: 226-2019
guthrie.house.gov   twitter RepGuthrie
CoS ....Eric Bergren   **LD** ....Joel Miller
Sch ....Jennifer Beil   **CD** ....Lauren Gaydos
Bio: b. 2/18/64 Florence, AL; Church of Christ; MPPM Yale
Univ., 1997; USA, 1987-90; USAR, 1990-2002; Automotive
Supply Company Executive; m. Beth
Comm.: Education & the Workforce; Energy & Commerce
Dist. Offices: Bowling Green, 270-842-9896

John Yarmuth (D-3rd)   202-225-5401
131 CHOB   6th Term/64%   98/99/92   Fax: 225-5776
yarmuth.house.gov   twitter repjohnyarmuth
CoS ....Julie Carr   **LD** ....Zack Marshall
EA ....Claire Elliott   **CD** ....Christopher Schuler
Bio: b. 11/4/47 Louisville, KY; Jewish; BA Yale Univ., 1969;
Newspaper Publisher & Columnist, Congressional Aide;
m. Cathy
Comm.: Budget (Rnk. Mem.)
Dist. Offices: Louisville, 502-582-5129; Louisville, 502-933-5863

Thomas Massie (R-4th)   202-225-3465
2453 RHOB   4th Term/71%   22/90/98   Fax: 225-0003
massie.house.gov   twitter RepThomasMassie
CoS ....Hans Hoeg   **Dep CoS**.......Seana Cranston
Sch ....Lauren Wills   **Press**................Lorenz Isidro
Bio: b. 1/13/71 Huntington, WV; Methodist; SM MIT, 1996;
Farmer, Technology Company Executive; m. Rhonda
Comm.: Oversight & Government Reform; Science, Space
& Technology; Transportation & Infrastructure
Dist. Offices: Crescent Springs, 859-426-0080; Ashland,
606-324-9898

Harold Rogers (R-5th)   202-225-4601
2406 RHOB   19th Term/Unc.   6/96/99   Fax: 225-0940
halrogers.house.gov   twitter RepHalRogers
CoS ....Megan Bell   **LD** ....Ryan Canfield
Sch ....Kelicia Rice   **CD** ....Danielle Smoot
Bio: b. 12/31/37 Barrier, KY; Baptist; LLB Univ. of KY, 1964;
KYNG, 1956-57, 1958-63; NCNG, 1957-58; Attorney; m.
Cynthia
Comm.: Appropriations
Dist. Offices: Somerset, 606-679-8346; Hazard, 606-439-
0794; Prestonsburg, 606-886-0844

Andy Barr (R-6th)   202-225-4706
1427 LHOB   3rd Term/61%   6/98/99   Fax: 225-2122
barr.house.gov   twitter RepAndyBarr
CoS ....Mary Rosado   **LD** ....Eric Bunning
Sch ....Gabriela Spence   **Dep CoS**.......Rick Van Meter
Bio: b. 7/24/73 Lexington, KY; Episcopal; JD Univ. of KY, 2001;
Lobbyist, Attorney, Congressional Aide; m. Carol
Comm.: Financial Services
Dist. Offices: Lexington, 859-219-1366; Ft. Wright, 859-578-
0188; Bowling Green, 270-781-1673

LOUISIANA
louisiana.gov

Pop.: 4,670,724 **Rank:** 25th
Caucasian: 63%
African-Am.: 33% **Nat. Am.:** 1%
Asian: 2% **Other:** 2% **Hisp.:** 5%
Reg. Voters: 2,976,695
Dem.: 46% **Rep.:** 28%
Other: 26%
Land Area: 43,204 sq. mi.
Rank: 33rd

Number of US House Seats:
5 Rep./1 Dem.

State Legislature
legis.state.la.us
Senate: 25R/14D   House: 58R/41D/3 Other
Session: 04/10/17 – 6/8/2017

Gov. John Bel Edwards (D)   225-342-7015
Next Election: 2019   1st Term/56%   Fax: 225-342-7099
twitter louisianagov
Bio: b. 4/18/79 Fort Worth, TX; Catholic; JD LA St. Univ.,
1999; USA, 1988-96; Attorney; m. Donna

PO Box 94004, Baton Rouge, LA 70804-9004

SENATE

Bill Cassidy (R)   202-224-5824
SH-520   1st Term/56%   55/85/99   Fax: 224-9735
cassidy.senate.gov   **twitter** BillCassidy
CoS .... James Quinn **LD** .... Christopher Gillott
Sch .... Allison Kapsner **CD** .... John Cummins
Bio: b. 9/28/57 Highland Park, IL; Christian; MD LA St. Univ.,
1983; Physician; m. Laura Layden Cassidy
Comm.: Energy & Natural Resources; Finance; Health, Edu-
cation, Labor & Pensions; Veterans' Affairs; Joint Economic
Dist. Offices: Baton Rouge, 225-929-7711; Metairie, 504-838-
0130; Lafayette, 337-261-1400; Alexandria, 318-448-7176

John N. Kennedy (R)   202-224-4623
SR-B11   1st Term/61%   Fax: 228-5061
kennedy.senate.gov   **twitter** SenJohnKennedy
CoS .... Preston Robinson **LD** .... Chris Stanley
Sch .... Scotty Wofford **CD** .... Michelle Millhollon
Bio: b. 11/21/51 Centreville, Miss; Methodist; BCL Oxford
Univ., 1979; Attorney, Aide; m. Becky
Comm.: Appropriations; Banking, Housing, & Urban Affairs;
Budget; Judiciary; Small Business & Entrepreneurship
Dist. Offices:

HOUSE

Steve Scalise (R-1st) *skuh-LEASE*   202-225-3015
2338 RHOB   6th Term/75%   8/98/98   Fax: 226-0386
scalise.house.gov   **twitter** SteveScalise
CoS .... Megan Bel Miller **LD** .... John Seale
Sch .... Ellen Gosnell **CD** .... Chris Bond
Bio: b. 10/6/65 Baton Rouge, LA; Catholic; BS LA St. Univ.,
1989; Software Engineer; m. Jennifer
Comm.: Energy & Commerce; Majority Whip
Dist. Offices: Metairie, 504-837-1259; Mandeville, 985-893-
9064; Houma, 985-879-2300

Louisiana

Cedric L. Richmond (D-2nd)   **202-225-6636**
420 CHOB   4th Term/70%   98/98/94   Fax: 225-1988
richmond.house.gov   **twitter** RepRichmond
CoS .... Virgil Miller **LD** .... Reginald Babin
Sch .... Kemah Dennis-Morial **CD** .... Brandon Gassaway
Bio: b. 9/13/73 New Orleans, LA; Baptist; JD Tulane Univ.,
1998; Attorney; m. Raquel Greenup
Comm.: Homeland Security; Judiciary
Dist. Offices: New Orleans, 504-288-3777; Baton Rouge,
225-636-5600; Gretna, 504-365-0390

Clay Higgins (R-3rd)   **202-225-2031**
1711 LHOB   1st Term/56%   Fax: 225-5724
clayhiggins.house.gov   **twitter**
CoS .... Kathee Facchiano **LD** .... Ward Cormier
Sch .... Jordan Lane **Press** .... Chris Comeaux
Bio: b. 8/24/61 New Orleans; Christian; Attended LA State
Univ.; LA National Guard, 1988-94; Public Information
Officer, Police Officer, Car Dealership Manager, Carpenter;
m. Becca
Comm.: Homeland Security; Science, Space & Technology;
Veterans' Affairs
Dist. Offices: TBA

Mike Johnson (R-4th)   **202-225-2777**
327 CHOB   1st Term/65%   Fax: 225-8039
mikejohnson.house.gov   **twitter** repmikejohnson
CoS .... Hayden Haynes **LD** .... Josh Hodges
Sch .... Ruth Ward **CD** .... Ainsley Holyfield
Bio: b. 1/30/72 Shreveport; Christian; JD LA St. Univ., 1998;
Attorney; m. Kelly
Comm.: Judiciary; Natural Resources
Dist. Offices: Bossier City, 318-840-0309; Leesville, 337-392-
3146; Natchitoches, 318-357-5731

Ralph Abraham (R-5th)   **202-225-8490**
417 CHOB   2nd Term/82%   7/99/100   Fax: 225-5639
abraham.house.gov   **twitter** RepAbraham
CoS .... Luke Letlow **LD** .... Ted Verrill
Sch .... Emma Herrock **CD** .... Cole Avery
Bio: b. 9/16/54 Monroe, LA; Baptist; MD LA St. Univ., 1994;
USA, 1986-89; Physician, Veterinarian; m. Dianne
Comm.: Agriculture; Armed Services; Science, Space &
Technology
Dist. Offices: Monroe, 318-322-3500; Alexandria, 318-
445-0818

Garret Graves (R-6th)   **202-225-3901**
430 CHOB   2nd Term/63%   9/96/99   Fax: 225-7313
garretgraves.house.gov   **twitter** RepGarretGraves
CoS .... Paul Sawyer **LD** .... Ian Bennitt
Sch .... Samantha Tillery **CD** .... Kevin Roig
Bio: b. 1/31/72 Baton Rouge, LA; Catholic; Attended AL
Univ., 1990-91; Attended LA Tech Univ., 1993-95; Attended
American Univ., 1996; Coastal Affairs Director, Congressional
Aide; m. Carissa
Comm.: Natural Resources; Transportation & Infrastructure
Dist. Offices: Baton Rouge, 225-442-1731; Livingston, 225-
686-4413; Thibodaux, 985-448-4103; Lake Charles, 337-277-
5398; Monroe, 318-324-2111; Shreveport, 318-798-3215

MAINE
maine.gov

Pop.: 1,329,328 **Rank:** 42nd
Caucasian: 95% **African-Am.:** 1% **Nat. Am.:** 1%
Asian: 1% **Other:** 2% **Hisp.:** 2%
Reg. Voters: 1,058,444
Dem.: 31% **Rep.:** 27% **Other:** 42%
Land Area: 30,843 sq. mi. **Rank:** 39th

Number of US House Seats: 1 Dem./1 Rep.

State Legislature
legislature.maine.gov
Senate: 18R/17D House: 77D/71R/5 Other
Session: 12/07/16 – 6/14/2017

Gov. Paul R. LePage (R)   **207-287-3531**
Next Election: 2018 2nd Term/48%   Fax: 207-287-1034
twitter governor_lepage
Bio: b. 10/9/48 Lewiston, ME; Catholic; MBA Univ. of Maine, 1975; Businessman; m. Ann

1 State House Station, Augusta, ME 04333-0001

SENATE

Susan Collins (R)   **202-224-2523**
SD-413   4th Term/68%   77/55/100   Fax: 224-2693
collins.senate.gov   twitter senatorcollins
CoS ....Darci Greenacre **CD** ....Betsy McDonnell
Sch ....Steve Abbott **LD** ....Annie Clark
Bio: b. 12/7/52 Caribou, ME; Catholic; BA St. Lawrence Univ., 1975; Businesswoman, Congressional Aide; m. Thomas Daffron
Comm.: Appropriations; Health, Education, Labor & Pensions; Select Intelligence; Special Aging (Chair)
Dist. Offices: Bangor, 207-945-0417; Augusta, 207-622-8414; Biddeford, 207-283-1101; Lewiston, 207-784-6969

Angus King (I)   **202-224-5344**
SH-133   1st Term/53%   93/85/99   Fax: 224-1946
king.senate.gov   twitter SenAngusKing
CoS ....Kay Rand **LD** ....Chad Metzler
Sch ....Matt Liscovitz **CD** ... Kathleen Connery Dawe
Bio: b. 3/31/44 Alexandria, VA; Episcopal; JD Univ. of VA, 1969; Attorney, Businessman; m. Mary J. Herman
Comm.: Armed Services; Budget; Energy & Natural Resources; Rules & Administration; Select Intelligence
Dist. Offices: Augusta, 207-622-8292; Presque Isle, 207-764-5124; Scarborough, 207-883-1588; Bangor, 207-945-8000

HOUSE

Chellie Pingree (D-1st) *Like "Shelley"*   **202-225-6116**
2162 RHOB   5th Term/58%   92/98/99   Fax: 225-5590
pingree.house.gov   twitter chelliepingree
CoS ....Jesse Connolly **LD** .... None
Sch ....Karen Sudbay **CD** ....Victoria Bonney
Bio: b. 4/2/55 Minneapolis, MN; Lutheran; BA Col. of the Atlantic, 1979; Inn Owner, Nonprofit Executive, Public Official; m. Donald Sussman
Comm.: Appropriations
Dist. Offices: Portland, 207-774-5019; Waterville, 207-873-5713

MAINE

Bruce Poliquin (R-2nd)   **202-225-6306**
1208 LHOB   2nd Term/54%   9/89/99   Fax: 225-2943
poliquin.house.gov   **twitter** RepPoliquin
CoS .... Matt Hutson **LD** .... Philip Swartzfager
Sch .... Danielle Branz **Press** .... Brendan Conley
Bio: b. 11/1/53 Waterville, ME; Catholic; AB Harvard Univ.,
1976; Real Estate Company Owner; wid.
Comm.: Financial Services; Veterans' Affairs
Dist. Offices: Bangor, 207-942-0583; Lewiston, 207-784-0768;
Presque Isle, 207-764-1968

MARYLAND
maryland.gov

Pop.: 6,006,401   **Rank:** 19th
Caucasian: 60%
African-Am.: 31%   **Nat. Am.:** 1%
Asian: 7%   **Other:** 3%   **Hisp.:** 10%
Reg. Voters: 3,900,090
Dem.: 54%   **Rep.:** 26%   **Other:** 20%
Land Area: 9,707 sq. mi.   **Rank:** 42nd

Number of US House Seats: 7 Dem./1 Rep.

State Legislature
mgaleg.maryland.gov
Senate: 32D/14R   House: 90D/51R
Session: 01/11/17 – 4/10/2017

Gov. Larry Hogan (R)   **410-974-3901**
Next Election: 2018 1st Term/51%   Fax: 410-974-3275
twitter larryhogan
Bio: b. 5/25/56 Washington, DC; Catholic; BA FL St. Univ.,
1978; Business Owner; m. Yumi

100 State Circle, Annapolis, MD 21401
Washington Office: 202-624-1430

SENATE

Benjamin L. Cardin (D)   **202-224-4524**
SH-509   2nd Term/56%   93/97/100   Fax: 224-1651
cardin.senate.gov   **twitter** SenatorCardin
CoS .... Christopher Lynch **LD** .... Vacant
Sch .... Debbie Yamada **CD** .... Sue Walitsky
Bio: b. 10/5/43 Baltimore, MD; Jewish; LLB Univ. of MD,
1967; Attorney; m. Myrna
Comm.: Environment & Public Works; Finance; Foreign
Relations (Rnk. Mem.); Small Business & Entrepreneurship
Dist. Offices: Baltimore, 410-962-4436; Bowie, 202-870-
1164; Salisbury, 410-546-4250; Cumberland, 301-777-2957;
Rockville, 301-762-2974

MARYLAND

Chris Van Hollen (D) 202-224-4654
SD-B40C   1st Term/60%   Fax: 224-8858
vanhollen.senate.gov   twitter chrisvanhollen
CoS .... Karen Robb LD .... Sarah Schenning
Sch .... Blaine Nolan CD .... Bridgett Frey
Bio: b. 1/10/59 Karachi, Pakistan; Episcopal; JD Georgetown Univ., 1990; Attorney, Gubernatorial Aide, Congressional Aide; m. Katherine Wilkens
Comm.: Agriculture, Nutrition & Forestry Committee; Appropriations; Banking, Housing, & Urban Affairs; Budget
Dist. Offices: Hagerstown, 301-797-2826; Rockville, 301-545-1500

HOUSE

Andy Harris (R-1st) 202-225-5311
1533 LHOB   4th Term/68%   9/98/99   Fax: 225-0254
harris.house.gov   twitter repandyharrismd
CoS .... John Dutton LD .... Tim Daniels
Sch .... Charlotte Heyworth Press .... Jacque Clark
Bio: b. 1/25/57 Brooklyn, NY; Catholic; MHS Johns Hopkins Univ., 1995; USNR, 1988-2005; Anesthesiologist; wid.
Comm.: Appropriations
Dist. Offices: Chester, 410-643-5425; Bel Air, 410-588-5670; Salisbury, 443-944-8624

C.A. Dutch Ruppersberger (D-2nd) 202-225-3061
2416 RHOB   8th Term/62%   81/92/99   Fax: 225-3094
dutch.house.gov   twitter Call_Me_Dutch
CoS ... Tara Linnehan-Oursler LD .... Walter Gonzales
Dep CoS .... Cori Duggins CD .... Jaime Lennon
Bio: b. 1/31/46 Baltimore, MD; Methodist; JD Univ. of Baltimore, 1970; Attorney, County Prosecutor; m. Kay
Comm.: Appropriations
Dist. Offices: Timonium, 410-628-2701

John Sarbanes (D-3rd) 202-225-4016
2444 RHOB   6th Term/63%   98/100/99   Fax: 225-9219
sarbanes.house.gov   twitter RepSarbanes
CoS .... Jason Gleason LD .... Raymond O'Mara
Sch .... Kate Gieron CD .... Daniel Jacobs
Bio: b. 5/22/62 Baltimore, MD; Greek Orthodox; JD Harvard Univ., 1988; Attorney, State Education Consultant; m. Dina
Comm.: Energy & Commerce; Oversight & Government Reform
Dist. Offices: Towson, 410-832-8890

Anthony G. Brown (D-4th) 202-225-8699
1505 LHOB   1st Term/74%   Fax: 225-8714
anthonybrown.house.gov   twitter AnthonyBrownMD4
CoS .... Maia Estes LD .... Eric Delaney
Sch .... Hannah Cooper CD .... Matthew Verghese
Bio: b. 11/21/61 Huntington, NY; Catholic; JD Harvard Univ., 1992; USA, 1984-89; USAR, 1989-2014; Attorney; m. Karmen
Comm.: Armed Services; Ethics; Natural Resources
Dist. Offices: Upper Marlboro, 301-985-2600

Steny H. Hoyer (D-5th) 202-225-4131
1705 LHOB   19th Term/67%   94/97/95   Fax: 225-4300
hoyer.house.gov   twitter WhipHoyer
CoS ...... Alexis Covey-Brandt LD .... Tom Mahr
Sch ... Jordan Sugar-Carlsgaard CD .... Katie Grant
Bio: b. 6/14/39 Manhattan, NY; Baptist; JD Georgetown Univ., 1966; Attorney; wid.
Comm.: Minority Whip
Dist. Offices: Greenbelt, 301-474-0119; Waldorf, 301-843-1577

MARYLAND

John Delaney (D-6th)   202-225-2721
1632 LHOB   3rd Term/55%   80/93/90   Fax: 225-2193
delaney.house.gov   twitter RepJohnDelaney
CoS .... Xan Fishman LD .... Lauren Santabar
Sch .... Elizabeth Virga CD .... Will McDonald
Bio: b. 4/16/63 Wood-Ridge, NJ; Catholic; JD Georgetown Univ., 1988; Entrepreneur, Businessman; m. April McClain-Delaney
Comm.: Financial Services; Joint Economic
Dist. Offices: Gaithersburg, 301-926-0300; Hagerstown, 301-733-2900

Elijah E. Cummings (D-7th)   202-225-4741
2163 RHOB   12th Term/75%   100/99/98   Fax: 225-3178
cummings.house.gov   twitter RepCummings
CoS .... Vernon Simms LD .... Suzanne Owen
Sch .... Jean Waskow CD .... Trudy Perkins
Bio: b. 1/18/51 Baltimore, MD; Baptist; JD Univ. of MD, 1976; Attorney; m. Maya
Comm.: Oversight & Government Reform (Rnk. Mem.); Transportation & Infrastructure
Dist. Offices: Baltimore, 410-685-9199; Catonsville, 410-719-8777; Ellicott City, 410-465-8259

Jamie Raskin (D-8th)   202-225-5341
431 CHOB   1st Term/59%   Fax: 225-0375
raskin.house.gov   twitter jamie_raskin
CoS .... Julie Tagen LD .... William Roberts
Sch .... Jack Frye Press .... Lauren Doney
Bio: b. 12/13/62 Washington, DC; Jewish Humanist; JD Harvard Univ., 1987; Attorney, Professor; m. Sarah
Comm.: House Administration; Judiciary; Oversight & Government Reform; Joint Printing
Dist. Offices: Rockville, 301-354-1000

MASSACHUSETTS
mass.gov

Pop.: 6,794,422
Rank: 15th
Caucasian: 82%
African-Am.: 8%
Nat. Am.: 1%
Asian: 7%   **Other:** 2%   **Hisp.:** 11%
Reg. Voters: 4,271,835
Dem.: 35%   **Rep.:** 11%   **Other:** 54%
Land Area: 7,800 sq. mi.   **Rank:** 45th

Number of US House Seats: 9 Dem.

State Legislature
mass.gov
Senate: 34D/6R   House: 125D/35R
Session: 01/04/17 – 11/15/2017

Gov. Charlie Baker (R)   617-725-4005
Next Election: 2018 1st Term/48%   Fax: 617-727-9725
twitter massgovernor
Bio: b. 11/13/56 Elmire, NY; Protestant; MBA Northwestern Univ., 1986; Businessman; m. Lauren

State House, Room 280, Boston, MA 02133
Washington Office: 202-624-7713

MASSACHUSETTS

SENATE

Elizabeth Warren (D)　　　　**202-224-4543**
SH-317　　1st Term/54%　　87/100/100　Fax: 228-2072
warren.senate.gov　　　　　　　　twitter senwarren
CoS .... Dan Geldon　**LD** .... Jon Donenberg
Sch .... Emily Ross　**Press** .... Lacey Rose
Bio: b. 6/22/49 Oklahoma City, OK; Methodist; JD Rutgers
Univ., 1976; Law Professor, Public Official; m. Bruce Mann
Comm.: Armed Services; Banking, Housing, & Urban Affairs;
Health, Education, Labor & Pensions; Special Aging
Dist. Offices: Boston, 617-565-3170; Springfield, 413-788-
2693

Edward J. Markey (D)　　　　**202-224-2742**
SD-255　　2nd Term/62%　　87/100/100　Fax: 224-8525
markey.senate.gov　　　　　　　　twitter SenMarkey
CoS .... Vacant　**LD** .... Vacant
Sch .... Sarah Butler　**CD** .... Giselle Barry
Bio: b. 7/11/46 Malden, MA; Catholic; JD Boston Col., 1972;
USAR, 1968-73; Attorney; m. Susan Blumenthal
Comm.: Commerce, Science & Transportation; Foreign Rela-
tions; Small Business & Entrepreneurship
Dist. Offices: Boston, 617-565-8519; Fall River, 508-677-0523;
Springfield, 413-785-4610

HOUSE

Richard E. Neal (D-1st)　　　　**202-225-5601**
341 CHOB　　15th Term/73%　　98/98/97　Fax: 225-8112
neal.house.gov　　　　　　　　twitter RepRichardNeal
CoS .... William Tranghese　**LD** .... Kara Getz
Sch .... Tim Ranstrom　**Press** .... William Tranghese
Bio: b. 2/14/49 Worcester, MA; Catholic; MPA Univ. of
Hartford, 1976; College Lecturer, Teacher, Mayoral Aide;
m. Maureen
Comm.: Ways & Means (Rnk. Mem.); Joint Taxation
Dist. Offices: Springfield, 413-785-0325; Pittsfield, 413-
442-0946

Jim McGovern (D-2nd)　　　　**202-225-6101**
438 CHOB　　11th Term/Unc.　100/98/98　Fax: 225-5759
mcgovern.house.gov　　　　　　　　twitter repmcgovern
CoS .... Jennifer Chandler　**LD** .... Cindy Buhl
Sch .... Daniel Holt　**Press** .... Abraham White
Bio: b. 11/20/59 Worcester, MA; Catholic; MPA American
Univ., 1984; Congressional Aide, Campaign Aide; m. Lisa
Comm.: Agriculture; Rules
Dist. Offices: Worcester, 508-831-7356; Northampton, 413-
341-8700; Leominster, 978-466-3552

Niki Tsongas (D-3rd) *SONG-gus*　　**202-225-3411**
1714 LHOB　　6th Term/69%　　96/98/98　Fax: 226-0771
tsongas.house.gov　　　　　　　　twitter nikiinthehouse
CoS .... Katie Enos　**LD** .... Sara Outterson
OM .... Bob Schneider　**CD** .... Michael Hartigan
Bio: b. 4/26/46 Chico, CA; Episcopal; JD Boston Univ., 1988;
Public Affairs Official, Attorney, Social Worker; wid.
Comm.: Armed Services; Natural Resources
Dist. Offices: Lowell, 978-459-0101

Joseph P. Kennedy III (D-4th)　　**202-225-5931**
434 CHOB　　3rd Term/70%　　98/98/92　Fax: 225-0182
kennedy.house.gov　　　　　　　　twitter RepJoeKennedy
CoS .... Greg Mecher　**LD** .... Sarah Curtis
Sch .... MS. Mariah Phillips　**Press** .... Dan Black
Bio: b. 10/4/80 Brighton, MA; Catholic; JD Harvard Univ.,
2009; County Prosecutor, Peace Corps Volunteer; m. Lauren
Comm.: Energy & Commerce
Dist. Offices: Attleboro, 508-431-1110; Newton, 617-332-
3333

Katherine M. Clark (D-5th)   **202-225-2836**
1415 LHOB   3rd Term/Unc.   98/99/99   Fax: 226-0092
katherineclark.house.gov   twitter RepKClark
CoS .... Brooke Scannell **LD** .... David Bond
Sch .... Mark McKinnon **CD** .... Justin Unga
Bio: b. 7/17/63 New Haven, CT; Protestant; MPA Harvard Univ., 1997; Attorney; m. Rodney S. Dowell
Comm.: Appropriations
Dist. Offices: Cambridge, 617-354-0292; Framingham, 508-319-9757

Seth Moulton (D-6th)   **202-225-8020**
1408 LHOB   2nd Term/Unc.   93/95/98   Fax: 225-5915
moulton.house.gov   twitter teammoulton
CoS ....Jeremy Joseph **Sr PA** .... Eric Kanter
Sch ....Anna Stolitzka **CD** .... Carrie Rankin
Bio: b. 10/24/78 Salem, MA; Christian; MBA/MPP Harvard Univ., 2011; USMC, 2002-08; Health Care Consultant, Rail Company Executive; single
Comm.: Armed Services; Budget
Dist. Offices: Salem, 978-531-1669

Michael E. Capuano *KAP-you-AH-no*
(D-7th)   **202-225-5111**
1414 LHOB   10th Term/Unc.   98/99/96   Fax: 225-9322
capuano.house.gov   twitter RepMikeCapuano
CoS ....Robert Primus **LD** .... Steven Carlson
Sch ....Mary Doherty **Press** .... Alison Mills
Bio: b. 1/9/52 Somerville, MA; Catholic; JD Boston Col., 1977; Attorney, State Legislative Aide; m. Barbara
Comm.: Financial Services; Transportation & Infrastructure
Dist. Offices: Cambridge, 617-621-6208

Stephen F. Lynch (D-8th)   **202-225-8273**
2268 RHOB   9th Term/72%   90/95/99   Fax: 225-3984
lynch.house.gov   twitter RepStephenLynch
CoS .... Kevin Ryan **LD** .... Bruce Fernandez
Sch ...... Megan Hollingshead **Press** .... Elizabeth Zappala
Bio: b. 3/31/55 Boston, MA; Catholic; MA Harvard Univ., 1998; Attorney, Ironworker; m. Margaret
Comm.: Financial Services; Oversight & Government Reform
Dist. Offices: Boston, 617-428-2000; Brockton, 508-586-5555; Quincy, 617-657-6305

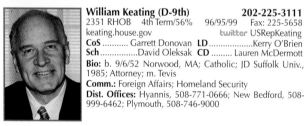

William Keating (D-9th)   **202-225-3111**
2351 RHOB   4th Term/56%   96/95/99   Fax: 225-5658
keating.house.gov   twitter USRepKeating
CoS .... Garrett Donovan **LD** .... Kerry O'Brien
Sch ....David Oleksak **CD** .... Lauren McDermott
Bio: b. 9/6/52 Norwood, MA; Catholic; JD Suffolk Univ., 1985; Attorney; m. Tevis
Comm.: Foreign Affairs; Homeland Security
Dist. Offices: Hyannis, 508-771-0666; New Bedford, 508-999-6462; Plymouth, 508-746-9000

MICHIGAN
michigan.gov

Pop.: 9,922,576
Rank: 10th
Caucasian: 80%
African-Am.: 14%   **Nat. Am.:** 1%
Asian: 3%   **Other:** 2%   **Hisp.:** 5%
Reg. Voters: 6,748,385
Party registration not required
Land Area: 56,539 sq. mi.   **Rank:** 22nd

Number of US House Seats: 9 Rep./5 Dem.

State Legislature
legislature.mi.gov
Senate: 27R/11D   House: 63R/47D
Session: 01/11/17 – 12/31/2017

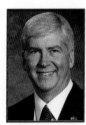

Gov. Rick Snyder (R)   517-373-3400
Next Election: 2018   2nd Term/51%   Fax: 517-335-6863
twitter onetoughnerd
Bio: b. 8/19/58 Battle Creek, MI; Presbyterian; JD Univ. of
MI, 1982; Accountant, Business Executive; m. Sue

PO Box 30013, Lansing, MI 48909
Washington Office: 202-624-5840

SENATE

Debbie Stabenow (D)   202-224-4822
SH-731   3rd Term/59%   89/92/98   Fax: 228-0325
stabenow.senate.gov   **twitter** SenStabenow
CoS .... Matt VanKuiken   **LD** .... Emily Carwell
Sch .... Anne Stanski   **Press**..... Miranda Margowsky
Bio: b. 4/29/50 Clare, MI; United Methodist; MSW MI St.
Univ., 1975; Training Consultant; div.
Comm.: Agriculture, Nutrition & Forestry (Rnk. Mem.);
Budget; Energy & Natural Resources; Finance; Joint Taxation
Dist. Offices: East Lansing, 517-203-1760; Detroit, 313-961-
4330; Grand Rapids, 616-975-0052; Flint, 810-720-4172;
Rochester, 248-608-8040; Traverse City, 231-947-7773

Gary Peters (D)   202-224-6221
SH-724   1st Term/55%   93/91/99   Fax: 224-7387
peters.senate.gov   **twitter** SenGaryPeters
CoS .... Eric Feldman   **LD** ....David Weinberg
Sch ....Angeli Chawla   **CD** .... Amber Moon
Bio: b. 12/1/58 Pontiac, MI; Episcopal; MA MI St. Univ., 2007;
USNR, 1993-2000, 01-05; College Instructor, Investment Firm
Branch Executive; m. Colleen Ochoa Peters
Comm.: Armed Services; Commerce, Science & Transpor-
tation; Homeland Security & Governmental Affairs; Joint
Economic
Dist. Offices: Detroit, 313-226-6020; Lansing, 517-377-1508;
Grand Rapids, 616-233-9150; Saginaw, 989-754-0112

HOUSE

Jack Bergman (R-1st)   202-225-4735
414 CHOB   1st Term/55%   Fax: 225-4710
bergman.house.gov   **twitter** RepJackBergman
CoS ....Tony Lis   **LD** .... Michelle Jelnicky
Sch ....Amelia Burns   **CD** .... Farahn Morgan
Bio: b. 2/2/47 Shakopee, MN; Lutheran; MBA Univ. of W.
FL, 1975; USMC, 1969-75 & 2003- 09; RING, 1975-78;
USMCR,; Military Officer; m. Cindy
Comm.: Budget; Natural Resources; Veterans' Affairs
Dist. Offices: Marquette, 906-273-2727; Traverse City, 231-
714-4785

MICHIGAN

Bill Huizenga (R-2nd) *HI-zing-uh*   **202-225-4401**
2232 RHOB   4th Term/68%   10/97/93   Fax: 226-0779
huizenga.house.gov   twitter RepHuizenga
CoS .... Jon DeWitte   **LD** .... Nathan Bult
Sch .... Sarah Lisman   **CD** .... Brian Patrick
Bio: b. 1/31/69 Zeeland, MI; Christian Reformed; BA Calvin Col., 1992; Private School Fundraiser, Congressional District Aide; m. Natalie
Comm.: Financial Services
Dist. Offices: Grand Haven, 616-414-5516; Grandville, 616-570-0917

Justin Amash (R-3rd) *ah-MAHSH*   **202-225-3831**
114 CHOB   4th Term/59%   22/87/99   Fax: 225-5144
amash.house.gov   twitter justinamash
CoS .... Poppy Nelson   **LD** .... Carolyn Iodice
Sch .... Jelena Matic   **CD** .... Corie Whalen
Bio: b. 4/18/80 Grand Rapids, MI; Eastern Orthodox; JD Univ. of MI, 2005; Attorney, Marketing Consultant; m. Kara
Comm.: Oversight & Government Reform
Dist. Offices: Grand Rapids, 616-451-8383

John Moolenaar (R-4th)   **202-225-3561**
117 CHOB   2nd Term/62%   9/98/99   Fax: 225-9679
moolenaar.house.gov   twitter RepMoolenaar
CoS .... Ryan Tarrant   **Dep CoS** .... Mike Telliga
Sch .... Eva Vrana   **CD** .... David Russell
Bio: b. 5/8/61 Midland, MI; Christian; MPP Harvard Univ., 1989; Charter School Administrator, Businessman, Chemist; m. Amy
Comm.: Appropriations
Dist. Offices: Midland, 989-631-2552; Cadillac, 231-942-5070

Dan Kildee (D-5th)   **202-225-3611**
227 CHOB   3rd Term/61%   98/99/99   Fax: 225-9679
dankildee.house.gov   twitter RepDanKildee
CoS .... Jennifer Cox   **LD** .... Maureen May
Sch .... Tina Reyes   **CD** .... Mitchell Rivard
Bio: b. 8/11/58 Flint, MI; Catholic; BS Central MI Univ., 2011; Nonprofit Executive, Public Official; m. Jennifer
Comm.: Financial Services
Dist. Offices: Flint, 810-238-8627

Fred Upton (R-6th)   **202-225-3761**
2183 RHOB   16th Term/59%   7/93/100   Fax: 225-4986
upton.house.gov   twitter RepFredUpton
CoS .... Joan Hillebrands   **LD** .... Mark Ratner
Sch .... Bits Thomas   **CD** .... Tom Wilbur
Bio: b. 4/23/53 St. Joseph, MI; Protestant; BA Univ. of MI, 1975; Congressional Aide, Budget Analyst; m. Amey
Comm.: Energy & Commerce
Dist. Offices: Kalamazoo, 269-385-0039; St. Joseph, 269-982-1986

Tim Walberg (R-7th)   **202-225-6276**
2436 RHOB   5th Term/55%   7/99/99   Fax: 225-6281
walberg.house.gov   twitter RepWalberg
CoS .... RJ Laukitis   **LD** .... Jonathan Hirte
Sch .... Carly Anderson   **CD** .... Dan Kotman
Bio: b. 4/12/51 Chicago, IL; Christian; MA Wheaton Col., 1978; Minister, Religious School Fundraiser; m. Sue
Comm.: Education & the Workforce; Energy & Commerce
Dist. Offices: Jackson, 517-780-9075

MICHIGAN

Mike Bishop (R-8th)   202-225-4872
428 CHOB   2nd Term/56%   9/97/99   Fax: 225-5820
mikebishop.house.gov   twitter repmikebishop
CoS .... Allan Filip **LD** ....Daniel Harder
Sch .... Susan Larson **CD** .... Kelli Ford
Bio: b. 3/18/67 Almont, MI; Congregationalist; JD Detroit
Col. of Law, 1993; Attorney, Real Estate Company Owner;
m. Cristina
Comm.: Ways & Means
Dist. Offices: Brighton, 810-227-8600

Sander M. Levin (D-9th)   202-225-4961
1236 LHOB   18th Term/58%   96/98/99   Fax: 226-1033
levin.house.gov   twitter Repsandylevin
CoS .... Hilarie Chambers **LD** .... Eddie Shimkus
Sch .... Hilarie Chambers **Press** .... Emily Del Morone
Bio: b. 9/6/31 Detroit, MI; Jewish; LLB Harvard Univ., 1957;
Attorney; m. Pamela Cole
Comm.: Ways & Means
Dist. Offices: Roseville, 586-498-7122

Paul Mitchell (R-10th)   202-225-2106
211 CHOB   1st Term/63%   Fax: 226-1169
mitchell.house.gov   twitter RepPaulMitchell
CoS .... Kyle Kizzier **LD** .... Pat Pelletier
Sch .... Molly Harrington **CD** .... Ann Tumolo
Bio: b. 11/14/56 Boston, MA; Protestant; BA MI St. Univ.
1978; Non-Profit Foundation President; m. Sherry
Comm.: Education & the Workforce; Oversight & Government
Reform; Transportation & Infrastructure
Dist. Offices: Shelby Township, 586-997-5010

Dave Trott (R-11th)   202-225-8171
1722 LHOB   2nd Term/53%   9/97/99   Fax: 225-2667
trott.house.gov   twitter repdavetrott
CoS .... Kyle Bonini **LD** ....Bridget Dobyan
Sch .... Marla Rondo **CD** ....Katie Vincentz
Bio: b. 10/16/60 Birmingham, MI; Catholic; JD Duke Univ.,
1985; Attorney, Business Owner, Congressional Aide; m.
Kathleen
Comm.: Financial Services
Dist. Offices: Troy, 248-528-0711

Debbie Dingell (D-12th)   202-225-4071
116 CHOB   2nd Term/64%   96/98/99   Fax: 226-0371
debbiedingell.house.gov   twitter RepDebDingell
CoS .... Peter Chandler **LD** .... Greg Sunstrum
Sch .... Jennifer Holland **CD** .... Hannah Smith
Bio: b. 11/23/53 Detroit, MI; Catholic; MA Georgetown Univ.,
1998; Nonprofit Executive, Lobbyist; m. John
Comm.: Energy & Commerce
Dist. Offices: Dearborn, 313-278-2936; Ypsilanti, 734-
481-1100

John Conyers, Jr. (D-13th)   202-225-5126
2426 RHOB   27th Term/77%   100/98/96   Fax: 225-0072
conyers.house.gov   twitter repjohnconyers
CoS .... Raymond Plowden **LD** .... Daniel Hervig
Sch .... Ammar Moussa **CD** ...Shadawn Reddick-Smith
Bio: b. 5/16/29 Detroit, MI; Baptist; LLB Wayne St. Univ.,
1958; MING, 1948-50; USA, 1950-54; USAR, 1954-57;
Attorney, Congressional District Aide; m. Monica
Comm.: Judiciary (Rnk. Mem.)
Dist. Offices: Detroit, 313-961-5670; Westland, 734-675-4084

MICHIGAN

Brenda Lawrence (D-14th)   **202-225-5802**
1213 LHOB   2nd Term/78%   96/99/98   Fax: 226-2356
lawrence.house.gov   twitter RepLawrence
CoS ....Duron Marshall **LD** ....Vacant
Sch ....Vacant **CD** ....Nicole Julius
Bio: b. 10/18/54 Detroit, MI; Christian; BS Central MI
Univ., 2005; Human Resources Investigator, Letter Carrier;
m. McArthur
Comm.: Oversight & Government Reform; Transportation
& Infrastructure
Dist. Offices: Southfield, 248-356-2052; Detroit, 313-423-
6183; Traverse City, 231-929-1031; Marquette, 906-228-8756

MINNESOTA
mn.gov

Pop.: 5,489,594   **Rank:** 21st
Caucasian: 85%   **African-Am.:** 6%
Nat. Am.: 1%   **Asian:** 5%
Other: 3%   **Hisp.:** 5%
Reg. Voters: 3,269,260
Party registration not required
Land Area: 79,627 sq. mi.
Rank: 14th

Number of US House Seats:
5 Dem./3 Rep.

State Legislature
leg.state.mn.us
Senate: 33D/33R   House: 76R/57D
Session: 01/03/17 – 5/22/2017

Gov. Mark Dayton (D)   **651-201-3400**
Next Election: 2018 2nd Term/50%   Fax: 651-797-1850
twitter govmarkdayton
Bio: b. 1/26/47 Minneapolis, MN; Presbyterian; BA Yale Univ.,
1969; Private Investor, Public Official; div.

130 State Capitol, 75 MLK Jr. Boulevard, St. Paul, MN 55155

SENATE

Amy Klobuchar (D) *KLO-buh-shar*   **202-224-3244**
SH-302   2nd Term/65%   90/90/96   Fax: 228-2186
klobuchar.senate.gov   twitter amyklobuchar
CoS ....Elizabeth Peluso **LD** ....Travis Talvitie
Sch ....Kelley Anne Carney **CD** ....Kate Childs Graham
Bio: b. 5/25/60 Plymouth, MN; Congregationalist; JD Univ. of
Chicago, 1985; Attorney, Lobbyist; m. John Bessler
Comm.: Agriculture, Nutrition & Forestry; Commerce, Science
& Transportation; Judiciary; Rules & Administration (Rnk.
Mem.); Joint Economic
Dist. Offices: Minneapolis, 612-727-5220; Moorhead, 218-
287-2219; Virginia, 218-741-9690; Rochester, 507-288-5321

Al Franken (D)   **202-224-5641**
SH-309   2nd Term/53%   90/96/96   Fax: 224-0044
franken.senate.gov   twitter SenFranken
CoS ....Jeff Lomonaco **LD** ....Ali Nouri
Sch ....Brynna Schmidt **CD** ....Ed Shelleby
Bio: b. 5/21/51 Manhattan, NY; Jewish; AB Harvard Univ.,
1973; Comedian, Writer, Radio Host; m. Franni
Comm.: Energy & Natural Resources; Health, Education,
Labor & Pensions; Judiciary; Indian Affairs
Dist. Offices: St. Paul, 651-221-1016; Moorhead, 218-284-
8721; Rochester, 507-288-2003; Duluth, 218-722-2390

Minnesota

HOUSE

Tim Walz (D-1st) *WALLS*   **202-225-2472**
2313 RHOB 6th Term/50% 85/91/98 Fax: 225-3433
walz.house.gov   twitter RepTimWalz
CoS ....Josh Syrjamaki **LD** .... Tim Bertocci
Sch ....Alyssa Berg **Dep CoS**.............Sara Severs
Bio: b. 4/6/64 West Point, NE; Lutheran; MS MN St. Univ.
- Mankato, 2001; NENG, 1981-96; MNNG, 1996-2005;
Mortgage Processor, Teacher; m. Gwen
Comm.: Agriculture; Veterans' Affairs (Rnk. Mem.)
Dist. Offices: Mankato, 507-388-2149; Rochester, 507-
206-0643

Jason Lewis (R-2nd)   **202-225-2271**
418 CHOB 1st Term/47% 10/97/98 Fax: 225-2595
jasonlewis.house.gov   twitter RepJasonLewis
CoS .... Amy Smith **LD** .... Katie Bloodgood
Sch .... Deborah Hansen **CD** .... Stephen Bradford
Bio: b. 9/23/55 Waterloo, IA; Catholic; MBA Univ. of CO -
Denver, 1992; Radio Talk Show Host; m. Leigh
Comm.: Budget; Education & the Workforce; Transportation
& Infrastructure
Dist. Offices: Burnsville, 651-846-2120

Erik Paulsen (R-3rd)   **202-225-2871**
127 CHOB 5th Term/57% 7/93/99 Fax: 225-6351
paulsen.house.gov   twitter RepErikPaulsen
CoS ....Laurie Esau **LD** .... Mike Stober
Sch .... Kate Paul **Press**........... Andrew Johnson
Bio: b. 5/14/65 Bakersfield, CA; Lutheran; BA St. Olaf Col.,
1987; Business Analyst, Congressional Aide; m. Kelly
Comm.: Ways & Means; Joint Economic
Dist. Offices: Eden Prairie, 952-405-8510

Betty McCollum (D-4th)   **202-225-6631**
2256 RHOB 9th Term/58% 98/99/99 Fax: 225-1968
mccollum.house.gov   twitter BettyMcCollum04
CoS .... Bill Harper **LD** .... Jenn Holcomb
Sch .... Ryan Houlihan **CD** .... Evan Hotlander
Bio: b. 7/12/54 Minneapolis, MN; Catholic; BA Col. of St.
Catherine, 1987; Teacher, Retail Salesperson; div.
Comm.: Appropriations
Dist. Offices: St. Paul, 651-224-9191

Keith Ellison (D-5th)   **202-225-4755**
2263 RHOB 6th Term/69% 100/98/94 Fax: 225-4886
ellison.house.gov   twitter Keithellison
CoS .... Kari Moe **LD** ....Carol Wayman
Sch .... Elyse Johnson **CD** ....Isaiah Breem
Bio: b. 8/4/63 Detroit, MI; Muslim; JD Univ. of MN, 1990;
Attorney, Nonprofit Law Firm Executive; div.
Comm.: Financial Services
Dist. Offices: Minneapolis, 612-522-1212

Tom Emmer (R-6th)   **202-225-2331**
315 CHOB 2nd Term/66% 6/96/98 Fax: 225-6475
emmer.house.gov   twitter reptomemmer
CoS .... David FitzSimmons **Sr Adv** ....Robert Boland
Sch .... Kate Braun **CD** ....Rebecca Alery
Bio: b. 3/3/61 South Bend, IN; Catholic; JD William Mitchell
Col. of Law, 1988; Lobbyist, Attorney; m. Jacquie
Comm.: Financial Services
Dist. Offices: Otsego, 763-241-6848

MINNESOTA

Collin C. Peterson (D-7th)   **202-225-2165**
2204 RHOB   14th Term/52%   24/51/98   Fax: 225-1593
collinpeterson.house.gov
CoS ....Allison Myhre **LD** ....Adam Durand
Sch .... Rebekah Solem **CD** ....Liz Friedlander
Bio: b. 6/29/44 Fargo, ND; Lutheran; BA Moorhead St. Col., 1966; MNNG, 1963-69; Accountant; div.
Comm.: Agriculture (Rnk. Mem.)
Dist. Offices: Detroit Lakes, 218-847-5056; Red Lake Falls, 218-253-4356; Willmar, 320-235-1061; Marshall, 507-537-2299

Rick Nolan (D-8th)   **202-225-6211**
2366 RHOB   6th Term/50%   91/96/94   Fax: 225-0699
nolan.house.gov   twitter usrepricknolan
CoS ....Jodie Torkelson **LD** ....Will Mitchell
Sch ....Taryn Brown **CD** .... Steven Johnson
Bio: b. 12/17/43 Brainerd, MN; Catholic; BA Univ. of MN, 1966; Businessman, Teacher; m. Mary
Comm.: Agriculture; Transportation & Infrastructure
Dist. Offices: Duluth, 218-464-5095

MISSISSIPPI
ms.gov

Pop.: 2,992,333   **Rank:** 32nd
Caucasian: 60%   **African-Am.:** 38%
Nat. Am.: 1%   **Asian:** 1%   **Other:** 1%
Hisp.: 3%
Reg. Voters: 1,905,605
Party registration not required
Land Area: 46,923 sq. mi.   **Rank:** 31st

Number of US House Seats: 3 Rep./1 Dem.

State Legislature
billstatus.ls.state.ms.us
Senate: 32R/19D House: 74R/48D
Session: 01/03/17 – 4/2/2017

Gov. Phil Bryant (R)   **601-359-3150**
Next Election: 2019 2nd Term/67%   Fax: 601-359-3741
twitter philbryantms
Bio: b. 12/9/54 Moorhead, MS; Methodist; MS MS Col., 1988; Public Official; m. Deborah

PO Box 139, Jackson, MS 39205

SENATE

Thad Cochran (R)   **202-224-5054**
SD-113   7th Term/60%   59/79/97   Fax: 224-5321
cochran.senate.gov   twitter SenThadCochran
CoS ....Brad White **Dep CoS**.............Adam Telle
Sch .... Doris Wagley **CD** .... Chris Gallegos
Bio: b. 12/7/37 Pontotoc, MS; Baptist; JD Univ. of MS, 1965; USN, 1959-61; Attorney; m. Kay Webber
Comm.: Agriculture, Nutrition & Forestry; Appropriations (Chair); Rules & Administration
Dist. Offices: Jackson, 601-965-4459; Oxford, 662-236-1018; Gulfport, 228-867-9710

MISSISSIPPI

Roger Wicker (R)   **202-224-6253**
SD-555   2nd Term/57%   50/89/96   Fax: 228-0378
wicker.senate.gov   **twitter** SenatorWicker
CoS ....Michelle Barlow **LD** ....Theda Khrestin
               Richardson
Sch .... Hall Carter **CD** .... Ryan Taylor
Bio: b. 7/5/51 Pontotoc, MS; Southern Baptist; JD Univ. of MS, 1975; USAF, 1976-80; USAFR, 1980-2004; Attorney; m. Gayle
Comm.: Armed Services; Commerce, Science & Transportation; Environment & Public Works; Rules & Administration
Dist. Offices: Jackson, 601-965-4644; Gulfport, 228-871-7017; Tupelo, 662-844-5010; Hernando, 662-429-1002

HOUSE

Trent Kelly (R-1st)   **202-225-4306**
1721 LHOB   2nd Term/69%   7/98/99   Fax: 225-3549
trentkelly.house.gov   **twitter** reptrentkelly
CoS .... Ted Maness **Dep CoS**........Elizabeth Parks
Sch .... Whitney Porter **CD** .... Susan Parker
Bio: b. 3/1/66 Union, MS; Christian; JD Univ. of MS, 1994; MSARNG, 1985-present; Prosecutor, Attorney; m. Sheila
Comm.: Agriculture; Armed Services; Small Business
Dist. Offices: Tupelo, 662-841-8808; Hernando, 662-449-3090; Columbus, 662-327-0748; Eupora, 662-258-7240; Mound Bayou, 662-741-9003; Jackson, 601-946-9003

Bennie Thompson (D-2nd)   **202-225-5876**
2466 RHOB   13th Term/67% 98/98/96   Fax: 225-5898
benniethompson.house.gov **twitter** BennieGThompson
CoS .... I. Lanier Avant **LD** .... Cory Horton
Sch ....Andrea Lee **CD** .... Andrea Lee
Bio: b. 1/28/48 Bolton, MS; United Methodist; MS Jackson St. Col., 1972; Teacher; m. London
Comm.: Homeland Security (Rnk. Mem.)
Dist. Offices: Bolton, 601-866-9003; Marks, 662-326-9003; Greenwood, 662-455-9003; Greenville, 662-335-9003; Starkville, 662-324-0007

Gregg Harper (R-3rd)   **202-225-5031**
2227 RHOB   5th Term/66%   9/97/96   Fax: 225-5797
harper.house.gov   **twitter** GreggHarper
CoS ....Michael Cravens **LD** .... Scot Malvaney
Sch .... Debra Boutwell **Press**........... Emerson George
Bio: b. 6/1/56 Jackson, MS; Southern Baptist; JD Univ. of MS, 1981; City Prosecutor, Attorney; m. Sidney
Comm.: Energy & Commerce; House Administration (Chair); Joint Library; Joint Printing (Chair)
Dist. Offices: Pearl, 601-932-2410; Meridian, 601-693-6681; Starkville, 662-324-0007; Brookhaven, 601-823-3400

Steven M. Palazzo (R-4th)   **202-225-5772**
2349 RHOB   4th Term/65%   9/98/90   Fax: 225-7074
palazzo.house.gov   **twitter** congpalazzo
CoS ....Casey Street **LD** .... Patrick Large
Sch ....Leslie Churchwell **CD** ....Jill Duckworth
Bio: b. 2/21/70 Gulfport, MS; Catholic; MBA Univ. of Southern MS, 1996; USMCR, 1988-96; MSNG, 1997-present; Accountant, Financial Manager; m. Lisa
Comm.: Appropriations
Dist. Offices: Biloxi, 228-864-7670; Hattiesburg, 601-582-3246; Pascagoula, 228-202-8104

MISSOURI
mo.gov

Pop.: 6,083,672   **Rank:** 18th
Caucasian: 83%
African-Am.: 12%
Nat. Am.: 1%   **Asian:** 2%
Other: 2%   **Hisp.:** 4%
Reg. Voters: 4,223,787
Party registration not required
Land Area: 68,742 sq. mi.
Rank: 18th

Number of US House Seats:
6 Rep./2 Dem.

State Legislature
moga.mo.gov
Senate: 24R/9D   House: 116R/46D/1Vac
Session: 01/04/17 – 5/12/2017

Gov. Eric Greitens (R)   573-751-3222
Next Election 2020   1st Term/51%   Fax: 573-526-3291
twitter ericgreitens

Bio: b. 4/10/74; St. Louis, MO; Jewish; Ph.D. Oxford Univ., 2000; USN 2001-17 (Lt. Cmdr.); Veterans Advocacy Nonprofit CEO; Author; m. Sheena

PO Box 720, Jefferson City, MO 65102

SENATE

Claire McCaskill (D)   202-224-6154
SH-503   2nd Term/55%   93/85/92   Fax: 228-6326
mccaskill.senate.gov   **twitter** mccaskilloffice
CoS .... Julie Dwyer   **LD** .... Nichole Distefano
Sch .... Lorenzo D'Aubert   **CD** .... John LaBombard
Bio: b. 7/24/53 Rolla, MO; Catholic; JD Univ. of MO, 1978; Attorney; m. Joseph Shepard
Comm.: Armed Services; Finance; Homeland Security & Governmental Affairs (Rnk. Mem.)
Dist. Offices: Kansas City, 816-421-1639; Cape Girardeau, 573-651-0964; St. Louis, 314-367-1364; Columbia, 573-442-7130; Columbia, 573-442-8151

Roy Blunt (R)   202-224-5721
SR-260   2nd Term/49%   43/86/96   Fax: 224-8149
blunt.senate.gov   **twitter** royblunt
CoS .... Stacey McBride   **LD** .... Tracy Henke
Sch .... Richard Eddings   **CD** .... Brian Hart
Bio: b. 1/10/50 Niangua, MO; Baptist; MA SW MO St. Univ., 1972; University President; m. Abigail
Comm.: Appropriations; Commerce, Science & Transportation; Rules & Administration; Select Intelligence; Joint Library (Chair); Joint Printing (Vice Chair)
Dist. Offices: Kansas City, 816-471-7141; Springfield, 417-877-7814; Clayton, 314-725-4484; Cape Girardeau, 573-334-7044

HOUSE

William Lacy Clay (D-1st)   202-225-2406
2428 RHOB   9th Term/76%   96/98/96   Fax: 226-3717
lacyclay.house.gov   **twitter** LacyClayMo1
CoS .... Yvette Cravins   **LD** .... Pauline Jamry
Sch .... Karyn Long   **CD** .... Steven Engelhardt
Bio: b. 7/27/56 St. Louis, MO; Catholic; BS Univ. of MD, 1983; Congressional Aide, Paralegal, Real Estate Agent; div.
Comm.: Financial Services; Natural Resources; Oversight & Government Reform
Dist. Offices: St. Louis, 314-367-1970; St. Louis, 314-669-9393; Florissant, 314-383-5240

MISSOURI

Ann Wagner (R-2nd)   **202-225-1621**
435 CHOB   3rd Term/59%   9/98/96   Fax: 225-2563
wagner.house.gov   twitter RepAnnWagner
CoS ....Christian Morgan LD ....Michael Lowry
Sch ....Meghan McCann CD .... Meghan Burris
Bio: b. 9/13/62 St. Louis, MO; Catholic; BSBA Univ. of MO,
1984; Homemaker, Campaign Aide, Public Official; m. Ray
Comm.: Financial Services; Foreign Affairs
Dist. Offices: Ballwin, 636-779-5449

Blaine Luetkemeyer (R-3rd)
LUTE-ka-myer   **202-225-2956**
2230 RHOB   5th Term/68%   8/99/97   Fax: 225-5712
luetkemeyer.house.gov   twitter RepBlainePress
CoS ....Seth Appleton LD ....Trey McKenzie
Sch ....Ann Vogel CD .... Kristina Weger
Bio: b. 5/7/52 Jefferson City, MO; Catholic; BA Lincoln Univ.,
1974; Bank Loan Officer, Insurance Agent; m. Jackie
Comm.: Financial Services; Small Business
Dist. Offices: Jefferson City, 573-635-7232; Wentzville, 636-
327-7055; Washington, 636-239-2276

Vicky Hartzler (R-4th)   **202-225-2876**
2235 RHOB   4th Term/68%   9/99/99   Fax: 225-0148
hartzler.house.gov   twitter RepHartzler
CoS .... Chris Connelly LD ....Joe Tvrdy
Sch .... Mallory Fields CD .... Kyle Buckles
Bio: b. 10/13/60 Archie, MO; Evangelical Christian; MS Central
MO St. Univ., 1992; Farmer, Business Owner; m. Lowell
Comm.: Agriculture; Armed Services
Dist. Offices: Columbia, 573-442-9311; Harrisonville, 816-
884-3411; Lebanon, 417-532-5582

Emanuel Cleaver II (D-5th)   **202-225-4535**
2335 RHOB   7th Term/58%   98/97/93   Fax: 225-4403
cleaver.house.gov   twitter repcleaver
CoS .... John Jones LD .... Christina Mahoney
Sch ....Alex Ndikum CD .... Heather Frierson
Bio: b. 10/26/44 Waxahachie, TX; Methodist; MDiv St. Paul
School of Theology, 1974; Pastor, Civic Activist, Business
Owner; m. Dianne
Comm.: Financial Services
Dist. Offices: Kansas City, 816-842-4545; Independence,
816-833-4545; Higginsville, 660-584-7373

Sam Graves (R-6th)   **202-225-7041**
1135 LHOB   9th Term/68%   10/98/94   Fax: 225-8221
graves.house.gov   twitter RepSamGraves
CoS ....Paul Sass LD ....Jack Ruddy
Sch ....Kristen Siegele CD .... Wesley Shaw
Bio: b. 11/7/63 Fairfax, MO; Baptist; BS Univ. of MO, 1986;
Farmer; sep.
Comm.: Armed Services; Transportation & Infrastructure
Dist. Offices: Kansas City, 816-792-3976; St. Joseph, 816-
749-0800

Billy Long (R-7th)   **202-225-6536**
2454 RHOB   4th Term/68%   7/99/99   Fax: 225-5604
long.house.gov   twitter USRepLong
CoS .... Joe Lillis LD ....Peter Stehouwer
Sch .... Drew McDowell CD ....Hannah Smith
Bio: b. 8/11/55 Springfield, MO; Presbyterian; Attended
Univ. of MO, 1973-74; Realtor, Auctioneer, Radio Talk Show
Host; m. Barbara
Comm.: Energy & Commerce
Dist. Offices: Springfield, 417-889-1800; Joplin, 417-781-1041

MISSOURI

Jason Smith (R-8th)   **202-225-4404**
1118 LHOB   3rd Term/74%   7/99/99   Fax: 226-0326
jasonsmith.house.gov   𝕥𝕨𝕚𝕥𝕥𝕖𝕣 RepJasonSmith
CoS .... Mark Roman   **LD** .... Justin Sok
Sch .... Adrienne Schrodt   **CD** .... Vacant
Bio: b. 6/16/80 St. Louis, MO; Assemblies of God; JD Oklahoma City Univ., 2004; Attorney, Realtor, Small Business Owner; single
Comm.: Budget; Ways & Means
Dist. Offices: Cape Girardeau, 573-335-0101; Rolla, 573-364-2455; Farmington, 573-756-9755; West Plains, 417-255-1515

MONTANA
montana.gov

Pop.: 1,032,949
Rank: 44th
Caucasian: 89%
African-Am.: 1%   **Nat. Am.:** 7%
Asian: 1%   **Other:** 3%
Hisp.: 4%
Reg. Voters: 696,357
Party registration not required
Land Area: 145,546 sq. mi.   **Rank:** 4th

·Great Falls   **1**
·Missoula   ★ **Helena**
Billings·

Number of US House Seats: 1 Vac.

State Legislature
leg.mt.gov
Senate: 32R/18D   House: 59R/41D
Session: 01/02/17 – 4/25/2017

Gov. Steve Bullock (D)   **406-444-3111**
Next Election: 2020   2nd Term/50%   Fax: 406-444-5529
𝕥𝕨𝕚𝕥𝕥𝕖𝕣 governorbullock
Bio: b. 4/11/66 Missoula, MT; Catholic; JD Columbia Univ., 1994; Attorney; m. Lisa

State Capitol, PO Box 200801, Helena, MT 59620-0801

SENATE

Jon Tester (D)   **202-224-2644**
SH-311   2nd Term/49%   83/87/100   Fax: 224-8594
tester.senate.gov   𝕥𝕨𝕚𝕥𝕥𝕖𝕣 SenatorTester
CoS .... Aaron Murphy   **LD** .... Dylan Laslovich
Sch .... Trecia McEvoy   **CD** .... Marnee Banks
Bio: b. 8/21/56 Havre, MT; Christian; BA Col. of Great Falls, 1978; Farmer, Teacher; m. Sharla
Comm.: Appropriations; Banking, Housing & Urban Affairs; Homeland Security & Governmental Affairs; Veterans' Affairs (Rnk. Mem.)
Dist. Offices: Helena, 406-449-5401; Billings, 406-252-0550; Missoula, 406-728-3003; Great Falls, 406-452-9585; Great Falls, 406-453-0148

Steve Daines (R)   **202-224-2651**
SH-320   1st Term/58%   47/93/100   Fax: 228-1236
daines.senate.gov   𝕥𝕨𝕚𝕥𝕥𝕖𝕣 stevedaines
CoS .... Jason Thielman   **LD** .... Darin Thacker
Sch .... Caitlin Dorman   **Press** .... Katie Waldman
Bio: b. 8/20/62 Van Nuys, CA; Presbyterian; BS MT St. Univ., 1984; Software Company Executive, Construction Company Manager; m. Cindy
Comm.: Agriculture, Nutrition & Forestry; Appropriations; Energy & Natural Resources; Homeland Security & Governmental Affairs; Indian Affairs
Dist. Offices: Helena, 406-443-3189; Billings, 406-245-6822; Missoula, 406-549-8198; Bozeman, 406-587-3446

MONTANA

HOUSE

Vacant (At Large)   **202-225-3211**
1419 LHOB
Rep. Ryan Zinke (R) resigned on February 28, 2017. A special election has been scheduled for May, 25, 2017.

**OPEN
SEAT**

NEBRASKA
nebraska.gov

Pop.: 1,896,190
Rank: 37th
Caucasian: 89%
African-Am.: 5%   **Nat. Am.:** 1%
Asian: 2%   **Other:** 2%   **Hisp.:** 10%
Reg. Voters: 1,211,113
Dem.: 31%   **Rep.:** 48%   **Other:** 21%
Land Area: 768,24 sq. mi.   **Rank:** 15th

Number of US House Seats: 3 Rep.

State Legislature
nebraskalegislature.gov
Senate: 49NON
Session: 01/04/17 – 6/2/2017

Gov. Pete Ricketts (R)   **402-471-2244**
Next Election: 2018 1st Term/57%   Fax: 402-471-6031
twitter govricketts
Bio: b. 8/19/64 Nebraska City, NE; Catholic; MBA Univ. of Chicago, 1991; Business Executive; m. Susanne

PO Box 94848, Lincoln, NE 68509-4848

SENATE

Deb Fischer (R)   **202-224-6551**
SR-454   1st Term/58%   53/96/100   Fax: 228-1325
fischer.senate.gov   twitter senatorfischer
CoS .... Joe Hack   **LD** .... Corey Astill
Sch .... Vaughan Wehr   **CD** .... Brianna Puccini
Bio: b. 3/1/51 Lincoln, NE; Presbyterian; BS Univ. of NE, 1988; Rancher; m. Bruce
Comm.: Armed Services; Commerce, Science & Transportation; Environment & Public Works; Rules & Administration; Special Aging
Dist. Offices: Lincoln, 402-441-4600; Omaha, 402-391-3411; Scottsbluff, 308-632-2329; Kearney, 308-233-2361

Ben Sasse (R) *SASS*   **202-224-4224**
SR-386A   1st Term/64%   41/88/98   Fax: 228-9642
sasse.senate.gov   twitter sensasse
CoS ....Derrick Morgan   **LD** .... Patrick Lehman
Sch .... Sarah Peer   **CD** .... James Wegmann
Bio: b. 2/22/72 Plainview, NE; Confessional Evangelical; PhD Yale Univ., 2004; University President, Professor, Government Aide; m. Melissa
Comm.: Armed Services; Banking, Housing, & Urban Affairs; Judiciary; Joint Economic
Dist. Offices: Lincoln, 402-476-1400; Kearney, 308-233-3677; Scottsbluff, 308-632-6032; Omaha, 402-550-8040

NEBRASKA

HOUSE

Jeff Fortenberry (R-1st)   **202-225-4806**
1514 LHOB   7th Term/70%   9/91/99   Fax: 225-5686
fortenberry.house.gov   twitter JeffFortenberry
CoS .... Reyn Archer **Dep CoS** ...... Alan Feyerherm
Sch .....Christine Capobianco **CD** .... James Crotty
Bio: b. 12/27/60 Baton Rouge, LA; Catholic; MDiv Franciscan Univ., 1996; Economist, Congressional Aide, Publishing Executive; m. Celeste
Comm.: Appropriations
Dist. Offices: Lincoln, 402-438-1598; Norfolk, 402-379-2064; Fremont, 402-727-0888

Don Bacon (R-2nd)   **202-225-4155**
1516 LHOB   1st Term/49%   Fax: 226-5452
bacon.house.gov   twitter RepDonBacon
CoS ....Mark Dreiling **LD** ....Jeff Kratz
Sch ....Jason Tyler **CD** ....Danielle Jensen
Bio: b. 8/16/63 Momence, IL; Non-denominational Christian; MA University of Phoenix 1995; USAF, 1985-2014; Professor, Aide, Military Officer; m. Angie
Comm.: Agriculture; Armed Services; Small Business
Dist. Offices: Omaha, 402-938-0300

Adrian Smith (R-3rd)   **202-225-6435**
320 CHOB   6th Term/Unc.   8/99/98   Fax: 225-0207
adriansmith.house.gov   twitter RepAdrianSmith
CoS ....Monica Didiuk **LD** ....Josh Jackson
Sch .... Jill Sims **CD** ....Emily Miller
Bio: b. 12/19/70 Scottsbluff, NE; Christian; BS Univ. of NE, 1993; Business Owner, Realtor; single
Comm.: House Administration; Ways & Means
Dist. Offices: Scottsbluff, 308-633-6333; Grand Island, 308-384-3900

NEVADA
nv.gov

Pop.: 2,890,845   **Rank:** 35th
Caucasian: 76%   **African-Am.:** 9%
Nat. Am.: 2%   **Asian:** 9%   **Other:** 5%
Hisp.: 28%
Reg. Voters: 1,467,263
Dem.: 39%   **Rep.:** 35%   **Other:** 26%
Land Area: 109,781 sq. mi.   **Rank:** 7th

Number of US House Seats: 3 Dem./1 Rep.

State Legislature
leg.state.nv.us
Senate: 11D/9R/1 Other   House: 27D/15R
Session: 02/06/17 – 6/5/2017

Gov. Brian Sandoval (R)   **775-684-5670**
Next Election: 2018 2nd Term/71%   Fax: 775-684-5683
twitter govsandoval
Bio: b. 8/5/63 Redding, CA; Catholic; JD OH St. Univ., 1989; Attorney; m. Kathleen

101 North Carson Street, Carson City, NV 89701
Washington Office: 202-624-5405

Nevada

SENATE

Dean Heller (R)　　　　　　　　**202-224-6244**
SH-324　　2nd Term/46%　　41/81/97　　Fax: 228-6753
heller.senate.gov　　　　　　　twitter SenDeanHeller
CoS ....Mac Abrams **Dep CoS**..............Sarah Paul
Sch ....Meron Bayu **CD** ....Neal Patel
Bio: b. 5/10/60 Castro Valley, CA; Mormon; BS Univ. of
Southern CA, 1985; Public Official, Stock Broker; m. Lynne
Comm.: Banking, Housing, & Urban Affairs; Commerce,
Science & Transportation; Finance; Veterans' Affairs
Dist. Offices: Reno, 775-686-5770; Las Vegas, 702-388-6605

Catherine Cortez Masto (D)　　　**202-224-3542**
SD-B40A　　1st Term/49%　　97/99/97　　Fax: 224-7327
cortezmasto.senate.gov　　　　　twitter SenCortezMasto
CoS .... Scott Fairchild **Dep CoS**........Laura Hatalsky
Sch ....Hilary Barrett **Press**............... Bianca Recto
Bio: b. 3/29/64 Las Vegas, NV; Catholic; JD Gonzaga Univ.,
1990; Vice Chancellor, Attorney, Prosecutor, Aide; m. Paul
Comm.: Banking, Housing, & Urban Affairs; Commerce,
Science & Transportation; Energy & Natural Resources; Rules
& Administration; Indian Affairs; Special Aging
Dist. Offices: Reno, 775-686-5750

HOUSE

Dina Titus (D-1st)　　　　　　**202-225-5965**
2464 RHOB　4th Term/62%　　96/97/92　　Fax: 225-3119
titus.house.gov　　　　　　　twitter repdinatitus
CoS ....Jay Gertsema **LD** ....David Rosenbaum
Sch .... Eva Hicks **CD** ....Kyle Roerink
Bio: b. 5/23/50 Thomasville, GA; Greek Orthodox; PhD FL
St. Univ., 1976; Professor, Public Official; m. Tom Wright
Comm.: Foreign Affairs; Transportation & Infrastructure
Dist. Offices: Las Vegas, 702-220-9823

Mark Amodei (R-2nd) *AM-uh-day*　**202-225-6155**
332 CHOB　4th Term/58%　　8/96/94　　Fax: 225-5679
amodei.house.gov　　　　　　twitter MarkAmodeiNV2
CoS .... Bruce Miller **LD** ....Jason Riederer
Sch ....Rachel Provost **CD** .... Logan Ramsey
Bio: b. 6/12/58 Carson City, NV; Christian; JD Univ. of the
Pacific, 1983; USA, 1983-87; Mining Association President,
Attorney; div.
Comm.: Appropriations
Dist. Offices: Reno, 775-686-5760; Elko, 775-777-7705

Jacky Rosen (D-3rd)　　　　　　**202-225-3252**
413 CHOB　1st Term/47%　　　　　　Fax: 225-2185
rosen.house.gov　　　　　　twitter RepJackyRosen
CoS ....David Furr **LD** ....Grant Dubler
Sch ....Nicole Echeto **CD** .... Ivana Blancaccio
Bio: b. 8/2/57 Chicago, IL; Jewish; BA Univ. of MN, 1979;
President, Developer, Programmer; m. Larry
Comm.: Armed Services; Science, Space & Technology
Dist. Offices: Las Vegas, 702-963-9500

Ruben Kihuen (D-4th) *KEE-when*　**202-225-9894**
313 CHOB　1st Term/48%　　　　　　Fax: 225-9783
kihuen.house.gov　　　　　　twitter RubenKihuen
CoS ....Dave Chase **LD** ....Mark Snyder
Sch ....Angie Toro **CD** ....Miguel Salazar
Bio: b. 4/25/80 Guadalajara, Jalisco, Mexico; Catholic; BS
UNLV, 2005; Consultant, Aide, Academic Advisor; single
Comm.: Financial Services
Dist. Offices: North Las Vegas, 702-963-9360

New Hampshire
nh.gov

Pop.: 1,330,608 **Rank:** 41st
Caucasian: 94% **African-Am.:** 2% **Nat. Am.:** 0%
Asian: 3% **Other:** 2% **Hisp.:** 3%
Reg. Voters: 872,171
Dem.: 26% **Rep.:** 30% **Other:** 44%
Land Area: 8,953 sq. mi. **Rank:** 44th

Number of US House Seats: 2 Dem.

State Legislature
gencourt.state.nh.us
Senate: 14R/10D House: 240R/184D
Session: 01/04/17 – 6/30/2017

Gov.Chris Sununu (R)   603-271-2121
Next Election 2018 1st Term/49%   Fax: 603-271-7680
twitter GovChrisSununu
Bio: b. 11/5/74; Salem, NH; Roman Catholic; BA MIT, 1998; Ski Resort Owner; Environmental Engineer, Management Consulting Firm Owner; m. Valeries

State House, 107 North Main Street, Concord, NH 03301

SENATE

Jeanne Shaheen (D)   202-224-2841
SH-506 2nd Term/51% 93/91/99 Fax: 228-3194
shaheen.senate.gov   twitter SenatorShaheen
CoS ....Maura Keefe **LD** ....Robert Diznoff
Sch ....Meaghan D'Arcy **CD** ....Ryan Nickel
Bio: b. 1/28/47 St. Charles, MO; Protestant; MSS Univ. of MS, 1973; Small Business Owner, Teacher; m. Bill
Comm.: Appropriations; Armed Services; Foreign Relations; Small Business & Entrepreneurship (Rnk. Mem.); Select Ethics
Dist. Offices: Manchester, 603-647-7500; Dover, 603-750-3004; Nashua, 603-883-0196; Claremont, 603-542-4872

Maggie Hassan (D)   202-224-3324
SR-B85 1st Term/48%   Fax: 224-4952
hassan.senate.gov   twitter SenatorHassan
CoS ....Marc Goldberg **LD** ....Jude McCartin
Sch ....Catherine George **Press** ....Meira Bernstein
Bio: b. 2/27/58 Boston, MA; United Church of Christ; JD Northeastern Univ., 1985; Attorney, State Officer; m. Thomas
Comm.: Commerce, Science & Transportation; Health, Education, Labor & Pensions; Homeland Security & Governmental Affairs; Joint Economic
Dist. Offices: Manchester, 603-662-2204

HOUSE

Carol Shea-Porter (D-1st)   202-225-5456
1530 LHOB 4th Term/44%   Fax: 225-5822
shea-porter.house.gov   twitter RepSheaPorter
CoS ....Naomi Andrews **LD** ....Chris Hillesheim
Sch ....Emily Mills **Press** ....Marjorie Connolly
Bio: b. 12/2/52 Brooklyn, NY; Catholic; JD Univ. of NH, 1979; Professor, Social Worker; m. Gene
Comm.: Armed Services; Education & the Workforce
Dist. Offices: Dover, 888-216-5373

New Hampshire

Ann McLane Kuster (D-2nd)   **202-225-5206**
137 CHOB   3rd Term/50%   83/94/99   Fax: 225-2946
kuster.house.gov   twitter RepAnnieKuster
CoS ......Abby Curran Horrell   LD ....Justin German
Sch ....Will Pisano   CD ....Nick Brown
Bio: b. 9/5/56 Concord, NH; Christian; JD Georgetown
Univ., 1984; Attorney, Lobbyist, Congressional Aide; m. Brad
Comm.: Agriculture; Veterans' Affairs
Dist. Offices: Concord, 603 226-1002; Nashua, 603 595-2006

New Jersey
newjersey.gov

Pop.: 8,958,013   **Rank:** 11th
Caucasian: 73%   **African-Am.:** 15%
Nat. Am.: 1%   **Asian:** 10%   **Other:** 2%
Hisp.: 20%
Reg. Voters: 5,836,592
Dem.: 32%   **Rep.:** 20%   **Other:** 48%
Land Area: 7,354 sq. mi.   **Rank:** 46th

Number of US House Seats: 7 Dem./5 Rep.

State Legislature
njleg.state.nj.us
Senate: 24D/16R   House: 52D/28R
Session: 01/10/17 – 1/9/2016

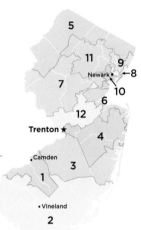

Gov. Chris Christie (R)   **609-292-6000**
Next Election: 2017   2nd Term/60%   Fax: 609-777-2922
twitter govchristie
Bio: b. 9/6/62 Newark, NJ; Catholic; JD Seton Hall Univ.,
1987; Attorney, Public Official; m. Mary Pat

PO Box 001, Trenton, NJ 08625
Washington Office: 202-638-0631

SENATE

Robert Menendez (D)   **202-224-4744**
SH-528   3rd Term/59%   86/92/98   Fax: 228-2197
menendez.senate.gov   twitter SenatorMenendez
CoS ....Fred Turner   LD ....Tim Del Monico
Sch ....Robert Kelly   CD ....Patricia Enright
Bio: b. 1/1/54 Manhattan, NY; Catholic; JD Rutgers Univ.,
1979; Attorney; eng. Alicia Mucci
Comm.: Banking, Housing & Urban Affairs; Finance; Foreign
Relations
Dist. Offices: Newark, 973-645-3030; Barrington, 856-757-5353

Cory Booker (D)   **202-224-3224**
SD-359   2nd Term/56%   87/100/97   Fax: 224-8378
booker.senate.gov   twitter SenBookerOffice
CoS ....Matt Klapper   LD ....Chris Slevin
Sch ....Unjin Lee   CD ....Jeff Giertz
Bio: b. 4/27/69 Washington, DC; Baptist; JD Yale Univ.,
1997; Attorney; single
Comm.: Commerce, Science & Transportation; Environment & Public Works; Foreign Relations; Small Business & Entrepreneurship
Dist. Offices: Newark, 973-639-8700; Camden, 856-338-8922

Donald Norcross (D-1st)   **202-225-6501**
1531 LHOB   3rd Term/59%   93/97/96   Fax: 225-6583
norcross.house.gov   twitter DonaldNorcross
CoS .... Michael Maitland   **LD** ...... Morgan Bradley-Jones
Sch .... Lara Weinstein   **CD** .... Matt Harringer
Bio: b. 12/13/58 Camden, NJ; Lutheran; AS Camden Comm.
Col., 1979; Union Representative, Electrician; m. Andrea
Doran:
Comm.: Armed Services; Education & the Workforce
Dist. Offices: Cherry Hill, 856-427-7000

Frank A. LoBiondo (R-2nd)   **202-225-6572**
2427 RHOB   12th Term/59%   15/83/100   Fax: 225-3318
lobiondo.house.gov   twitter RepLoBiondo
CoS .... Jason Galanes   **LD** .... Matthew Satterley
Sch ..... Mehgan Perez-Acosta   **CD** .... Jason Galanes
Bio: b. 5/12/46 Bridgeton, NJ; Catholic; BS St. Joseph's Univ.,
1968; Businessman; m. Tina Ercole
Comm.: Armed Services; Transportation & Infrastructure;
Select Intelligence
Dist. Offices: Mays Landing, 609-625-5008

Tom MacArthur (R-3rd)   **202-225-4765**
506 CHOB   2nd Term/60%   6/89/97   Fax: 225-0778
macarthur.house.gov   twitter RepTomMacArthur
CoS .... Ryan Carney   **LD** .... Jeff Brabant
Sch .... Heather Smith   **CD** .... Camille Gallow
Bio: b. 10/16/60 Hebron, CT; Episcopal; BA Hofstra Univ.,
1982; Insurance Company Executive; m. Debbie
Comm.: Financial Services
Dist. Offices: Marlton, 856-267-5182; Toms River, 732-
569-6495

Christopher H. Smith (R-4th)   **202-225-3765**
2373 RHOB   19th Term/64%   15/87/98   Fax: 225-7768
chrissmith.house.gov   twitter RepChrisSmith
CoS .... Mary Noonan   **LD** .... Cate Benedetti
Sch .... Daniel Tillson   **CD** .... Jeff Beck
Bio: b. 3/4/53 Rahway, NJ; Catholic; BA Trenton St. Col.,
1975; Sporting Goods Wholesaler; m. Marie
Comm.: Foreign Affairs
Dist. Offices: Hamilton, 609-585-7878; Plumsted, 609-286-
2571; Freehold, 732-780-3035

Josh Gottheimer (D-5th)   **202-225-4465**
213 CHOB   1st Term/50%   Fax: 225-9048
gottheimer.house.gov   twitter JoshGottheimer
CoS .... Tricia Russell   **LD** .... Michael Lukso
Sch .... Emma Goldstein   **CD** .... Melissa Miller
Bio: b. 3/8/75 North Caldwell, NJ; Jewish; JD Harvard; At-
torney, Political Advisor; m. Marla Tusk
Comm.: Financial Services
Dist. Offices: Glen Rock, 888-216-5646

Frank Pallone, Jr. (D-6th)   **202-225-4671**
237 CHOB   16th Term/63%   98/100/97   Fax: 225-9665
pallone.house.gov   twitter FrankPallone
CoS .... Janice Fuller   **Dep CoS** .... Brian Laughlin
Sch .... Alexander Gristina   **CD** .... Anton Becker
Bio: b. 10/30/51 Long Branch, NJ; Catholic; JD Rutgers Univ.,
1978; Attorney; m. Sarah Hospodor-Pallone
Comm.: Energy & Commerce (Rnk. Mem.)
Dist. Offices: Long Branch, 732-571-1140; New Brunswick,
732-249-8892

Leonard Lance (R-7th)   **202-225-5361**
2352 RHOB   5th Term/55%   6/93/100   Fax: 225-9460
lance.house.gov   twitter RepLanceNJ7
CoS .... Todd Mitchell **Dep CoS** ....John Byers
Sch .... Anna Pellecchia **CD** ....John Byers
Bio: b. 6/25/52 Easton, PA; Catholic; MPA Princeton Univ.,
1982; Attorney, Gubernatorial Aide; m. Heidi A. Rohrbach
Comm.: Energy & Commerce; Ethics
Dist. Offices: Westfield, 908-518-7733; Flemington, 908-788-6900

Albio Sires (D-8th) *SEAR-eez (like "series")* **202-225-7919**
2342 RHOB   7th Term/77%   92/95/89   Fax: 226-0792
sires.house.gov   twitter RepSires
CoS ....Gene Martorony **LD** .... Kaylan Koszela
AD ....Judi Wolford **CD** .... Erica Daughtrey
Bio: b. 1/26/51 Bejucal, Cuba; Catholic; MA Middlebury
Col., 1985; Business Owner; m. Adrienne
Comm.: Foreign Affairs; Transportation & Infrastructure
Dist. Offices: Jersey City, 201-309-0301; West New York,
201-558-0800; Elizabeth, 908-820-0692

Bill Pascrell, Jr. (D-9th)   **202-225-5751**
2370 RHOB   11th Term/70%   96/98/95   Fax: 225-5782
pascrell.house.gov   twitter BillPascrell
CoS .... Ben Rich **LD** ....Alyssa Penna
Sch ....Aileen Monahan **CD** ....Timothy Carroll
Bio: b. 1/25/37 Paterson, NJ; Catholic; MA Fordham Univ.,
1961; USA, 1961; USAR, 1962-67; Teacher; m. Elsie
Comm.: Ways & Means
Dist. Offices: Paterson, 973-523-5152

Donald M. Payne, Jr. (D-10th)   **202-225-3436**
132 CHOB   4th Term/86%   95/98/86   Fax: 225-4160
payne.house.gov   twitter repdonaldpayne
CoS .... LaVerne Alexander **PD:**..........LaVerne Alexander
Sch ....Jay Bhargava **CD** .... Michael Burns
Bio: b. 12/16/58 Newark, NJ; Baptist; Attended Kean Col.,
1976-78; School Transportation Director; m. Beatrice
Comm.: Homeland Security; Transportation & Infrastructure
Dist. Offices: Newark, 973-645-3213; Jersey City, 201-369-0392; Hillside, 862-229-2294

Rodney Frelinghuysen (R-11th)
    FREE-ling-high-zen   **202-225-5034**
2306 RHOB   12th Term/58%   6/95/98   Fax: 225-3186
frelinghuysen.house.gov   twitter USRepRodney
CoS ....Kathleen Hazlett **LD** .... Austin Bone
Sch ....Chris Hansell **Press**.................Steve Wilson
Bio: b. 4/29/46 Manhattan, NY; Episcopal; BA Hobart Col.,
1969; USA, 1969-71; Public Official; m. Virginia Robinson
Comm.: Appropriations (Chair)
Dist. Offices: Morristown, 973-984-0711

Bonnie Watson Coleman (D-12th)   **202-225-5801**
1535 LHOB   2nd Term/63%   98/100/99   Fax: 225-6025
watsoncoleman.house.gov   twitter RepBonnie
CoS ....James Gee **LD** .... Michael Reed
Sch .... Jaimee Gilmartin **CD** .... Kirsten Allen
Bio: b. 2/6/45 Camden, NJ; Baptist; BA Thomas Edison St. Col.,
1985; State Civil Rights Office Director; m. William Coleman
Comm.: Homeland Security; Oversight & Government Reform
Dist. Offices: Ewing, 609-883-0026

NEW MEXICO
newmexico.gov

Pop.: 2,085,109   **Rank:** 36th
Caucasian: 83%   **African-Am.:** 3%
Nat. Am.: 11%   **Asian:** 2%
Other: 3%   **Hisp.:** 48%
Reg. Voters: 1,197,953
Dem.: 46%   **Rep.:** 31%   **Other:** 23%
Land Area: 121,298 sq. mi.   **Rank:** 5th

Number of US House Seats:
2 Dem./1 Rep.

State Legislature
nmlegis.gov
Senate: 27D/16R   House: 38D/32R
Session: 01/17/17 – 3/18/2017

Gov. Susana Martinez (R)   **505-476-2200**
Next Election: 2018   2nd Term/57%   Fax: 505-476-2226
Bio: b. 7/14/59 El Paso, TX; Catholic; JD Univ. of OK, 1986;
Attorney; m. Chuck Franco

490 Old Santa Fe Trail, Room 400, Santa Fe, NM 87501

SENATE

Tom Udall (D)   **202-224-6621**
SH-531   2nd Term/56%   90/97/99   Fax: 228-3261
tomudall.senate.gov   **twitter** SenatorTomUdall
CoS ..Bianca Ortiz Wertheim **LD** .... Andrew Wallace
Sch .... Devon Wohl **CD** .... Jennifer Talhelm
Bio: b. 5/18/48 Tucson, AZ; Mormon; JD Univ. of NM, 1977;
Attorney, Congressional Aide; m. Jill Cooper
Comm.: Appropriations; Commerce, Science & Transporta-
tion; Foreign Relations; Rules & Administration; Indian Affairs
(Vice Chair); Joint Printing
Dist. Offices: Albuquerque, 505-346-6791; Las Cruces, 575-
526-5475; Santa Fe, 505-988-6511; Carlsbad, 575-234-0366

Martin Heinrich (D) *HINE-rick*   **202-224-5521**
SH-303   1st Term/51%   90/96/99   Fax: 228-2841
heinrich.senate.gov   **twitter** martinheinrich
CoS .... Joe Britton **LD** .... Virgilio Barrera
Sch .... Mike DeSpain **CD** .... Whitney Potter
Bio: b. 10/17/71 Fallon, NV; Lutheran; BS Univ. of MO, 1995;
Consultant, Nonprofit Director; m. Julie
Comm.: Armed Services; Energy & Natural Resources; Select
Intelligence; Joint Economic (Rnk. Mem.)
Dist. Offices: Albuquerque, 505-346-6601; Santa Fe, 505-988-
6647; Farmington, 505-325-5030; Las Cruces, 575-523-6561;
Portales, 575-356-6811

HOUSE

Michelle Lujan Grisham (D-1st)   **202-225-6316**
214 CHOB   3rd Term/65%   92/95/97   Fax: 225-4975
lujangrisham.house.gov   **twitter** replujangrisham
CoS .... Dominic Gabello **LD** .... Nathan Schelble
Sch .... Natalie Armijo **CD** .... Gilbert Gallegos
Bio: b. 10/24/59 Los Alamos, NM; Catholic; JD Univ. of NM,
1987; Health Consultant, State Agency Director, Attorney;
eng. Manuel Cordova
Comm.: Agriculture; Budget
Dist. Offices: Albuquerque, 505-346-6781; Socorro, 855-
473-2723; Alamogordo, 855-473-2723

New Mexico

Steve Pearce (R-2nd)   **202-225-2365**
2432 RHOB   7th Term/63%   8/97/91   Fax: 225-9599
pearce.house.gov   twitter repstevepearce
CoS .... Todd Willens **Dep CoS**............. Patrick Cuff
Sch ....Kristine Nichols **Press**........Keeley Christensen
Bio: b. 8/24/47 Lamesa, TX; Baptist; MBA Eastern NM Univ.,
1991; USAF, 1970-76; Business Owner; m. Cynthia
Comm.: Financial Services; Natural Resources
Dist. Offices: Las Cruces, 855-473-2723; Hobbs, 855-473-
2723; Los Lunas, 855-473-2723; Roswell, 855-473-2723;
Socorro, 855-473-2723

Ben Ray Luján (D-3rd)   **202-225-6190**
2231 RHOB   5th Term/63%   96/96/98   Fax: 226-1528
lujan.house.gov   twitter repBenRayLujan
CoS ....Angela Ramirez **LD**...............Graham Mason
Sch ....Chris Garcia **Press**.............Joe Shoemaker
Bio: b. 6/7/72 Santa Fe, NM; Catholic; BBA NM Highlands
Univ., 2007; Human Resources Manager, State Government
Aide; single
Comm.: Energy & Commerce
Dist. Offices: Santa Fe, 505-984-8950; Las Vegas, 505-454-
3038; Rio Rancho, 505-994-0499; Farmington, 505-324-1005;
Tucumcari, 575-461-3029

New York
ny.gov

Pop.: 19,795,791   **Rank:** 4th
Caucasian: 70%
African-Am.: 18%
Nat. Am.: 1%
Asian: 9%
Other: 3%
Hisp.: 19%

Reg. Voters: 11,476,433
Dem.: 49%   **Rep.:** 24%   **Other:** 27%
Land Area: 47,126 sq. mi.   **Rank:** 30th

Number of US House Seats: 18 Dem./9 Rep.

State Legislature
nysenate.gov
Senate: 32D/31R   House: 106D/43R/1 Other
Session: 01/04/17 – 12/31/2017

Gov. Andrew M. Cuomo (D)   **518-474-8390**
Next Election: 2018 2nd Term/54%   Fax: 518-474-1513
twitter nygovcuomo
Bio: b. 12/6/57 Queens, NY; Catholic; JD Albany Law School,
1982; Attorney; div.

State Capitol, Albany, NY 12224
Washington Office: 202-434-7112

SENATE

Charles E. Schumer (D)   **202-224-6542**
SH-322   4th Term/70%   93/99/100   Fax: 228-3027
schumer.senate.gov   twitter SenSchumer
CoS ....Mike Lynch **LD**................... Meghan Taira
Sch ....Michelle Mittler **CD** ....Matt House
Bio: b. 11/23/50 Brooklyn, NY; Jewish; JD Harvard Univ.,
1974; Public Official; m. Iris Weinshall
Comm.: Rules & Administration; Joint Library; Joint Printing;
Minority Leader
Dist. Offices: New York, 212-486-4430; Buffalo, 716-846-
4111; Rochester, 585-263-5866; Albany, 518-431-4070

NEW YORK

Kirsten Gillibrand (D)
KEER-sten JILL-uh-brand   **202-224-4451**
SR-478   2nd Term/72%   90/99/93   Fax: 228-0282
gillibrand.senate.gov   twitter SenGillibrand
CoS ....Jess Fassler   **LD** ....Brooke Jamison
Sch .... Kinsey Spears   **CD** ....Marc Barumer
Bio: b. 12/9/66 Albany, NY; Catholic; JD Univ. of CA - Los
Angeles, 1991; Attorney; m. Jonathan
Comm.: Agriculture, Nutrition & Forestry; Armed Services;
Special Aging
Dist. Offices: New York, 212-688-6262; Albany, 518-431-
0120; Buffalo, 716-854-9725; Rochester, 585-263-6250;
Binghamton, 607-772-6792; Syracuse, 315-423-5471; Peek-
skill, 914-734-1532; Melville, 631-753-0978

HOUSE

Lee Zeldin (R-1st)   **202-225-3826**
1517 LHOB   2nd Term/59%   6/94/99   Fax: 225-3143
zeldin.house.gov   twitter RepLeeZeldin
CoS .... Eric Amidon   **LD** ....Kevin Dowling
Sch ....Nicole Paciello   **CD** ....Jennifer DiSiena
Bio: b. 1/30/80 East Meadow, NY; Jewish; JD Albany Law
School, 2003; USA, 2003-07; USAR, 2007-present; Attorney,
Military Prosecutor; m. Diana
Comm.: Financial Services; Foreign Affairs
Dist. Offices: Patchogue, 631-289-1097; Riverhead, 631-
209-4235

Peter T. King (R-2nd)   **202-225-7896**
339 CHOB   13th Term/62%   7/93/98   Fax: 226-2279
peteking.house.gov   twitter RepPeteKing
CoS .... Kevin Fogarty   **LD** ....Jamie Matese
Sch .... Kevin Fogarty   **CD** ....Kevin Fogarty
Bio: b. 4/5/44 Manhattan, NY; Catholic; JD Univ. of Notre
Dame, 1968; NYNG, 1968-73; Attorney; m. Rosemary
Comm.: Financial Services; Homeland Security; Select
Intelligence
Dist. Offices: Massapequa Park, 516-541-4225

Tom Suozzi (D-3rd) *SWAH-zee*   **202-225-3335**
226 CHOB   1st Term/52%   Fax: 225-4669
suozzi.house.gov   twitter RepTomSuozzi
CoS ....Mike Florio   **LD** .... Diane Shuste
Sch ....Ellie Arbeit   **Press** ....Lou Wasson
Bio: b. 8/31/62 Glen Cove; Catholic; JD Fordham Univ.,
1989; Attorney; m. Helene
Comm.: Armed Services; Foreign Affairs
Dist. Offices: Huntington, 631-923-4100

Kathleen Rice (D-4th)   **202-225-5516**
1508 LHOB   2nd Term/59%   84/94/93   Fax: 225-5758
kathleenrice.house.gov   twitter RepKathleenRice
CoS ....Nell Reilly   **LD** ....Colleen Nguyen
Sch ....Amanda Walsh   **CD** ....Coleman Lamb
Bio: b. 2/15/65 Manhattan, NY; Catholic; JD Touro Law
Center, 1991; County Prosecutor; single
Comm.: Homeland Security; Veterans' Affairs
Dist. Offices: Garden City, 516-739-3008

Gregory W. Meeks (D-5th)   **202-225-3461**
2234 RHOB   11th Term/86%   92/98/91   Fax: 226-4169
meeks.house.gov   twitter GregoryMeeks
CoS ....Sophia Lafargue   **LD** ....Ernie Jolly
Sch ....Kim Fuller   **CD** ....Jordan Morris
Bio: b. 9/25/53 Manhattan, NY; African Methodist Episco-
pal; JD Howard Univ., 1978; City Prosecutor, Attorney; m.
Simone-Marie
Comm.: Financial Services; Foreign Affairs
Dist. Offices: Arverne, 347-230-4032; Jamaica, 718-725-6000

New York

Grace Meng (D-6th)　　　　　**202-225-2601**
1317 LHOB　3rd Term/72%　94/98/95　Fax: 225-1589
meng.house.gov　　　　　　**twitter** RepGraceMeng
CoS .... Justin Oswald　**LD** .... David Bagby
Sch .... Brenda Connolly　**CD** .... Jordan Goldes
Bio: b. 10/1/75 Queens, NY; Christian; JD Yeshiva Univ., 2002; Attorney; m. Wayne Kye
Comm.: Appropriations
Dist. Offices: Flushing, 718-358-6364; Forest Hills, 718-358-6364

Nydia M. Velázquez (D-7th)　　**202-225-2361**
2302 RHOB　13th Term/91%　98/100/98　Fax: 226-0327
velazquez.house.gov　　　　　**twitter** NydiaVelazquez
CoS .... Adam Minehardt　**LD** .... Justin Pelletier
Sch .... Tera Proby　**CD** .... Alex Haurek
Bio: b. 3/28/53 Yabucoa, PR; Catholic; MA NYU, 1976; Professor, Congressional Staff; div.
Comm.: Financial Services; Small Business (Rnk. Mem.)
Dist. Offices: Brooklyn, 718-599-3658; Brooklyn, 718-222-5819; New York, 212-619-2606

Hakeem Jeffries (D-8th) *HA-keem*　**202-225-5936**
1607 LHOB　3rd Term/93%　98/99/95　Fax: 225-1018
jeffries.house.gov　　　　　　**twitter** RepJeffries
CoS .... Cedric Grant　**LD** .... Chris Randle
Sch .... Audrey Litvak　**CD** .... Michael Hardaway
Bio: b. 8/4/70 Brooklyn, NY; Baptist; JD NYU, 1997; Attorney; m. Kennisandra
Comm.: Budget; Judiciary
Dist. Offices: Brooklyn, 718-373-0033; Brooklyn, 718-237-2211

Yvette D. Clarke (D-9th)　　　**202-225-6231**
2058 RHOB　6th Term/92%　98/100/97　Fax: 226-0112
clarke.house.gov　　　　　　**twitter** RepYvetteClarke
CoS .... LaDavia Drane　**Dep CoS** .... Asi Ofosu
Sch .... Shawnta Goins　**Press** .... Christine Bennett
Bio: b. 11/21/64 Brooklyn, NY; Christian; Attended Oberlin Col., 1982-86; Economic Development Director, Legislative Aide; single
Comm.: Energy & Commerce; Ethics; Small Business
Dist. Offices: Brooklyn, 718-287-1142

Jerrold Nadler (D-10th) *NAD-ler*　**202-225-5635**
2109 RHOB　14th Term/78%　98/99/86　Fax: 225-6923
nadler.house.gov　　　　　　**twitter** RepJerryNadler
CoS .... Amy Rutkin　**LD** .... Lisette Morton
Sch .... Janice Siegel　**CD** .... Daniel Schwarz
Bio: b. 6/13/47 Brooklyn, NY; Jewish; JD Fordham Univ., 1978; Attorney, State Legislative Aide; m. Joyce Miller
Comm.: Judiciary; Transportation & Infrastructure
Dist. Offices: New York, 212-367-7350; Brooklyn, 718-373-3198

Dan Donovan (R-11th)　　　　**202-225-3371**
1541 LHOB　2nd Term/62%　7/90/100　Fax: 226-1272
donovan.house.gov　　　　　　**twitter** RepDanDonovan
CoS .... Ronald Carara　**LD** .... Vacant
Dep CoS .... Blaire Bartlett　**CD** .... Patrick Ryan
Bio: b. 11/6/56 Staten Island, NY; Catholic; JD Fordham Univ., 1988; County Government Aide, City Prosecutor, Attorney; eng. Serena Stonick
Comm.: Foreign Affairs; Homeland Security
Dist. Offices: Staten Island, 718-351-1062; Brooklyn, 718-630-5277

Carolyn B. Maloney (D-12th) 202-225-7944
2308 RHOB 13th Term/83% 96/98/94 Fax: 225-4709
maloney.house.gov twitter RepMaloney
CoS .... Michael Iger **LD** .... Christina Parisi
Sch .... Rebecca Tulloch **Press** .... Jennifer Bell
Bio: b. 2/19/46 Greensboro, NC; Presbyterian; AB Greensboro Col., 1968; Educator; wid.
Comm.: Financial Services; Oversight & Government Reform; Joint Economic
Dist. Offices: New York, 212-860-0606; Astoria, 718-932-1804

Adriano Espaillat (D-13th)
ah-dri-AN-o ess-PIE-yot **202-225-4365**
1630 LHOB 1st Term/89% Fax: 225-0816
espaillat.house.gov twitter EspaillatNY
CoS .... Aneiry Batista **LD** .... Valeria Carranza
Sch .... Raphael Dominguez **CD** ... Candace Randle Person
Bio: b. 9/27/54 Santiago, Dominican Republic; Catholic; BS Queens Col., 1978; Non-Profit Director; m. Marthera Madera
Comm.: Education & the Workforce; Foreign Affairs; Small Business
Dist. Offices: Harlem, 212-663-3900

Joseph Crowley (D-14th) 202-225-3965
1035 LHOB 10th Term/83% 96/100/96 Fax: 225-1909
crowley.house.gov twitter repjoecrowley
CoS .... Kate Keating **LD** .... Nicole Cohen
Sch .... Jessica Vallejo **CD** .... Courtney Gidner
Bio: b. 3/16/62 Queens, NY; Catholic; BA Queens Col., 1985; Public Official; m. Kasey
Comm.: Ways & Means
Dist. Offices: Queens, 718-779-1400; Bronx, 718-931-1400

José E. Serrano (D-15th) 202-225-4361
2354 RHOB 15th Term/95% 98/100/98 Fax: 225-6001
serrano.house.gov twitter RepJoseSerrano
CoS .... Matthew Alpert **LD** .... Angel Nigaglioni
Sch .... Frederick Velez **CD** .... Paola Amador
Bio: b. 10/24/43 Mayaguez, PR; Catholic; Attended Lehman Col., 1979-80; USA, 1964-66; School Administrator, Banker; div.
Comm.: Appropriations
Dist. Offices: Bronx, 718-620-0084

Eliot L. Engel (D-16th) 202-225-2464
2462 RHOB 15th Term/95% 96/98/93 Fax: 225-5513
engel.house.gov twitter RepEliotEngel
CoS .... Bill Weitz **LD** .... Brian Skretny
Sch .... Darlene Murray **Press** .... Bryant Daniels
Bio: b. 2/18/47 Bronx, NY; Jewish; JD NY Law School, 1987; Teacher; m. Patricia
Comm.: Energy & Commerce; Foreign Affairs (Rnk. Mem.)
Dist. Offices: Bronx, 718-796-9700; Mt. Vernon, 914-699-4100; Bronx, 718-320-2314

Nita M. Lowey (D-17th) 202-225-6506
2365 RHOB 15th Term/Unc. 94/98/99 Fax: 225-0546
lowey.house.gov twitter NitaLowey
CoS .... Elizabeth Stanley **LD** .... Dana Acton
Sch .... Kelly Healton **CD** .... Roy Loewenstein
Bio: b. 7/5/37 Bronx, NY; Jewish; BA Mt. Holyoke Col., 1959; Homemaker, State Government Aide; m. Stephen
Comm.: Appropriations (Rnk. Mem.)
Dist. Offices: White Plains, 914-428-1707; New City, 845-639-3485

NEW YORK

Sean Patrick Maloney (D-18th)   **202-225-5441**
1027 LHOB   3rd Term/55%   80/92/97   Fax: 225-3289
seanmaloney.house.gov   twitter RepSeanMaloney
CoS ....Tim Persico LD ....Tom Mintz
Sch ....Kevin Golden CD ....Caitlin Girouard
Bio: b. 7/30/66 Sherbrooke, Canada; Catholic; JD Univ. of VA, 1992; Attorney, White House Aide; m. Randy Florke
Comm.: Agriculture; Transportation & Infrastructure
Dist. Offices: Newburgh, 845-561-1259

John J. Faso (R-19th) *FASO (like "lasso")* **202-225-5614**
1616 LHOB   1st Term/55%   Fax: 225-1168
faso.house.gov   twitter RepJohnFaso
CoS ....Dain Pascocello LD ....Patrick Rooney
Sch ....Hope Costa CD ....Courtney Weaver
Bio: b. 8/25/52 Massapequa, NY; Catholic; JD Georgetown Univ., 1979; Attorney; m. Mary Frances
Comm.: Agriculture; Budget; Transportation & Infrastructure
Dist. Offices: Delhi, 607-746-9537; Kinderhook, 518-610-8133; Kingston, 845-514-2322

Paul Tonko (D-20th)   **202-225-5076**
2463 RHOB   5th Term/68%   98/98/98   Fax: 225-5077
tonko.house.gov   twitter RepPaulTonko
CoS ....Clinton Britt LD ....Jeff Morgan
OM ....David Mastrangelo **Press**............Matt Sonneborn
Bio: b. 6/18/49 Amsterdam, NY; Catholic; BS Clarkson Univ., 1971; Public Works Engineer; single
Comm.: Energy & Commerce; Science, Space & Technology
Dist. Offices: Albany, 518-465-0700; Amsterdam, 518-843-3400; Schenectady, 518-374-4547

Elise Stefanik (R-21st) *stef-AH-nick* **202-225-4611**
318 CHOB   2nd Term/66%   9/87/99   Fax: 226-0621
stefanik.house.gov   twitter RepStefanik
CoS ....Lindley Kratovil LD ....Courtney Carrow
Sch ....Emily Cosci CD ....Tom Flanagin
Bio: b. 7/2/84 Albany, NY; Catholic; AB Harvard Univ., 2006; Sales Director, Campaign Aide, White House Aide; eng.
Comm.: Armed Services; Education & the Workforce; Select Intelligence
Dist. Offices: Watertown, 315-782-3150; Glens Falls, 518-743-0964; Plattsburgh, 518-561-2324

Claudia Tenney (R-22nd)   **202-225-3665**
512 CHOB   1st Term/47%   Fax: 225-1891
tenney.house.gov   twitter claudiatenney
CoS ....Margaux Matter LD ....Nick Stewart
Sch ....Teri Dorn **Press**..........Hannah Andrews
Bio: b. 2/4/61 Utica, NY; Presbyterian; JD Univ. of Cincinnati, 1987; Publisher, Attorney, Yugoslavian Consulate Aide; div.
Comm.: Financial Services
Dist. Offices: New Hartford, 315-732-0713

Tom Reed (R-23rd)   **202-225-3161**
2437 RHOB   5th Term/58%   6/93/98   Fax: 226-6599
reed.house.gov   twitter RepTomReed
CoS ....Tim Kolpien LD ....Drew Wayne
OM ....Don Castellucci CD ....Samantha Cotten
Bio: b. 11/18/71 Joliet, IL; Catholic; JD OH Northern Univ., 1996; Attorney, Business Owner; m. Jean
Comm.: Ways & Means
Dist. Offices: Corning, 607-654-7566; Geneva, 315-759-5229; Ithaca, 607-222-2027; Jamestown, 716-708-6369; Olean, 716-379-8434

New York

John Katko (R-24th)
202-225-3701
1620 LHOB   2nd Term/61%   9/84/98   Fax: 225-4042
katko.house.gov   twitter RepJohnKatko
CoS .... Brad Gentile **LD** .... Zach Howell
Sch .... Elizabeth Kilgallin **CD** .... Erin O'Connor
Bio: b. 11/9/62 Syracuse, NY; Catholic; JD Syracuse Univ.,
1988; Federal Prosecutor, Attorney; m. Robin
Comm.: Homeland Security; Transportation & Infrastructure
Dist. Offices: Syracuse, 315-423-5657; Auburn, 315-253-
4068; Oswego, TBA; Lyons, TBA

Louise M. Slaughter (D-25th)
202-225-3615
2469 RHOB   16th Term/55%   98/98/98   Fax: 225-7822
louise.house.gov   twitter louiseslaughter
CoS .... Liam Fitzsimmons **LD** .... Colleen Bell
Sch .... Yodit Tewelde **CD** .... Jeff Gohringer
Bio: b. 8/14/29 Harlan Co., KY; Episcopal; MPH Univ. of KY,
1953; Microbiologist; wid.
Comm.: Rules (Rnk. Mem.)
Dist. Offices: Rochester, 585-232-4850

Brian Higgins (D-26th)
202-225-3306
2459 RHOB   7th Term/74%   92/97/97   Fax: 226-0347
higgins.house.gov   twitter RepBrianHiggins
CoS .... Matthew Fery **LD** .... Matthew Fery
Sch .... Kayla Williams **CD** .... Theresa Kennedy
Bio: b. 10/6/59 Buffalo, NY; Catholic; MPA Harvard Univ.,
1996; Public Official; m. Mary Jane Hannon
Comm.: Budget; Ways & Means
Dist. Offices: Buffalo, 716-852-3501; Niagara Falls, 716-
282-1274

Chris Collins (R-27th)
202-225-5265
1117 LHOB   3rd Term/68%   8/97/96   Fax: 225-5910
chriscollins.house.gov   twitter RepChrisCollins
CoS .... Michael Hook **LD** .... Ted Alexander
Sch .... Taylor Elliot **CD** .... Michael McAdams
Bio: b. 5/20/50 Schenectady, NY; Catholic; MBA Univ. of
AL - Birmingham, 1975; Business Owner; m. Mary
Comm.: Energy & Commerce
Dist. Offices: Williamsville, 716-634-2324; Geneseo, 585-
519-4002

North Carolina
nc.gov

Pop.: 10,042,802   **Rank:** 9th
Caucasian: 71%   **African-Am.:** 22%
Nat. Am.: 2%   **Asian:** 3%   **Other:** 2%   **Hisp.:** 9%
Reg. Voters: 6,924,296
Dem.: 41%   **Rep.:** 30%   **Other:** 29%
Land Area: 48,618 sq. mi.   **Rank:** 29th

Number of US House Seats: 10 Rep./3 Dem.

State Legislature
ncga.state.nc.us
Senate: 35R/15D   House: 74R/46D
Session: 01/11/17 – 8/1/2017

North Carolina

Gov. Roy Cooper (D)　　　　**919-814-2000**
Next Election 2020　1st Term/49%　Fax: 919-733-2120

twitter nc_governor

Bio: b. 6/13/57; Nashville, NC; Presbyterian; JD Univ. of NC, 1982; Attorney; m. Kristin

20301 Mail Service Center, Raleigh, NC 27699-0301
Washington Office: 202-624-5833

SENATE

Richard M. Burr (R)　　　　**202-224-3154**
SR-217　　　3rd Term/51%　57/81/100　Fax: 228-2981
burr.senate.gov　　　　　　　　twitter senatorburr
CoS ....Dean Myers　**LD** .... Natasha Hickman
Sch ....Molly Harper　**Press**............. Taylor Holgate
Bio: b. 11/30/55 Charlottesville, VA; Methodist; BA Wake Forest Univ., 1978; Marketing Manager; m. Brooke
Comm.: Finance; Health, Education, Labor & Pensions; Select Intelligence (Chair); Special Aging
Dist. Offices: Winston-Salem, 336-631-5125; Wilmington, 910-251-1058; Asheville, 828-350-2437; Gastonia, 704 833-0854

Thom Tillis (R)　　　　**202-224-6342**
SD-185　　　1st Term/49%　52/88/99　Fax: 228-2563
tillis.senate.gov　　　　　　　　twitter senthomtillis
CoS ....Jordan Shaw　**LD** ....Courtney Temple
Sch ....Angela Schulze　**CD** ....Daniel Keylin
Bio: b. 8/30/60 Jacksonville, FL; Catholic; BS Univ. of MD - Univ. Col., 1997; Business Consultant, Information Technology Manager; m. Susan
Comm.: Armed Services; Banking, Housing, & Urban Affairs; Judiciary; Veterans' Affairs; Special Aging
Dist. Offices: Charlotte, 704 509-9087; Greenville, 252 329-0371; Raleigh, 919 856-4630; High Point, 336-885-0685; Rocky Mount, 252-977-9522

HOUSE

G.K. Butterfield (D-1st)　　　　**202-225-3101**
2080 RHOB　8th Term/69%　96/97/92　Fax: 225-3354
butterfield.house.gov　　　　　　twitter gkbutterfield
CoS .... Troy Clair　**LD** ....Saul Hernandez
Sch ....Lindsey Bowen　**CD** .... Meaghan Lynch
Bio: b. 4/27/47 Wilson, NC; Baptist; JD NC Central Univ., 1974; USA, 1968-70; Judge, Attorney; div.
Comm.: Energy & Commerce
Dist. Offices: Wilson, 252-237-9816; Durham, 919-908-0164

George Holding (R-2nd)　　　　**202-225-3032**
1110 LHOB　3rd Term/57%　7/98/99　Fax: 225-5662
holding.house.gov　　　　　　　twitter RepHolding
CoS .... Tucker Knott　**LD** ....Kris Denzel
Sch ....Katie Smith　**CD** ....William Glenn
Bio: b. 4/17/68 Raleigh, NC; Baptist; JD Wake Forest Univ., 1996; Attorney, Congressional Aide; m. Lucy
Comm.: Ways & Means
Dist. Offices: Raleigh, 919-782-4400

Walter B. Jones (R-3rd)　　　　**202-225-3415**
2333 RHOB　12th Term/67%　37/78/95　Fax: 225-3286
jones.house.gov　　　　　　　twitter RepWalterJones
CoS .... Joshua Bowlen　**LD** ....Bradley Ryon
Sch .... Maggie Ayera　**CD** ....Allison Tucker
Bio: b. 2/10/43 Farmville, NC; Catholic; BA Atlantic Christian Col., 1968; NCNG, 1967-71; Businessman; m. Joe Anne
Comm.: Armed Services
Dist. Offices: Greenville, 252-931-1003

North Carolina

David E. Price (D-4th)　　　　**202-225-1784**
2108 RHOB　15th Term/68%　96/98/96　Fax: 225-2014
price.house.gov　　　　　*twitter* RepDavidEPrice
CoS .... Asher Hildebrand　LD .... James Hunter
Sch .... Bayly Hassell　Press .... Lawrence Kluttz
Bio: b. 8/17/40 Erwin, TN; Baptist; PhD Yale Univ., 1969; Professor; m. Lisa
Comm.: Appropriations
Dist. Offices: Raleigh, 919-859-5999; Chapel Hill, 919-688-3004; Fayetteville, 910-323-0260

Virginia Foxx (R-5th)　　　　**202-225-2071**
2262 RHOB　7th Term/58%　7/97/95　Fax: 225-2995
foxx.house.gov　　　　　*twitter* virginiafoxx
CoS .... Cyrus Artz　LD .... Carson Middleton
Sch .... Rochelle Colburn　CD .... Sheridan Watson
Bio: b. 6/29/43 Bronx, NY; Catholic; EdD Univ. of NC - Greensboro, 1985; Business Owner, Educator; m. Tom
Comm.: Education & the Workforce (Chair); Oversight & Government Reform
Dist. Offices: Clemmons, 336-778-0211; Boone, 828-265-0240

Mark Walker (R-6th)　　　　**202-225-3065**
1305 LHOB　2nd Term/59%　9/99/95　Fax: 225-8611
walker.house.gov　　　　　*twitter* repmarkwalker
CoS .... Scott Luginbill　LD .... Ryan Walker
Sch .... Katie Abrames　CD .... Jack Minor
Bio: b. 5/20/69 Dothan, AL; Baptist; BA Piedmont Baptist Col., 1999; Pastor; m. Kelly
Comm.: House Administration; Oversight & Government Reform; Joint Printing
Dist. Offices: Graham, 336-229-0159; Greensboro, 336-333-5005

David Rouzer (R-7th)　　　　**202-225-2731**
424 CHOB　2nd Term/61%　7/99/100　Fax: 225-5773
rouzer.house.gov　　　　　*twitter* repdavidrouzer
CoS .... Melissa Murphy　LD .... Kyle Sanders
EA .... Kelley Billy　CD .... Danielle Adams
Bio: b. 2/16/72 Landstuhl, Germany; Southern Baptist; BA/BS NC St. Univ., 1994; Business Owner, Congressional Aide, University Administrator; single
Comm.: Agriculture; Natural Resources; Transportation & Infrastructure
Dist. Offices: Bolivia, 910-253-6111; Four Oaks, 919-938-3040; Wilmington, 910-395-0202

Richard Hudson (R-8th)　　　　**202-225-3715**
429 CHOB　3rd Term/59%　8/100/94　Fax: 225-4036
hudson.house.gov　　　　　*twitter* RepRichHudson
CoS .... Chris Carter　LD .... Aaron Ringel
Sch .... Summer Fields　CD .... Tatum Gibson
Bio: b. 11/4/71 Franklin, VA; Christian; BA Univ. of NC - Charlotte, 1996; Congressional Aide, Business Owner; m. Renee
Comm.: Energy & Commerce
Dist. Offices: Concord, 704-786-1612; Rockingham, 910-997-2070

Robert Pittenger (R-9th)　　　　**202-225-1976**
224 CHOB　3rd Term/58%　8/98/96　Fax: 225-3389
pittenger.house.gov　　　　　*twitter* reppittenger
CoS .... Stephen Billy　Dep CoS .... Clark Fonda
Sch ...... Hayden Bumgardner　CD .... Jamie Bowers
Bio: b. 8/15/48 Dallas, TX; Protestant; BA Univ. of TX, 1970; Real Estate Investor, Fundraiser; m. Suzanne
Comm.: Financial Services
Dist. Offices: Charlotte, 704-362-1060; Fayetteville, 910-303-0669; Monroe, 704-917-9573

NORTH CAROLINA

Patrick T. McHenry (R-10th)   **202-225-2576**
2334 RHOB   7th Term/63%   7/99/99   Fax: 225-0316
mchenry.house.gov   twitter PatrickMcHenry
CoS .... Jeff Butler **LD** .... Matt Mulder
Sch .... Lindsey Shackelford **Press** .... Jeff Butler
Bio: b. 10/22/75 Charlotte, NC; Catholic; BA Belmont Abbey Col., 2000; Realtor, Campaign Aide; m. Giulia
Comm.: Financial Services
Dist. Offices: Hickory, 828-327-6100; Gastonia, 704-833-0096; Black Mountain, 828-669-0600

Mark Meadows (R-11th)   **202-225-6401**
1024 LHOB   3rd Term/64%   6/98/99   Fax: 226-6422
meadows.house.gov   twitter RepMarkMeadows
CoS .... Paul Fitzpatrick **LD** .... Graham Haile
Sch .... Eliza Thurston **CD** .... Ben Williamson
Bio: b. 7/28/59 Maginot Bks, Verdun, France; Christian; AA Univ. of S. FL, 1980; Business Owner; m. Debbie
Comm.: Foreign Affairs; Oversight & Government Reform; Transportation & Infrastructure
Dist. Offices: Hendersonville, 828-693-5660; Lenoir, 828-426-8701; Waynesville, 828-452-6022; Spruce Pine, 828-765-0573

Alma Adams (D-12th)   **202-225-1510**
222 CHOB   3rd Term/67%   98/99/95   Fax: 225-1512
adams.house.gov   twitter RepAdams
CoS .... Rhonda Foxx **LD** .... Margaret Franklin
Sch .... Sandra Brown **Press** .... Hailey Barringer
Bio: b. 5/27/46 High Point, NC; Baptist; PhD OH St. Univ., 1981; Professor, Artist, Teacher; div.
Comm.: Agriculture; Education & the Workforce; Small Business; Joint Economic
Dist. Offices: Charlotte, 704-344-9950; Greensboro, 336-275-9950

Ted Budd (R-13th)   **202-225-4531**
118 CHOB   1st Term/56%   Fax: 225-0181
budd.house.gov   twitter RepTedBudd
CoS .... Andrew Bell **LD** .... Alex Vargo
Sch .... Jeanna Buck **Press** .... Melissa Brown
Bio: b. 10/21/71 Winston Salem; Non-denominational Christian; MBA Wake Forest, 2007; Business Owner, Executive; m. Amy Kate
Comm.: Financial Services
Dist. Offices: Advance, 336-998-1313; Mooresville, TBA

NORTH DAKOTA
nd.gov

Williston

1

Grand Forks •

★ Bismarck

Fargo

Pop.: 756,927   **Rank:** 47th
Caucasian: 89%
African-Am.: 2%
Nat. Am.: 6%   **Asian:** 1%
Other: 2%   **Hisp.:** 4%
Reg. Voters: No voter registration
Land Area: 69,001 sq. mi.   **Rank:** 17th

Number of US House Seats: 1 Rep.

State Legislature
legis.nd.gov
Senate: 38R/9D   House: 81R/13D
Session: 01/03/17 – 4/26/2017

North Dakota

Gov. Doug Burgum (R) **701-328-2200**
Next Election 2020   1st Term/77%   Fax: 701-328-2205
twitter DougBurgum

Bio: b. 8/1/1956; Arthur, ND; Unspecified; MBA Stanford Univ., 1980; Real Estate Investor, Software Company Executive, Federal Reserve System Policy Advisor; Management Consultant; m. Kathryn

600 East Boulevard Avenue, Bismarck, ND 58505-0100
Washington Office: 703-519-1207

SENATE

John Hoeven (R) *HO-ven* **202-224-2551**
SR-338   2nd Term/79%   53/86/98   Fax: 224-7999
hoeven.senate.gov   **twitter** SenJohnHoeven
CoS .... Ryan Bernstein **LD** .... Tony Eberhard
Sch .... Jennifer Newman **CD** .... Don Canton
Bio: b. 3/13/57 Bismarck, ND; Catholic; MBA Northwestern Univ., 1981; Bank Executive; m. Mical
Comm.: Agriculture, Nutrition & Forestry; Appropriations; Energy & Natural Resources; Homeland Security & Governmental Affairs; Indian Affairs
Dist. Offices: Bismarck, 701-250-4618; Fargo, 701-239-5389; Grand Forks, 701 746-8972; Minot, 701 838-1361

Heidi Heitkamp (D) **202-224-2043**
SH-516   1st Term/50%   73/61/99   Fax: 224-7776
heitkamp.senate.gov   **twitter** SenatorHeitkamp
CoS .... Tessa Gould **LD** .... Tracee Sutton
Sch .... Stacy Austad **CD** .... Abigail McDonough
Bio: b. 10/30/55 Breckenridge, MN; Catholic; JD Lewis & Clark Col., 1980; Attorney, Homemaker; m. Darwin Lange
Comm.: Agriculture, Nutrition & Forestry; Banking, Housing, & Urban Affairs; Homeland Security & Governmental Affairs; Small Business & Entrepreneurship; Indian Affairs
Dist. Offices: Bismarck, 701-258-4648; Fargo, 701-232-8030; Grand Forks, 701-775-9601; Minot, 701-852-0703

HOUSE

Kevin Cramer (R-At Large) **202-225-2611**
1717 LHOB   3rd Term/69%   8/98/97   Fax: 226-0893
cramer.house.gov   **twitter** RepKevinCramer
CoS .... Mark Gruman **LD** .... Mark Gruman
Sch .... Rachel Buening **CD** .... Adam Jorde
Bio: b. 1/21/61 Rolette, ND; Evangelical Christian; MM Univ. of Mary, 2003; University Fundraiser, Economic Development Director; m. Kris
Comm.: Energy & Commerce
Dist. Offices: Bismarck, 701-224-0355; Fargo, 701-356-2216; Grand Forks, 701-738-4880; Minot, 701-839-0255

Ohio
ohio.gov

Pop.: 11,613,423   **Rank:** 7th
Caucasian: 83%
African-Am.: 13%
Nat. Am.: 0%   **Asian:** 2%
Other: 2%   **Hisp.:** 4%
Reg. Voters: 7,861,025
Party registration not required
Land Area: 40,861 sq. mi.
Rank: 35th

Number of US House Seats:
12 Rep./4 Dem.

State Legislature
legislature.state.oh.us
Senate: 24R/9D   House: 66R/33D
Session: 01/02/17 – 12/31/2017

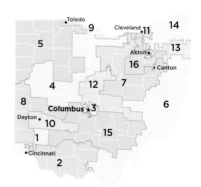

OHIO

Gov. John R. Kasich (R)   **614-466-3555**
Next Election: 2018   2nd Term/64%   Fax: 614-466-9354
twitter johnkasich

Bio: b. 5/13/52 McKees Rocks, PA; Christian; BA OH St.
Univ., 1974; Legislative Aide, Public Official, Commentator; m. Karen

77 South High Street, Riffe Center, 30th Floor,
Columbus, OH 43215-6117

SENATE

Sherrod Brown (D)   **202-224-2315**
SH-713   2nd Term/51%   88/96/97   Fax: 228-6321
brown.senate.gov   **twitter** SenSherrodBrown
CoS .... Sarah Benzing   **LD** ....Jeremy Hekhuis
Sch ....Diana Baron   **CD** .... Jennifer Donohue
Bio: b. 11/9/52 Mansfield, OH; Lutheran; MA OH St. Univ.,
1981; Educator; m. Connie Schultz
Comm.: Agriculture, Nutrition & Forestry; Banking, Housing & Urban Affairs (Rnk. Mem.); Finance; Veterans' Affairs
Dist. Offices: Cleveland, 216-522-7272; Cincinnati, 513-684-1021; Columbus, 614-469-2083; Lorain, 440-242-4100

Rob Portman (R)   **202-224-3353**
SR-448   2nd Term/58%   59/72/99   Fax: 224-9075
portman.senate.gov   **twitter** senrobportman
CoS ....Mark Isakowitz   **LD** .... Pam Thiessen
Sch .... Angie Youngen   **CD** .... Kevin Smith
Bio: b. 12/19/55 Cincinnati, OH; Methodist; JD Univ. of MI,
1984; Attorney; m. Jane
Comm.: Energy & Natural Resources; Finance; Foreign
Relations; Homeland Security & Governmental Affairs;
Joint Economic
Dist. Offices: Columbus, 614-469-6774; Cincinnati, 513-684-3265; Cleveland, 216-522-7095; Toledo, 419-259-3895

HOUSE

Steve Chabot (R-1st) *SHAB-it*   **202-225-2216**
2371 RHOB   11th Term/60%   9/99/99   Fax: 225-3012
chabot.house.gov   **twitter** repstevechabot
CoS .... Stacy Barton   **LD** ....Jonathan Lowe
Sch ....Lisa McGhie   **CD** ....Brian Griffith
Bio: b. 1/22/53 Cincinnati, OH; Catholic; JD Northern KY
Univ., 1978; Attorney; m. Donna
Comm.: Foreign Affairs; Judiciary; Small Business (Chair)
Dist. Offices: Cincinnati, 513-684-2723; Lebanon, 513-421-8704

Brad Wenstrup (R-2nd)   **202-225-3164**
2419 RHOB   3rd Term/67%   9/98/97   Fax: 225-1992
wenstrup.house.gov   **twitter** repbradwenstrup
CoS ....Derek Harley   **LD** ....Lisa Langenderfer
Sch ....April Lyman   **CD** ....Hailey Sadler
Bio: b. 6/17/58 Cincinnati, OH; Catholic; DPM Dr. William
M. Scholl Col. of Podiatric Medicine, 1985; USAR, 1998-present; Surgeon; m. Monica
Comm.: Armed Services; Veterans' Affairs; Select Intelligence
Dist. Offices: Cincinnati, 513-474-7777; Peebles, 513-605-1380

Joyce Beatty (D-3rd)   **202-225-4324**
133 CHOB   3rd Term/68%   96/98/97   Fax: 225-1984
beatty.house.gov   **twitter** RepBeatty
CoS .... Kimberly Ross   **LD** .... Jennifer Storipan
EA .... Juan L. Negron   **CD** .... Dominic Manecke
Bio: b. 3/12/50 Dayton, OH; Baptist; MS Wright St. Univ.,
1975; Business Owner, Management Consultant; m. Otto
Comm.: Financial Services
Dist. Offices: Columbus, 614-220-0003

Jim Jordan (R-4th)   202-225-2676
2056 RHOB   6th Term/68%   6/98/98   Fax: 226-0577
jordan.house.gov   twitter Jim_Jordan
CoS ....Ray Yonkura **LD** ....Jared Dilley
Sch ....Melissa Wade **Press**.................Darin Miller
Bio: b. 2/17/64 Troy, OH; Christian; JD Capital Univ., 2001;
College Wrestling Coach; m. Polly
Comm.: Judiciary; Oversight & Government Reform
Dist. Offices: Lima, 419-999-6455; Norwalk, 419-663-1426

Bob Latta (R-5th)   202-225-6405
2448 RHOB   6th Term/71%   9/99/97   Fax: 225-1985
latta.house.gov   twitter BobLatta
CoS .... Allison Witt Poulios **LD** ....Jason Isakovic
Sch .... Erin Partee **CD** .... Drew Griffin
Bio: b. 4/18/56 Bluffton, OH; Catholic; JD Univ. of Toledo,
1981; Attorney; m. Marcia
Comm.: Energy & Commerce
Dist. Offices: Bowling Green, 419-354-8700; Defiance, 419-
782-1996; Findlay, 419-422-7791

Bill Johnson (R-6th)   202-225-5705
1710 LHOB   4th Term/71%   7/98/99   Fax: 225-5907
billjohnson.house.gov   twitter repbilljohnson
CoS ....Mike Smullen **LD** .... Elise Conner
Sch .... Lisl Davis **CD** .... Benjamin Keeler
Bio: b. 11/10/54 Roseboro, NC; Protestant; MS GA Tech.,
1984; USAF, 1973-99; Military Officer, Business Executive;
m. LeeAnn
Comm.: Budget; Energy & Commerce
Dist. Offices: Marietta, 740-376-0868; Salem, 330-337-6951;
Ironton, 740-534-9431; Cambridge, 740-432-2366

Bob Gibbs (R-7th)   202-225-6265
2446 RHOB   4th Term/64%   7/98/99   Fax: 225-3394
gibbs.house.gov   twitter RepBobGibbs
CoS ....Meredith Dolan **LD** .... Hillary Gross
Sch Rachael van Mersbergen **Press**.............. Dallas Gerber
Bio: b. 6/14/54 Peru, IN; Methodist; AAS OH St. Univ., 1974;
Farmer; m. Jody
Comm.: Agriculture; Transportation & Infrastructure
Dist. Offices: Ashland, 419-207-0650

Warren Davidson (R-8th)   202-225-6205
1004 LHOB   2nd Term/69%   4/97/99   Fax: 225-0704
davidson.house.gov   twitter WarrenDavidson
CoS .... Jason Yaworske **LD** ....Matthew Silver
Sch ....Lisa Christian **CD** .... Alexei Woltornist
Bio: b. 3/1/70 Sidney, Ohio; Protestant; MBA, Univ. of Notre
Dame, 2005; USA, 1989-2000; Metal Manufacturing Com-
pany Executive; m. Lisa
Comm.: Financial Services
Dist. Offices: West Chester, 513-779-5400; Troy, 937-339-1524

Marcy Kaptur (D-9th)   202-225-4146
2186 RHOB   18th Term/69%   98/97/96   Fax: 225-7711
kaptur.house.gov   twitter RepMarcyKaptur
CoS ....Steve Katich **LD** .... Jenny Perrino
Sch .... Courtney Hruska **Press**.............. Joshua Stewart
Bio: b. 6/17/46 Toledo, OH; Catholic; MUP Univ. of MI,
1974; Urban Planner; single
Comm.: Appropriations
Dist. Offices: Toledo, 419-259-7500; Lorain, 440-288-1500;
Cleveland, 216-767-5933

Ohio

Michael R. Turner (R-10th)　　　**202-225-6465**
2368 RHOB　8th Term/65%　9/94/92　Fax: 225-6754
turner.house.gov　　　twitter RepMikeTurner
CoS ....Adam Howard　LD..................Jeffrey Wilson
Sch ....Emily Ziegler　CD ....Lauren O'Toole
Bio: b. 1/11/60 Dayton, OH; Protestant; MBA Univ. of Dayton, 1992; Attorney; div.
Comm.: Armed Services; Select Intelligence
Dist. Offices: Dayton, 937-225-2843

Marcia L. Fudge (D-11th)　　　**202-225-7032**
2344 RHOB　6th Term/80%　94/99/98　Fax: 225-1339
fudge.house.gov　　　twitter RepMarciaFudge
CoS .... Veleter Mazyck　LD ....Clifton Williams
Sch ....Lewis Myers　Press............Lauren Williams
Bio: b. 10/29/52 Cleveland, OH; Baptist; JD Cleveland St. Univ., 1983; Law Clerk, Congressional Aide; single
Comm.: Agriculture; Education & the Workforce
Dist. Offices: Warrensville Heights, 216-522-4900; Akron, 330-835-4758

Pat Tiberi (R-12th) *TEA-berry*　　　**202-225-5355**
1203 LHOB　9th Term/67%　6/97/92　Fax: 226-4523
tiberi.house.gov　　　twitter pattiberi
CoS ....Kelli Briggs　LD ..... Whitney Koch Daffner
Sch ....Laura Engquist　Press..................Olivia Hnat
Bio: b. 10/21/62 Columbus, OH; Catholic; BA OH St. Univ., 1985; Congressional Aide, Real Estate Agent; m. Denice
Comm.: Ways & Means; Joint Economic (Chair)
Dist. Offices: Columbus, 614-523-2555

Tim Ryan (D-13th)　　　**202-225-5261**
1126 LHOB　8th Term/68%　94/98/96　Fax: 225-3719
timryan.house.gov　　　twitter RepTimRyan
CoS ....Ron Grimes　LD .... Anne Sokolov
Sch ....Erin Isenberg　CD ....Michael Zetts
Bio: b. 7/16/73 Niles, OH; Catholic; JD Franklin Pierce Law Center, 2000; Congressional Aide, Public Official; m. Andrea
Comm.: Appropriations
Dist. Offices: Akron, 330-630-7311; Warren, 800-856-4152; Youngstown, 330-740-0193

David Joyce (R-14th)　　　**202-225-5731**
1124 LHOB　3rd Term/63%　6/93/96　Fax: 225-3307
joyce.house.gov　　　twitter RepDaveJoyce
CoS ....Dino DiSanto　LD .... Chris Cooper
Sch ....Anna Alburger　CD .... Vacant
Bio: b. 3/17/57 Cleveland, OH; Catholic; JD Univ. of Dayton, 1982; County Public Defender; m. Kelly
Comm.: Appropriations
Dist. Offices: Painesville, 440-352-3939; Twinsburg, 330-425-9291

Steve Stivers (R-15th)　　　**202-225-2015**
1022 LHOB　4th Term/66%　8/96/94　Fax: 225-3529
stivers.house.gov　　　twitter repstevestivers
CoS ......Courtney Whetstone　Dep CoS...............Nick Bush
Sch ....Sara Donlon　CD ....Tim Alford
Bio: b. 3/24/65 Cincinnati, OH; Methodist; MBA OH St. Univ., 1996; OHNG, 1988-present; Bank Executive, Lobbyist; m. Karen
Comm.: Financial Services
Dist. Offices: Hilliard, 614-771-4968; Lancaster, 740-654-2654; Wilmington, 937-283-7049

OHIO

James B. Renacci (R-16th) *reh-NAY-see* **202-225-3876**
328 CHOB   4th Term/65%   6/96/98   Fax: 225-3059
renacci.house.gov   twitter RepJimRenacci
CoS ....Surya Gunasekara **LD** .... Randy Herndon
Sch ....Michelle Runk **Press**................Kelsey Knight
Bio: b. 12/3/58 Monongahela, PA; Catholic; BS Indiana
Univ. of PA, 1980; Business Consultant, Business Owner,
Accountant; m. Tina
Comm.: Budget; Ways & Means
Dist. Offices: Wadsworth, 330-334-0040; Parma, 440-882-
6779

OKLAHOMA
ok.gov

Pop.: 3,911,338   **Rank:** 28th
Caucasian: 75%   **African-Am.:** 8%
Nat. Am.: 9%   **Asian:** 2%   **Other:** 6%
Hisp.: 10%
Reg. Voters: 2,161,881
Dem.: 43%   **Rep.:** 44%   **Other:** 13%
Land Area: 68,595 sq. mi.   **Rank:** 19th

Number of US House Seats: 5 Rep.

State Legislature
lsb.state.ok.us
Senate: 42R/6D   House: 74R/26D/1 Other
Session: 02/06/17 – 5/26/2017

Gov. Mary Fallin (R)   **405-521-2342**
Next Election: 2018 2nd Term/56%   Fax: 405-521-3353
twitter govmaryfallin
Bio: b. 12/9/54 Warrensburg, MO; Christian; BS OK St. Univ.,
1977; Real Estate Broker, Public Official; m. Wade Christensen

2300 North Lincoln Boulevard, Room 212,
Oklahoma City, OK 73105

SENATE

James M. Inhofe (R) *IN-hoff*   **202-224-4721**
SR-205   5th Term/68%   46/95/94   Fax: 228-0380
inhofe.senate.gov   twitter jiminhofe
CoS ....Ryan Jackson **LD** ....Luke Holland
Sch ....Wendi Price **CD** ....Daisy Letendre
Bio: b. 11/17/34 Des Moines, IA; Presbyterian; BA Univ. of
Tulsa, 1973; USA, 1957-58; Insurance Executive; m. Kay
Comm.: Armed Services; Commerce, Science & Transpor-
tation; Environment & Public Works; Small Business &
Entrepreneurship
Dist. Offices: Oklahoma City, 405-608-4381; Tulsa, 918
-748-5111; Enid, 580-234-5105; McAlester, 918-426-0933

James Lankford (R)   **202-224-5754**
SH-316   1st Term/68%   50/85/99   Fax: 228-1015
lankford.senate.gov   twitter SenatorLankford
CoS ....Greg Slavonic **LD** ....Michelle Altman
Sch ....Jaclyn O'Neil **CD** ......................D.J. Jordan
Bio: b. 3/4/68 Dallas, TX; Baptist; MDiv Southwestern Baptist
Theological Seminary, 1994; Youth Camp Director; m. Cindy
Comm.: Appropriations; Homeland Security & Governmental
Affairs; Indian Affairs; Select Intelligence
Dist. Offices: Oklahoma City, 405-231-4941; Tulsa, 918-
581-7651

OKLAHOMA

Jim Bridenstine (R-1st)   **202-225-2211**
216 CHOB   3rd Term/Unc.   6/99/97   Fax: 225-9187
bridenstine.house.gov   twitter repjbridenstine
CoS ....Joe Kaufman **LD**....................James Mazol
Sch ....Megan Wenrich **CD** .... Sheryl Kaufman
Bio: b. 6/15/75 Ann Arbor, MI; Baptist; MBA Cornell Univ., 2009; USN, 1998-2007; USNR, 2010-present; Naval Aviator, Marketing Consultant, Museum Director; m. Michelle
Comm.: Armed Services; Science, Space & Technology
Dist. Offices: Tulsa, 918-935-3222

Markwayne Mullin (R-2nd)   **202-225-2701**
1113 LHOB   3rd Term/71%   8/99/98   Fax: 225-3038
mullin.house.gov   twitter RepMullin
CoS ....Michael Stopp **LD** ....Jonathan Gray
Sch ....Madison Thomas **Press**.............Amy Lawrence
Bio: b. 7/26/77 Tulsa, OK; Pentacostal; AAS OK St. Univ. Inst. of Tech., 2010; Plumbing Company Owner, Rancher; m. Christie
Comm.: Energy & Commerce
Dist. Offices: Muskogee, 918-687-2533; McAlester, 918-423-5951

Frank D. Lucas (R-3rd)   **202-225-5565**
2405 RHOB   13th Term/79%   9/98/100   Fax: 225-8698
lucas.house.gov   twitter RepFrankLucas
CoS ....Stacey Glasscock **Dep CoS**....Courtney Lincoln
Sch ....Molly Johnson **CD** .... Andrew Witmer
Bio: b. 1/6/60 Cheyenne, OK; Baptist; BS OK St. Univ., 1982; Farmer, Rancher; m. Lynda
Comm.: Agriculture; Financial Services; Science, Space & Technology
Dist. Offices: Yukon, 405-373-1958

Tom Cole (R-4th)   **202-225-6165**
2467 RHOB   8th Term/70%   7/96/99   Fax: 225-3512
cole.house.gov   twitter tomcoleok04
CoS ....Sean Murphy **Dep CoS**..........Maria Bowie
Sch ....Sabrina Parker **CD** ....Teresa Davis
Bio: b. 4/28/49 Shreveport, LA; Methodist; PhD Univ. of OK, 1984; Professor, Political Consultant, Congressional Aide; m. Ellen
Comm.: Appropriations; Budget; Rules
Dist. Offices: Norman, 405-329-6500; Lawton, 580-357-2131; Ada, 580-436-5375

Steve Russell (R-5th)   **202-225-2132**
128 CHOB   2nd Term/57%   13/96/98   Fax: 226-1463
russell.house.gov   twitter RepRussell
CoS ....Stephen Moffitt **Dep CoS**...........Alex Hutkin
Sch ....Hannah Dirks **Press**............Daniel Susskind
Bio: b. 5/25/63 Oklahoma City, OK; Southern Baptist; BA Ouachita Baptist Univ., 1985; USA, 1985-2006; Army Officer, Gun Store Owner, Motivational Speaker; m. Cindy
Comm.: Armed Services; Education & the Workforce; Oversight & Government Reform
Dist. Offices: Del City, 405-602-3074

OREGON
oregon.gov

Pop.: 4,028,977 **Rank:** 27th
Caucasian: 88%
African-Am.: 2%
Nat. Am.: 2% **Asian:** 4%
Other: 4% **Hisp.:** 13%
Reg. Voters: 2,571,722
Dem.: 38% **Rep.:** 30%
Other: 32%
Land Area: 95,988 sq. mi.
Rank: 10th

Number of US House Seats: 4 Dem./1 Rep.

State Legislature
oregonlegislature.gov
Senate: 17D/13R House: 35D/25R
Session: 02/01/17 – 7/10/2017

Gov. Kate Brown (D)   503-378-4582
Next Election: 2020 2nd Term/51% Fax: 503-378-6827

twitter oregongovbrown

Bio: b. 6/1/60 Madrid, Spain; Not Stated; JD Lewis and Clark Law School, 1985; Attorney; m. Dan Little

160 State Capitol, 900 Court Street NE, Salem, OR 97301
Washington Office: 202-508-3850

SENATE

Ron Wyden (D)   202-224-5244
SD-221 5th Term/57% 90/100/98 Fax: 228-2717
wyden.senate.gov twitter ronwyden
CoS .... Jeff Michels **LD** .... Sarah Bittleman
Sch ....Montana Judd **CD** .... Keith Chu
Bio: b. 5/3/49 Wichita, KS; Jewish; JD Univ. of OR, 1974; Legal Services Executive, Seniors Advocate; m. Nancy Bass-Wyden
Comm.: Budget; Energy & Natural Resources; Finance (Rnk. Mem.); Select Intelligence; Joint Taxation
Dist. Offices: Portland, 503-326-7525; Eugene, 541-431-0229; Bend, 541-330-9142; LaGrande, 541-962-7691

Jeff Merkley (D)   202-224-3753
SH-313 2nd Term/56% 90/99/99 Fax: 228-3997
merkley.senate.gov twitter SenJeffMerkley
CoS ....Michael Zamore **LD** .... Jeremiah Baumann
Sch ....Jennifer Piorkowski **CD** ....Ray Zaccaro
Bio: b. 10/24/56 Eugene, OR; Lutheran; MPA Princeton Univ., 1982; Business Owner, Budget Analyst; m. Mary Sorteberg
Comm.: Appropriations; Budget; Environment & Public Works; Foreign Relations
Dist. Offices: Portland, 503-326-3386; Eugene, 541-465-6750; 541-608-9102; Pendleton, 541-278-1129; Bend, 541-318-1298; Salem, 503-362-8102

HOUSE

Suzanne Bonamici (D-1st)
bon-a-ME-chee
    202-225-0855
439 CHOB 4th Term/60% 98/99/95 Fax: 225-9497
bonamici.house.gov twitter RepBonamici
CoS .... Rachael Bornstein **LD** .... Allison Smith
Sch .... James Puerini **Press** .... Maggie Rousseau
Bio: b. 10/14/54 Detroit, MI; Not Stated; JD Univ. of OR, 1983; State Legislative Aide, Homemaker, Attorney; m. Michael H. Simon
Comm.: Education & the Workforce; Science, Space & Technology
Dist. Offices: Beaverton, 503-469-6010

Oregon

Greg Walden (R-2nd)   202-225-6730
2185 RHOB 10th Term/72% 7/96/99 Fax: 225-5774
walden.house.gov   twitter repgregwalden
CoS .... Lorissa Bounds **Dep CoS**.... Andrew Malcolm
Sch .... Jenny Forrest **CD** .... Andrew Malcolm
Bio: b. 1/10/57 The Dalles, OR; Episcopal; BS Univ. of OR, 1981; Radio Station Owner, Congressional Aide; m. Mylene
Comm.: Energy & Commerce (Chair)
Dist. Offices: Medford, 541-776-4646; Bend, 541-389-4408; La Grande, 541-624-2400

Earl Blumenauer (D-3rd)   202-225-4811
1111 LHOB 12th Term/73% 96/99/96 Fax: 225-8941
blumenauer.house.gov   twitter repblumenauer
CoS .... Willie Smith **LD** .... Laura Thrift
Sch .... Lena Spilman **CD** .... Nicole L'Esperance
Bio: b. 8/16/48 Portland, OR; Not Stated; JD Lewis & Clark Col., 1976; Public Official; m. Margaret Kirkpatrick
Comm.: Ways & Means
Dist. Offices: Portland, 503-231-2300

Peter A. DeFazio (D-4th)   202-225-6416
2134 RHOB 16th Term/56% 92/95/96 Fax: 226-3493
defazio.house.gov   twitter RepPeterDeFazio
CoS .... Kristie Greco **LD** .... Kris Pratt
Sch .... Matt Leasure **CD** .... Beth Schoenbach
Bio: b. 5/27/47 Needham, MA; Catholic; MS Univ. of OR, 1977; USAF, 1967-71; Congressional Aide; m. Myrnie Daut
Comm.: Transportation & Infrastructure (Rnk. Mem.)
Dist. Offices: Eugene, 541-465-6732; Coos Bay, 541-269-2609; Roseburg, 541-440-3523

Kurt Schrader (D-5th)   202-225-5711
2431 RHOB 5th Term/54% 79/84/95 Fax: 225-5699
schrader.house.gov   twitter repschrader
CoS .... Paul Gage **Dep CoS**... Chris Huckleberry
Sch .... Whitlee Preim-Siddon **CD** .... Carlee Griffeth
Bio: b. 10/19/51 Bridgeport, CT; Episcopal; DVM Univ. of IL, 1977; Veterinarian, Small Business Owner, Farmer; m. Susan Mora
Comm.: Energy & Commerce
Dist. Offices: Salem, 503-588-9100; Oregon City, 503-557-1324

Pennsylvania
pa.gov

Pop.: 12,802,503
Rank: 6th
Caucasian: 83%
African-Am.: 12%
Nat. Am.: 0%
Asian: 3%
Other: 2%
Hisp.: 7%
Reg. Voters: 8,722,977
Dem.: 49% **Rep.:** 37% **Other:** 14%
Land Area: 44,743 sq. mi. **Rank:** 32nd

Number of US House Seats: 13 Rep./5 Dem.

State Legislature
legis.state.pa.us
Senate: 34R/16D House: 136R/94D/1Vac
Session: 01/03/17 – 12/31/2017

Pennsylvania

Gov. Tom Wolf (D)　　　　**717-787-2500**
Next Election: 2018　1st Term/55%　　Fax: 717-772-8284
twitter governortomwolf
Bio: b. 11/17/48 York, PA; Methodist; PhD MIT, 1981; Businessman; m. Frances

225 Main Capitol Building, Harrisburg, PA 17120

SENATE

Bob Casey (D)　　　　**202-224-6324**
SR-393　　2nd Term/54%　93/92/98　Fax: 228-0604
casey.senate.gov　　　　**twitter** SenBobCasey
CoS .... Kristen Gentile　**LD** .... Derek Miller
Sch .... Alina Meltaus　**CD** .... John Rizzo
Bio: b. 4/13/60 Scranton, PA; Catholic; JD Catholic Univ., 1988; Attorney; m. Terese
Comm.: Agriculture, Nutrition & Forestry; Finance; Health, Education, Labor & Pensions; Special Aging (Rnk. Mem.)
Dist. Offices: Harrisburg, 717-231-7540; Philadelphia, 215-405-9660; Pittsburgh, 412-803-7370; Scranton, 570-941-0930; Pittsburgh, 412-803-3501; Scranton, 570-941-3540; Johnstown, 814-266-5970

Patrick J. Toomey (R)　　　　**202-224-4254**
SR-248　　2nd Term/49%　52/94/87　Fax: 228-0284
toomey.senate.gov　　　　**twitter** SenToomey
CoS .... Daniel Brandt　**LD** .... Vacant
Sch .... Danielle Quercia　**CD** .... ER Anderson
Bio: b. 11/17/61 Providence, RI; Catholic; AB Harvard Univ., 1984; Investment Banker, Restaurateur; m. Kris
Comm.: Banking, Housing & Urban Affairs; Budget; Finance
Dist. Offices: Allentown, 610-434-1444; Erie, 814-453-3010; Harrisburg, 717-782-3951; Philadelphia, 215-241-1090

HOUSE

Robert A. Brady (D-1st)　　　　**202-225-4731**
2004 RHOB　11th Term/82%　96/98/96　Fax: 225-0088
brady.house.gov　　　　**twitter** RepBrady
CoS .... Stan White　**LD** .... Eriade Williams
Sch .... Zach Rosen　**CD** .... Karen Warrington
Bio: b. 4/7/45 Philadelphia, PA; Catholic; HS Diploma; Carpenter, Union Official; m. Debra
Comm.: Armed Services; House Administration (Rnk. Mem.); Joint Library; Joint Printing
Dist. Offices: Philadelphia, 215-389-4627; Philadelphia, 267-519-2252; Chester, 610-874-7094; Philadelphia, 215-426-4616

Dwight Evans (D-2nd)　　　　**202-225-4001**
1105 LHOB　2nd Term/90%　100/96/98　Fax: 226-0311
evans.house.gov　　　　**twitter** RepDwightEvans
CoS .... Kim Turner　**LD** .... Kendra Brown
Sch .... Felicia Parker-Cox　**CD** .... Becca Brukman
Bio: b. 5/16/54 Philadelphia, PA; Baptist; BA LaSalle Col., 1975; Community Organizer, Teacher; single
Comm.: Agriculture; Small Business
Dist. Offices: Philadelphia, 215-276-0340

PENNSYLVANIA

Mike Kelly (R-3rd)   **202-225-5406**
1707 LHOB   4th Term/Unc.   7/97/99   Fax: 225-3103
kelly.house.gov   twitter MikeKellyPA
CoS ....Matthew Stroia **PD**........................Lori Prater
Sch .... Tim Butler **CD** ....Tom Qualtere
Bio: b. 5/10/48 Pittsburgh, PA; Catholic; BA Univ. of Notre Dame, 1970; Car Dealership Owner; m. Victoria
Comm.: Ways & Means
Dist. Offices: Butler, 724-282-2557; Erie, 814-454-8190; Sharon, 724-342-7170

Scott Perry (R-4th)   **202-225-5836**
1207 LHOB   3rd Term/66%   7/99/99   Fax: 226-1000
perry.house.gov   twitter RepScottPerry
CoS ....Lauren Muglia **LD** ....John Drzewicki
Sch .... Carol Wiest **CD** ....Brandy Brown
Bio: b. 5/27/62 San Diego, CA; Christian; BS PA St. Univ. - Harrisburg, 1991; PANG, 1980-present; Business Owner; m. Christy
Comm.: Foreign Affairs; Homeland Security; Transportation & Infrastructure
Dist. Offices: York, 717-600-1919; Gettysburg, 717-338-1919; Wormleysburg, 717-635-9504

Glenn Thompson (R-5th)   **202-225-5121**
124 CHOB   5th Term/67%   9/97/99   Fax: 225-5796
thompson.house.gov   twitter congressmanGT
CoS ....Matthew Brennan **LD** ....John Busovsky
Sch ....Lindsay Reusser **CD** ....Renee Gamela
Bio: b. 7/27/59 Bellefonte, PA; Protestant; MEd Temple Univ., 1998; Rehabilitation Therapist; m. Penny Ammerman-Thompson
Comm.: Agriculture; Education & the Workforce; Natural Resources
Dist. Offices: Bellefonte, 814-353-0215; Titusville, 814-827-3985

Ryan A. Costello (R-6th)   **202-225-4315**
326 CHOB   2nd Term/57%   9/82/99   Fax: 225-8440
costello.house.gov   twitter RepRyanCostello
CoS ....Lauryn Schothorst **Dep CoS**........ Dante Cutrona
Sch .... Chelsea Caulfield **CD** .... Natalie Gillam
Bio: b. 9/7/76 Phoenixville, PA; Presbyterian; JD Villanova Univ., 2002; Attorney; m. Christine
Comm.: Energy & Commerce
Dist. Offices: West Chester, 610-696-2982; Wyomissing, 610-376-7630

Patrick Meehan (R-7th)   **202-225-2011**
2305 RHOB   4th Term/60%   7/86/99   Fax: 226-0280
meehan.house.gov   twitter repmeehan
CoS .... Michael Kirlin **LD** ....Julie Nolan
Sch .... Colleen Gallagher **CD** ....John Elizandro
Bio: b. 10/20/55 Cheltenham, PA; Catholic; JD Temple Univ., 1986; Attorney, Congressional Aide, Hockey Referee; m. Carolyn
Comm.: Ethics; Ways & Means
Dist. Offices: Springfield, 610-690-7323

Brian Fitzpatrick (R-8th)   **202-225-4276**
514 CHOB   1st Term/55%   Fax: 225-9511
brianfitzpatrick.house.gov   twitter RepBrianFitz
CoS ....Justin Rusk **LC** ....Joseph Knowles
Sch ....Emery Boyer **CD** .... Aaron Clark
Bio: b. 12/17/73 Philadelphia; Catholic; JD/MBA Penn State, 2001; Attorney, Agent, Consultant; single
Comm.: Foreign Affairs; Homeland Security; Small Business
Dist. Offices: Langhorne, 215-579-8102

Bill Shuster (R-9th)　　**202-225-2431**
2079 RHOB　9th Term/63%　7/97/99　Fax: 225-2486
shuster.house.gov　　twitter RepBillShuster
CoS .... Eric Burgeson　**LD** .... Dennis Wirtz
Sch .... Brittany Smith　**CD** .... Casey Contres
Bio: b. 1/10/61 McKeesport, PA; Lutheran; MBA American Univ., 1987; Car Dealership Owner; sep.
Comm.: Armed Services; Transportation & Infrastructure (Chair)
Dist. Offices: Hollidaysburg, 814-696-6318; Chambersburg, 717-264-8308; Indiana, 724-463-0516

Tom Marino (R-10th)　　**202-225-3731**
2242 RHOB　4th Term/70%　8/98/88　Fax: 225-9594
marino.house.gov　　twitter RepTomMarino
CoS .... Sara Rogers　**LD** .... Jeff Wieand
Sch .... Elizabeth Hyers　**CD** .... Ryan Barton
Bio: b. 8/13/52 Williamsport, PA; Catholic; JD Dickinson School of Law, 1988; Attorney, Prosecutor; m. Edie
Comm.: Foreign Affairs; Homeland Security; Judiciary
Dist. Offices: Williamsport, 570-322-3961; Selinsgrove, 570-374-9469; Lake Ariel, 570-689-6024

Lou Barletta (R-11th)　　**202-225-6511**
2049 RHOB　4th Term/64%　8/96/93　Fax: 226-6250
barletta.house.gov　　twitter RepLouBarletta
CoS .... Andrea Niethold　**LD** .... Mira Lezell
Sch .... Courtney Uckele　**CD** .... Vacant
Bio: b. 1/28/56 Hazleton, PA; Catholic; Attended Bloomsburg St. Col., 1973-76; Business Owner; m. Mary Grace
Comm.: Education & the Workforce; Homeland Security; Transportation & Infrastructure
Dist. Offices: Hazleton, 570-751-0050; Carlisle, 717-249-0190; Sunbury, 570-988-7801; Harrisburg, 717-525-7002

Keith Rothfus (R-12th)　　**202-225-2065**
1205 LHOB　3rd Term/62%　9/99/98　Fax: 225-5709
rothfus.house.gov　　twitter KeithRothfus
CoS .... Alex Shively　**LD** .... David Goldfarb
EA .... Kirsten Hasler　**CD** .... Kate Rosario
Bio: b. 4/25/62 Endicott, NY; Catholic; JD Univ. of Notre Dame, 1990; Attorney, University Administrator; m. Elsie
Comm.: Financial Services
Dist. Offices: Pittsburgh, 412-837-1361; Johnstown, 814-619-3659; Beaver, 724-359-1626

Brendan F. Boyle (D-13th)　　**202-225-6111**
1133 LHOB　2nd Term/Unc.　92/96/98　Fax: 226-0611
boyle.house.gov　　twitter RepBrendanBoyle
CoS .... John McCarthy　**LD** .... Helena Mastrogianis
Sch .... Dan Maher　**CD** .... Sean Tobin
Bio: b. 2/6/77 Philadelphia, PA; Catholic; MPP Harvard Univ., 2005; Information Technology Analyst; m. Jennifer
Comm.: Budget; Foreign Affairs
Dist. Offices: Philadelphia, 215-335-3355; Glenside, 215-517-6572; Olney, 267-335-5643

Mike Doyle (D-14th)　　**202-225-2135**
239 CHOB　12th Term/74%　96/98/95　Fax: 225-3084
doyle.house.gov　　twitter USRepMikeDoyle
CoS .... David Lucas　**LD** .... Philip Murphy
Sch .... Ellen Young　**Press** .... Matt Dinkel
Bio: b. 8/5/53 Pittsburgh, PA; Catholic; BS PA St. Univ., 1975; Businessman, Legislative Aide; m. Susan
Comm.: Energy & Commerce
Dist. Offices: Pittsburgh, 412-390-1499; Penn Hills, 412-241-6055; McKeesport, 412-664-4049

PENNSYLVANIA

Charlie Dent (R-15th) 202-225-6411
2082 RHOB   7th Term/58%   7/88/99   Fax: 226-0778
dent.house.gov   **twitter** RepCharlieDent
CoS .... Drew Kent   **LD** .... Sean Snyder
Sch .... Heather Smith   **CD** .... Shawn Millan
Bio: b. 5/24/60 Allentown, PA; Presbyterian; MPA Lehigh Univ., 1993; Congressional Aide, Public Official; m. Pamela
Comm.: Appropriations
Dist. Offices: Allentown, 610-770-3490; Hershey, 717-533-3959; Annville, 717-867-1026; Hamburg, 717-393-0667; East Greenville, 215-541-4106

Lloyd K. Smucker (R-16th) 202-225-2411
516 CHOB   1st Term/54%   Fax: 225-2013
smucker.house.gov   **twitter** RepSmucker
CoS .... Greg Facchiano   **LD** .... Andrew Robreno
Sch .... Kelsey Kelleher   **Press** .... Bill Jaffee
Bio: b. 1/23/64 Lancaster; Lutheran; Attended Franklin & Marshall College; Attended Lebanon Valley College; Construction Company Owner; m. Cindy
Comm.: Budget; Education & the Workforce; Transportation & Infrastructure
Dist. Offices: Lancaster, 717-393-0667

Matt Cartwright (D-17th) 202-225-5546
1034 LHOB   3rd Term/54%   96/98/98   Fax: 226-0996
cartwright.house.gov   **twitter** RepCartwright
CoS .... Hunter Ridgway   **Dep CoS** .... Jeremy Marcus
Sch .... Emily Sweda   **CD** .... Colleen Gerrity
Bio: b. 5/1/61 Erie, PA; Catholic; JD Univ. of PA, 1986; Attorney; m. Marion Munley Cartwright
Comm.: Appropriations; Oversight & Government Reform
Dist. Offices: Scranton, 570-341-1050; Easton, 484-546-0776; Pottsville, 570-624-0140

Tim Murphy (R-18th) 202-225-2301
2332 RHOB   8th Term/Unc.   9/96/99   Fax: 225-1844
murphy.house.gov   **twitter** RepTimMurphy
CoS .... Susan Mosychuk   **LD** .... Scott Dziengelski
Sch .... Megan Dornan   **Press** .... Carly Atchison
Bio: b. 9/11/52 Cleveland, OH; Catholic; PhD Univ. of Pittsburgh, 1979; USNR, 2009-present; Psychologist; m. Nan Missig Murphy
Comm.: Energy & Commerce
Dist. Offices: Pittsburgh, 412-344-5583; Greensburg, 724-850-7312

RHODE ISLAND
ri.gov

Pop.: 1,056,298   **Rank:** 43rd
Caucasian: 85%   **African-Am.:** 8%
Nat. Am.: 1%   **Asian:** 4%   **Other:** 3%
Hisp.: 14%
Reg. Voters: 770,875
Dem.: 41%   **Rep.:** 10%   **Other:** 49%
Land Area: 1,034 sq. mi.   **Rank:** 50th

Number of US House Seats: 2 Dem.

State Legislature
rilin.state.ri.us
Senate: 33D/5R   House: 64D/11R
Session: 01/03/17 – 6/30/2017

RHODE ISLAND

Gov. Gina Raimondo (D)   **401-222-2080**
Next Election: 2018   1st Term/41%   Fax: 401-273-8096
twitter ginaraimondo
Bio: b. 5/17/71 Smithfield, RI; Catholic; JD Yale Univ., 1998;
Business Investor; m. Andrew Moffit

State House, 82 Smith Street, Providence, RI 02903

SENATE

Jack Reed (D)   **202-224-4642**
SH-728   4th Term/71%   93/96/100 Fax: 224-4680
reed.senate.gov   twitter SenJackReed
CoS ....Neil Campbell **LD** ....Elyse Wasch
Sch ....Rosanne Haroian **Press**.................. Chip Unruh
Bio: b. 11/12/49 Providence, RI; Catholic; JD Harvard Univ.,
1982; USA, 1971-79; USAR, 1979-91; Attorney; m. Julia
Comm.: Appropriations; Armed Services (Rnk. Mem.); Bank-
ing, Housing & Urban Affairs
Dist. Offices: Cranston, 401-943-3100; Providence, 401-
528-5200

Sheldon Whitehouse (D)   **202-224-2921**
SH-530   2nd Term/65%   93/96/99   Fax: 228-6362
whitehouse.senate.gov   twitter SenWhitehouse
CoS ....Sam Goodstein **LD** ....Josh Karetny
Sch ....Leah Seigle **CD** ....Caleb Gibson
Bio: b. 10/20/55 Manhattan, NY; Episcopal; JD Univ. of VA,
1982; Attorney; m. Sandra
Comm.: Budget; Environment & Public Works; Health, Educa-
tion, Labor & Pensions; Judiciary; Special Aging
Dist. Offices: Providence, 401-453-5294

HOUSE

David Cicilline (D-1st) *sis-uh-LEE-nee* **202-225-4911**
2244 RHOB   4th Term/64%   94/98/97   Fax: 225-3290
cicilline.house.gov   twitter repcicilline
CoS ....Peter Karafotas **LD** .... Sarah Trister
Sch ....Alisa Sarkisian **CD** ....Richard Luchette
Bio: b. 7/15/61 Providence, RI; Jewish; JD Georgetown Univ.,
1986; Attorney; single
Comm.: Foreign Affairs; Judiciary
Dist. Offices: Pawtucket, 401-729-5600

Jim Langevin (D-2nd) *LAN-juh-vin* **202-225-2735**
2077 RHOB   9th Term/58%   93/95/99   twitter jimlangevin
langevin.house.gov   Fax: 225-5976
CoS .... Todd Adams **LD** .... Nick Leiserson
Sch .... Stu Rose **CD** .... Vacant
Bio: b. 4/22/64 Warwick, RI; Catholic; MPA Harvard Univ.,
1994; Public Official; single
Comm.: Armed Services; Homeland Security
Dist. Offices: Warwick, 401-732-9400

SOUTH CAROLINA
sc.gov

Pop.: 4,896,146   **Rank:** 23rd
Caucasian: 68%   **African-Am.:** 28%
Nat. Am.: 1%   **Asian:** 2%   **Other:** 2%
Hisp.: 6%
Reg. Voters: 2,722,287
Party registration not required
Land Area: 30,061 sq. mi.   **Rank:** 40th

Number of US House Seats: 5 Rep./1 Dem./1 Vac.

State Legislature
scstatehouse.gov
Senate: 27R/18D/1Vac   House: 79R/44R/1Vac
Session: 01/10/17 – 6/1/2017

Gov. Henry McMaster (R)   **803-734-2100**
Next Election: 2018 1st Term/Appt.   Fax: 803-734-5167
Bio: b. 5/27/47 Columbia, Presbyterian; JD Univ. of SC, 1973; USAR, 1967-75; Lawyer, Congressional Aide; m. Peggy

1100 Gervais Street, Columbia, SC 29201

SENATE

Lindsey Graham (R)   **202-224-5972**
SR-290   3rd Term/54%   65/70/83   Fax: 224-3808
lgraham.senate.gov   **twitter** GrahamBlog
CoS ....Richard Perry **LD** ....Matt Rimkunas
Sch .... Alice James **CD** ....Kevin Bishop
Bio: b. 7/9/55 Seneca, SC; Southern Baptist; JD Univ. of SC, 1981; USAF, 82-88; SCANG, 89-96; USAFR, 88-89,03-15; Attorney; single
Comm.: Appropriations; Armed Services; Budget; Judiciary
Dist. Offices: Columbia, 803-933-0112; Mt. Pleasant, 843-849-3887; Florence, 843-669-1505; Rock Hill, 803-366-2828

Tim Scott (R)   **202-224-6121**
SH-717   3rd Term/61%   48/95/98   Fax: 228-5143
scott.senate.gov   **twitter** SenatorTimScott
CoS .... Jennifer DeCasper **LD** ....Charles Cogar
Sch ....John Don **Press**..............Michele Exner
Bio: b. 9/19/65 North Charleston, SC; Christian; BS Charleston Southern Univ., 1988; Insurance Agency Owner, Financial Adviser; single
Comm.: Banking, Housing & Urban Affairs; Finance; Health, Education, Labor & Pensions; Small Business & Entrepreneurship; Special Aging
Dist. Offices: Columbia, 803-771-6112; Greenville, 864-233-5366; North Charleston, 843-727-4525

HOUSE

Mark Sanford (R-1st)   **202-225-3176**
2211 RHOB   6th Term/59%   13/91/97   Fax: 225-3407
sanford.house.gov   **twitter** RepSanfordSC
CoS ....Matthew Taylor **LD** .... Jay Fields
Sch ....Evan Gillissie **Press**..................Scott Jeffrey
Bio: b. 5/28/60 Ft. Lauderdale, FL; Episcopal; MBA Univ. of VA, 1988; USAFR, 2002-11; Real Estate Investment Company Owner; div.
Comm.: Budget; Oversight & Government Reform; Transportation & Infrastructure
Dist. Offices: Mount Pleasant, 843-352-7572; Beaufort, 843-521-2530

SOUTH CAROLINA

Joe Wilson (R-2nd)　　　　**202-225-2452**
1436 LHOB　9th Term/62%　7/99/99　Fax: 225-2455
joewilson.house.gov　　　　twitter RepJoeWilson
CoS ....Jonathan Day　**LD** ....Taylor Andreae
Sch ....Emily Saleeby　**CD** ....Leacy Burke
Bio: b. 7/31/47 Charleston, SC; Presbyterian; JD Univ. of SC, 1972; USAR, 1972-75; SCNG, 1975-2003; Attorney; m. Roxanne
Comm.: Armed Services; Education & the Workforce; Foreign Affairs
Dist. Offices: West Columbia, 803-939-0041; Aiken, 803-642-6416

Jeff Duncan (R-3rd)　　　　**202-225-5301**
2229 RHOB　4th Term/73%　8/99/96　Fax: 225-3216
jeffduncan.house.gov　　　　twitter RepJeffDuncan
CoS ....Lance Williams　**LD** ....Joshua Gross
Sch ....Lauren Valainis　**Dep CoS**...........Allen Klump
Bio: b. 1/7/66 Greenville, SC; Baptist; BA Clemson Univ., 1988; Business Owner, Real Estate Broker, Banker; m. Melody
Comm.: Foreign Affairs; Homeland Security
Dist. Offices: Anderson, 864-224-7401; Laurens, 864-681-1028

Trey Gowdy (R-4th)　　　　**202-225-6030**
2418 RHOB　4th Term/67%　8/100/97　Fax: 226-1177
gowdy.house.gov　　　　twitter tgowdysc
CoS ....Cindy Crick　**Dep CoS**...........Anna Bartlett
Sch ......Mary-Langston Willis　**Press**........Amanda Gonzalez
Bio: b. 8/22/64 Greenville, SC; Baptist; JD Univ. of SC, 1989; Attorney, Prosecutor; m. Terri
Comm.: Ethics; Judiciary; Oversight & Government Reform; Select Intelligence
Dist. Offices: Greenville, 864-241-0175; Spartanburg, 864- 583-3264

OPEN SEAT

Vacant (5th)　　　　**202-225-5501**
2350 RHOB　　　　Fax: 225-0464
Mick Mulvaney (R) resigned on February 16, 2017. A special election has been scheduled for June 20, 2017.

James E. Clyburn (D-6th)　　　　**202-225-3315**
242 CHOB　13th Term/69%　100/98/95　Fax: 225-2313
clyburn.house.gov　　　　twitter Clyburn
CoS ....Yelberton Watkins　**LD** ....Craig Link
Sch ....Lindy Birch Kelly　**CD** ....Patrick Devlin
Bio: b. 7/21/40 Sumter, SC; African Methodist Episcopal; BA SC St. Col., 1962; Educator; m. Emily England Clyburn
Comm.: Assistant Minority Leader
Dist. Offices: Columbia, 803-799-1100; Kingstree, 843-355-1211; Santee, 803-854-4700

Tom Rice (R-7th)　　　　**202-225-9895**
223 CHOB　3rd Term/61%　9/98/98　Fax: 225-9690
rice.house.gov　　　　twitter RepTomRice
CoS ....Jennifer Watson　**LD** ....Walker Barrett
Sch ....Terra Davis　**Press**............Cassie Boehm
Bio: b. 8/4/57 Charleston, SC; Episcopal; JD/MAcc Univ. of SC, 1982; Attorney, Accountant; m. Wrenzie
Comm.: Ways & Means
Dist. Offices: Myrtle Beach, 843-445-6459; Florence, 843-679-9781

SOUTH DAKOTA
sd.gov

Pop.: 858,469   Rank: 46th
Caucasian: 86%
African-Am.: 2%   Nat. Am.: 9%
Asian: 1%   Other: 2%
Hisp.: 4%
Reg. Voters: 547,833
Dem.: 33%   Rep.: 46%   Other: 21%
Land Area: 75,811 sq. mi.   Rank: 16th

Number of US House Seats: 1 Rep.

State Legislature
sdlegislature.gov
Senate: 29R/6D   House: 59R/10D/1Vac
Session: 01/10/17 – 3/27/2017

Gov. Dennis Daugaard (R)　　605-773-3212
Next Election: 2018   2nd Term/70%   Fax: 605-773-4711
twitter sdgovdaugaard
Bio: b. 6/11/53 Garretson, SD; Christian; JD Northwestern Univ., 1978; Bank Executive, Non-profit Development Director; m. Linda

500 East Capitol Avenue, Pierre, SD 57501

SENATE

John Thune (R)　　202-224-2321
SD-511　　3rd Term/72%　　52/93/99　　Fax: 228-5429
thune.senate.gov　　twitter senjohnthune
CoS .... Ryan Nelson　**LD** .... Jane Lucas
Sch .... Daffnei Riedel　**CD** .... Ryan Wrasse
Bio: b. 1/7/61 Pierre, SD; Protestant; MBA Univ. of SD, 1984; Lobbyist, Association Executive; m. Kimberley
Comm.: Agriculture, Nutrition & Forestry; Commerce, Science & Transportation (Chair); Finance
Dist. Offices: Sioux Falls, 605-334-9596; Rapid City, 605-348-7551; Aberdeen, 605-225-8823

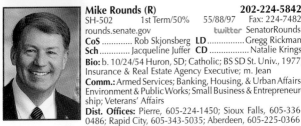

Mike Rounds (R)　　202-224-5842
SH-502　　1st Term/50%　　55/88/97　　Fax: 224-7482
rounds.senate.gov　　twitter SenatorRounds
CoS .... Rob Skjonsberg　**LD** .... Gregg Rickman
Sch .... Jacqueline Juffer　**CD** .... Natalie Krings
Bio: b. 10/24/54 Huron, SD; Catholic; BS SD St. Univ., 1977; Insurance & Real Estate Agency Executive; m. Jean
Comm.: Armed Services; Banking, Housing, & Urban Affairs; Environment & Public Works; Small Business & Entrepreneurship; Veterans' Affairs
Dist. Offices: Pierre, 605-224-1450; Sioux Falls, 605-336-0486; Rapid City, 605-343-5035; Aberdeen, 605-225-0366

HOUSE

Kristi Noem (R-At Large) *NOHM*　　202-225-2801
2457 RHOB　　4th Term/64%　　9/96/98　　Fax: 225-5823
noem.house.gov　　twitter RepKristiNoem
CoS .... Jordan Stoick　**Dep CoS** .... Andrew Christianson
Sch .... Christiana Frazee　**CD** .... Brittany Comins
Bio: b. 11/30/71 Watertown, SD; Evangelical Christian; BS SD St. Univ., 2011; Farmer, Rancher; m. Bryon
Comm.: Ways & Means
Dist. Offices: Watertown, 605-878-2868; Sioux Falls, 605-275-2868; Rapid City, 605-791-4673

TENNESSEE
tennessee.gov

Pop.: 6,600,299
Rank: 17th

Caucasian: 79% **African-Am.:** 17% **Nat. Am.:** 0% **Asian:** 2%
Other: 2% **Hisp.:** 5%
Reg. Voters: 3,553,293 *Party registration not required*
Land Area: 41,235 sq. mi. **Rank:** 34th

Number of US House Seats: 7 Rep./2 Dem.

State Legislature
legislature.state.tn.us
Senate: 28R/5D House: 74R/25D
Session: 01/10/17 – 4/14/2017

Gov. Bill Haslam (R)   615-741-2001
Next Election: 2018 2nd Term/70% Fax: 615-532-9711
twitter billhaslam
Bio: b. 8/23/58 Knoxville, TN; Presbyterian; BA Emory Univ.,
1980; Businessman; m. Crissy

State Capitol, 1st Floor, Nashville, TN 37243-0001

SENATE

Lamar Alexander (R)   202-224-4944
SD-455   3rd Term/62%   70/69/98   Fax: 228-3398
alexander.senate.gov   twitter SenAlexander
CoS .... David Cleary **LD** .... Allison Martin
Sch .... Victoria Souza **CD** .... Liz Wolgemuth
Bio: b. 7/3/40 Maryville, TN; Presbyterian; JD NYU, 1965;
Public Official, University President, Attorney; m. Honey
Comm.: Appropriations; Energy & Natural Resources; Health,
Education, Labor & Pensions (Chair), Rules & Administration
Dist. Offices: Nashville, 615-736-5129; Knoxville, 865-545-
4253; Memphis, 901-544-4224; Chattanooga, 423-752-5337;
Nacogdoches, 936-715-9514

Bob Corker (R)   202-224-3344
SD-425   2nd Term/65%   57/93/98   Fax: 228-0566
corker.senate.gov   twitter SenBobCorker
CoS .... Todd Womack **LD** .... Rob Strayer
Sch .... Hallie Williams **CD** .... Micah Johnson
Bio: b. 8/24/52 Orangeburg, SC; Protestant; BS Univ. of TN,
1974; Businessman; m. Elizabeth
Comm.: Banking, Housing, & Urban Affairs; Budget; Foreign
Relations (Chair); Special Aging
Dist. Offices: Chattanooga, 423-756-2757; Knoxville, 865-
637-4180; Jonesborough, 423-753-2263; Jackson, 731-664-
2294; Jackson, 731-423-9344; Blountville, 423-325-6240

HOUSE

Phil Roe (R-1st)   202-225-6356
336 CHOB   5th Term/78%   9/99/99   Fax: 225-5714
roe.house.gov   twitter DrPhilRoe
CoS .... Matt Meyer **LD** .... Aaron Bill
Sch .... Catherine Bartley **CD** .... Vacant
Bio: b. 7/21/45 Clarksville, TN; Methodist; MD Univ. of TN,
1973; USA, 1973-74; Physician; m. Pam
Comm.: Education & the Workforce; Veterans' Affairs (Chair)
Dist. Offices: Kingsport, 423-247-8161; Morristown, 423-
254-1400

TENNESSEE

John J. Duncan, Jr. (R-2nd)　　**202-225-5435**
2207 RHOB　16th Term/76%　24/92/99　Fax: 225-6440
duncan.house.gov　　**twitter** RepJohnDuncanJr
CoS ....Bob Griffitts **LD** ....Scott Fischer
Sch ....Denise Lambert **Acting Press** ......Don Walker
Bio: b. 7/21/47 Lebanon, TN; Presbyterian; JD George Washington Univ., 1973; TNNG, 1970-87; Attorney, Judge; m. Lynn
Comm.: Oversight & Government Reform; Transportation & Infrastructure
Dist. Offices: Knoxville, 865-523-3772; Maryville, 865-984-5464

Chuck Fleischmann (R-3rd)　　**202-225-3271**
2410 RHOB　4th Term/66%　7/97/100　Fax: 225-3494
fleischmann.house.gov　　**twitter** repchuck
CoS ....Jim Hippe **LD** ....Daniel Tidwell
Sch ....Holly Hendrix **CD** ....Vacant
Bio: b. 10/11/62 Manhattan, NY; Catholic; JD Univ. of TN, 1986; Attorney; m. Brenda
Comm.: Appropriations
Dist. Offices: Chattanooga, 423-756-2342; Oak Ridge, 865-576-1976; Athens, 423-745-4671

Scott DesJarlais (R-4th) *DAY-zhur-lay*　**202-225-6831**
2301 RHOB　4th Term/58%　9/99/92　Fax: 226-5172
desjarlais.house.gov　　**twitter** DesJarlaisTN04
CoS ....Richard Vaughn **LD** ....Richard Wilkins
Sch ....Allison Mills **CD** ....Brendan Thomas
Bio: b. 2/21/64 Des Moines, IA; Episcopal; MD Univ. of SD, 1991; Physician; m. Amy
Comm.: Agriculture; Armed Services; Oversight & Government Reform
Dist. Offices: Columbia, 931-381-9920; Murfreesboro, 615-896-1986; Winchester, 931-962-3180; Cleaveland, 423-472-7500

Jim Cooper (D-5th)　　**202-225-4311**
1536 LHOB　14th Term/63%　72/82/97　Fax: 226-1035
cooper.house.gov　　**twitter** repjimcooper
CoS ....Lisa Quigley **Dep CoS**...........Jason Lumia
Sch ....Savannah Darnall **Press**...............Chris Carroll
Bio: b. 6/19/54 Nashville, TN; Episcopal; JD Harvard Univ., 1980; Business Owner, Attorney; m. Martha
Comm.: Armed Services; Oversight & Government Reform
Dist. Offices: Nashville, 615-736-5295

Diane Black (R-6th)　　**202-225-4231**
1131 LHOB　4th Term/71%　6/100/91　Fax: 225-6887
black.house.gov　　**twitter** RepDianeBlack
CoS ....Teresa Koeberlein **Dep CoS**.....Dean Thompson
Sch ....Greg Dowell **CD** ....Jonathan Frank
Bio: b. 1/16/51 Baltimore, MD; Christian; BSN Belmont Univ., 1992; Nurse, College Instructor; m. David
Comm.: Budget (Chair); Ways & Means
Dist. Offices: Gallatin, 615-206-8204; Cookeville, 931-854-0069

Marsha Blackburn (R-7th)　　**202-225-2811**
2266 RHOB　8th Term/72%　8/100/96　Fax: 225-3004
blackburn.house.gov　　**twitter** MarshaBlackburn
CoS ....Mike Platt **LD** ....Charles Flint
Sch ....Grace Burch **CD** ....Stefanie Wheeler
Bio: b. 6/6/52 Laurel, MS; Presbyterian; BS MS St. Univ., 1973; Business Owner; m. Chuck
Comm.: Energy & Commerce
Dist. Offices: Clarksville, 931-503-0391; Franklin, 615-591-5161

TENNESSEE

David Kustoff (R-8th)   **202-225-4714**
508 CHOB   1st Term/69%   Fax: 225-1765
kustoff.house.gov   **twitter** repdavidkustoff
CoS ....Tyler Threadgill **LD**....................Justin Melvin
Sch .... Anderson Briggs **Press**.................Casey Black
Bio: b. 10/8/66 Memphis, TN; Jewish; JD Memphis St. Univ.,
1992; Attorney; m. Roberta
Comm.: Financial Services
Dist. Offices: Dyersburg, 731-412-1031; Martin, 731-412-
1043; Memphis, 901-682-4422; Jackson, 731-423-4848

Steve Cohen (D-9th)   **202-225-3265**
2404 RHOB   6th Term/79%   92/98/95   Fax: 225-5663
cohen.house.gov   **twitter** RepCohen
CoS .... Marilyn Dillihay **LD** .... Matt Weisman
Sch .... Patrick Cassidy **CD** .... Michael Eisenstatt
Bio: b. 5/24/49 Memphis, TN; Jewish; JD Memphis St. Univ.,
1973; Attorney; single
Comm.: Ethics; Judiciary; Transportation & Infrastructure
Dist. Offices: Memphis, 901-544-4131

TEXAS
texas.gov

Pop.: 27,469,114   **Rank:** 2nd
Caucasian: 80%   **African-Am.:** 13%
Nat. Am.: 1%
Asian: 5%
Other: 2%
Hisp.: 39%
Reg. Voters: 14,954,095
Party registration not required
Land Area: 261,232 sq. mi.
Rank: 2nd

Number of US House Seats: 25 Rep./11 Dem.

State Legislature
legis.state.tx.us
Senate: 20R/11D   House: 95R/55D
Session: 01/10/17 – 5/29/2017

Gov. Greg Abbott (R)   **512-463-2000**
Next Election: 2018 1st Term/59%   Fax: 512-463-1849
twitter govabbott
Bio: b. 11/13/57 Wichita Falls, TX; Catholic; JD Vanderbilt
Univ., 1984; Attorney; m. Cecilia

State Insurance Building, 1100 San Jacinto, Austin, TX 78701
Washington Office: 202-638-3927

SENATE

John Cornyn (R)   **202-224-2934**
SH-517   3rd Term/62%   62/94/95   Fax: 228-2856
cornyn.senate.gov   **twitter** JohnCornyn
CoS ....Beth Jafari **LD** .... Stephen Tausend
Sch .... Aaricka Oliver **CD** ....Drew Brandewie
Bio: b. 2/2/52 Houston, TX; Christian Non-Denominational;
LLM Univ. of VA, 1995; Attorney, Realtor; m. Sandy
Comm.: Finance; Judiciary; Select Intelligence; Majority Whip
Dist. Offices: Austin, 512-469-6034; Dallas, 972-239-1310;
Houston, 713-572-3337; San Antonio, 210-224-7485

TEXAS

Ted Cruz (R)   **202-224-5922**
SR-404   1st Term/56%   44/81/50   Fax: 228-0755
cruz.senate.gov   **twitter** sentedcruz
CoS ....David Polyansky **LD**.................. Steve Chartan
Sch .... Amy Herot **CD** ....Rachael Slobodien
Bio: b. 12/22/70 Calgary, Canada; Baptist; JD Harvard Univ., 1995; Attorney; m. Heidi
Comm.: Armed Services; Commerce, Science & Transportation; Judiciary; Rules & Administration; Joint Economic
Dist. Offices: Austin, 512-916-5834; Dallas, 214-599-8749; Houston, 713-718-3057; San Antonio, 210-340-2885; Harlingen, 956-423-0162; Lubbock, 806-472-7533; Tyler, 903-593-0902

HOUSE

Louie Gohmert (R-1st)   **202-225-3035**
2243 RHOB   7th Term/74%   4/98/96   Fax: 226-1230
gohmert.house.gov   **twitter** replouiegohmert
CoS .... Connie Hair **LD** .... Brad Watts
Sch ....Chelsea Cohen **CD** ......Kimberly Willingham
Bio: b. 8/18/53 Pittsburg, TX; Baptist; JD Baylor Univ., 1977; USA, 1978-82; Judge, Attorney; m. Kathy
Comm.: Judiciary; Natural Resources
Dist. Offices: Tyler, 903-561-6349; Longview, 903-236-8597; Lufkin, 936-632-3180; Marshall, 903-938-8386; Nacogdoches, 936-715-9514

Ted Poe (R-2nd)   **202-225-6565**
2132 RHOB   7th Term/61%   8/98/67   Fax: 225-5547
poe.house.gov   **twitter** JudgeTedPoe
CoS .... Gina Foote **Dep CoS**............. Tim Tarpley
OM ...... Alexandria Vandiver **CD** ....Shaylyn Hynes
Bio: b. 9/10/48 Temple, TX; Church of Christ; JD Univ. of Houston, 1973; USAFR, 1970-76; Judge; m. Carol
Comm.: Foreign Affairs; Judiciary
Dist. Offices: Kingwood, 281-446-0242

Sam Johnson (R-3rd)   **202-225-4201**
2304 RHOB   14th Term/61%   9/99/86   Fax: 225-1485
samjohnson.house.gov   **twitter** SamsPressShop
CoS ....David Eiselsberg **LD** .... Jett Thompson
Sch ....Amanda Hamilton **CD** .... Adrienne Rimmer
Bio: b. 10/11/30 San Antonio, TX; Methodist; MSIA George Washington Univ., 1974; USAF, 1951-79; Air Force Pilot, Home Builder; wid.
Comm.: Ways & Means; Joint Taxation
Dist. Offices: Plano, 469-304-0382

John Ratcliffe (R-4th)   **202-225-6673**
325 CHOB   2nd Term/88%   6/99/99   Fax: 225-3332
ratcliffe.house.gov   **twitter** RepRatcliffe
CoS ....Daniel Kroese **LD** ....Emily Leviner
Sch .... Hayley D'Antuono **Press**.......... Rachel Stephens
Bio: b. 10/20/65 Mount Prospect, IL; Catholic; JD Southern Methodist Univ., 1989; Attorney, Federal Prosecutor; m. Michele
Comm.: Homeland Security; Judiciary
Dist. Offices: Rockwall, 972-771-0100; Texarkana, 903-823-3173; Sherman, 903-813-5270

Jeb Hensarling (R-5th) *HENN-sur-ling*   **202-225-3484**
2228 RHOB   8th Term/79%   10/99/98   Fax: 226-4888
hensarling.house.gov   **twitter** RepHensarling
CoS ....Andrew Duke **LD** ....Kyle Jackson
Sch ....Jennifer Stalzer **CD** .... Liz Hill
Bio: b. 5/29/57 Stephenville, TX; Episcopal; JD Univ. of TX, 1982; Business Owner, Attorney, Congressional Aide; m. Melissa
Comm.: Financial Services (Chair)
Dist. Offices: Dallas, 214-349-9996; Athens, 903-675-8288

TEXAS

Joe L. Barton (R-6th)　　　**202-225-2002**
2107 RHOB　17th Term/58%　10/98/97　Fax: 225-3052
joebarton.house.gov　　　　**twitter** RepJoeBarton
CoS ....Ryan Thompson　**LD** ....Krista Rosenthall
Sch ....Linda Gillespie　**CD** ....Daniel Rhea
Bio: b. 9/15/49 Waco, TX; Methodist; MS Purdue Univ.,
1973; Engineer; m. Terri
Comm.: Energy & Commerce
Dist. Offices: Arlington, 817-543-1000; Ennis, 972-875-8488

John Culberson (R-7th)　　　**202-225-2571**
2161 RHOB　9th Term/56%　7/97/98　Fax: 225-4381
culberson.house.gov　　　　**twitter** CongCulberson
CoS ....Jamie Gahun　**LD** ....Corey Inglee
Sch ....Emily Taylor　**CD** ....Emily Taylor
Bio: b. 8/24/56 Houston, TX; Methodist; JD S. TX Col. of Law,
1988; Attorney; m. Belinda
Comm.: Appropriations
Dist. Offices: Houston, 713-682-8828

Kevin Brady (R-8th)　　　**202-225-4901**
1011 LHOB　11th Term/Unc.　7/99/96　Fax: 225-5524
kevinbrady.house.gov　　　　**twitter** RepKevinBrady
CoS .... David Davis　**LD** .... Sahra Su
Sch ....Jen Jett　**CD** ....Tracee Evans
Bio: b. 4/11/55 Vermillion, SD; Catholic; BS Univ. of SD,
1990; Commerce Executive; m. Cathy
Comm.: Ways & Means (Chair); Joint Taxation (Chair)
Dist. Offices: Conroe, 936-441-5700; Huntsville, 936-439-
9532

Al Green (D-9th)　　　**202-225-7508**
2347 RHOB　7th Term/91%　96/96/96　Fax: 225-2947
algreen.house.gov　　　　**twitter** RepAlGreen
CoS ....Gregg Orton　**LD** .... Vacant
Sch ....Keenan Hale　**CD** ....Michael Mouton
Bio: b. 9/1/47 New Orleans, LA; Baptist; JD TX Southern
Univ., 1973; Attorney; div.
Comm.: Financial Services
Dist. Offices: Houston, 713-383-9234

Michael McCaul (R-10th)　　　**202-225-2401**
2001 RHOB　7th Term/57%　8/98/95　Fax: 225-5955
mccaul.house.gov　　　　**twitter** RepMcCaul
CoS ....Jessica Nalepa　**LD** ....Thomas Hester
Sch ....Kelly Cotner　**CD** ....Elizabeth Litzow
Bio: b. 1/14/62 Dallas, TX; Catholic; JD St. Mary's Univ.,
1987; Attorney, Federal Prosecutor; m. Linda
Comm.: Foreign Affairs; Homeland Security (Chair)
Dist. Offices: Austin, 512-473-2357; Tomball, 281-255-8372

K. Michael Conaway (R-11th)　　　**202-225-3605**
2430 RHOB　7th Term/90%　11/98/100　Fax: 225-1783
conaway.house.gov　　　　**twitter** ConawayTX11
CoS ....Mark Williams　**LD** ....Matt Russell
Sch ....Emily Keener　**Press**.................Emily Hytha
Bio: b. 6/11/48 Borger, TX; Baptist; BBA E. TX St. Univ., 1970;
USA, 1970-72; Accountant; m. Suzanne
Comm.: Agriculture (Chair); Armed Services; Select Intel-
ligence
Dist. Offices: Llano, 325-247-2826; Midland, 432-687-2390;
San Angelo, 325-659-4010; Brownwood, 325-646-1950;
Odessa, 432-331-9667; Granbury, 682-937-2577

TEXAS

Kay Granger (R-12th)　　　　**202-225-5071**
1026 LHOB　11th Term/69%　8/97/90　Fax: 225-5683
kaygranger.house.gov　　　twitter RepKayGranger
CoS .... Eric Wiese　LD .... Ben Kochman
Sch .... Lynn Miller　Press .... Alex Jakubowich
Bio: b. 1/18/43 Greenville, TX; Methodist; BS TX Wesleyan
Univ., 1965; Teacher, Business Owner; div.
Comm.: Appropriations
Dist. Offices: Ft. Worth, 817-338-0909

Mac Thornberry (R-13th)　　　　**202-225-3706**
2208 RHOB　12th Term/90%　9/97/98　Fax: 225-3486
thornberry.house.gov　　　twitter MacTXPress
CoS .... Josh Martin　LD .... Michael Seeds
Sch .... Ariel McCord　Press .... Jon Corley
Bio: b. 7/15/58 Clarendon, TX; Presbyterian; JD Univ. of TX,
1983; Rancher, Attorney; m. Sally
Comm.: Armed Services (Chair)
Dist. Offices: Amarillo, 806-371-8844; Wichita Falls, 940-
692-1700

Randy Weber (R-14th)　　　　**202-225-2831**
1708 LHOB　3rd Term/62%　6/98/99　Fax: 225-0271
weber.house.gov　　　twitter TXRandy14
CoS .... Chara McMichael　LD .... Sarah Noack
Sch .... Christy Kortokrax　CD .... Elizabeth Burton-Jones
Bio: b. 7/2/53 Houston, TX; Baptist; BS Univ. of Houston - Clear
Lake, 1977; Small Business Owner; m. Brenda
Comm.: Science, Space & Technology; Transportation &
Infrastructure
Dist. Offices: League City, 281-316-0231; Lake Jackson, 979-
285-0231; Beaumont, 409-835-0108

Vicente Gonzalez (D-15th)　　　　**202-225-2531**
113 CHOB　1st Term/57%　　　Fax: 225-5688
gonzalez.house.gov　　　twitter RepGonzalez
CoS .... Jose Borjon　LD .... Julie Merberg
Sch .... Paulina Carrillo　CD .... Vacant
Bio: b. 9/4/67 Corpus Christi; Catholic; JD Texas Wesleyan,
1996; Attorney; m. Lorette Saenz
Comm.: Financial Services
Dist. Offices: Edinburg, 956-682-5545

Beto O'Rourke (D-16th) *BET-oh*　　**202-225-4831**
1330 LHOB　3rd Term/86%　96/98/93　Fax: 225-2016
orourke.house.gov　　　twitter RepBetoORourke
CoS .... David Wysong　LD .... Aaron Woolf
Sch .... Samantha Stiles　CD .... John Meza
Bio: b. 9/26/72 El Paso, TX; Catholic; BA Columbia Univ.,
1995; Business Owner; m. Amy Sanders O'Rourke
Comm.: Armed Services; Veterans' Affairs
Dist. Offices: El Paso, 915-541-1400

Bill Flores (R-17th)　　　　**202-225-6105**
2440 RHOB　4th Term/65%　8/99/97　Fax: 225-0350
flores.house.gov　　　twitter RepBillFlores
CoS .... Jon Oehmen　LD .... Eric Gustafson
Sch .... Jessica Harrison　CD .... Andre Castro
Bio: b. 2/25/54 Warren AFB, WY; Baptist; MBA Houston
Baptist Univ., 1985; Businessman; m. Gina
Comm.: Energy & Commerce
Dist. Offices: Waco, 254-732-0748; Bryan, 979-703-4037;
Austin, 512-373-3378

TEXAS

Sheila Jackson Lee (D-18th)   **202-225-3816**
2187 RHOB   12th Term/73%   96/97/87   Fax: 225-3317
jacksonlee.house.gov   twitter JacksonLeeTX18
CoS .... Glenn Rushing **LD** .... Gregory Berry
Sch ...... LaDedra Drummond **Press** .... Russell Rucks
Bio: b. 1/12/50 Queens, NY; Seventh-Day Adventist; JD Univ. of VA, 1975; Attorney, Congressional Aide; m. Elwyn Lee
Comm.: Budget; Homeland Security; Judiciary
Dist. Offices: Houston, 713-655-0050; Houston, 713-861-4070; Houston, 713-691-4882; Houston, 713-227-7740

Jodey C. Arrington (R-19th)   **202-225-4005**
1029 LHOB   1st Term/87%   Fax: 225-9615
arrington.house.gov   twitter JodeyArrington
CoS .... Russell Thomasson **LD** .... Benjamin Cantrell
Sch .... Kyla Nations **CD** .... Kate McBrayer
Bio: b. 3/9/72 Lubbock; Evangelical; MPA Texas Tech, 1998; President, Vice Chancellor, Aide; m. Anne
Comm.: Agriculture; Budget; Veterans' Affairs
Dist. Offices: Abilene, 325-675-5038; Lubbock, 806-767-9168

Joaquin Castro (D-20th)   **202-225-3236**
1221 LHOB   3rd Term/80%   96/99/86   Fax: 225-1915
castro.house.gov   twitter joaquincastrotx
CoS .... Danny Meza **LD** .... Ben Thomas
Sch .... Jacqueline Sanchez **Press** .... Erin Hatch
Bio: b. 9/16/74 San Antonio, TX; Catholic; JD Harvard Univ., 2000; Attorney; m. Anna Flores
Comm.: Foreign Affairs; Select Intelligence
Dist. Offices: San Antonio, 210-348-8216

Lamar Smith (R-21st)   **202-225-4236**
2409 RHOB   16th Term/57%   8/99/98   Fax: 225-8628
lamarsmith.house.gov   twitter LamarSmithTX21
CoS .... Ashlee Vinyard **LD** .... Abby Gunderson-Schwarz
Sch .... Christa Danford **Press** .... Jennifer Pett
Bio: b. 11/19/47 San Antonio, TX; Christian Science; JD Southern Methodist Univ., 1975; Attorney, Rancher; m. Beth
Comm.: Homeland Security; Judiciary; Science, Space & Technology (Chair)
Dist. Offices: San Antonio, 210-821-5024; Kerrville, 830-896-0154; Austin, 512-912-7508

Pete Olson (R-22nd)   **202-225-5951**
2133 RHOB   5th Term/60%   7/100/99   Fax: 225-5241
olson.house.gov   twitter reppeteolson
CoS .... Bill Zito **LD** .... Sarah Moxley
Sch .... Victoria Blackwell **CD** .... Melissa Kelly
Bio: b. 12/9/62 Ft. Lewis, WA; United Methodist; JD Univ. of TX, 1988; USN, 1988-98; Congressional Aide; m. Nancy
Comm.: Energy & Commerce
Dist. Offices: Sugar Land, 281-494-2690

Will Hurd (R-23rd)   **202-225-4511**
317 CHOB   2nd Term/48%   7/97/99   Fax: 225-2237
hurd.house.gov   twitter hurdonthehill
CoS .... Stoney Burke **LD** .... Matthew Haskins
Sch .... Nancy Pack **Acting CD** .... Rachel Holland
Bio: b. 8/19/77 San Antonio, TX; Christian; BS TX A&M Univ., 2000; Cyber Security Consultant, CIA Agent; single
Comm.: Homeland Security; Oversight & Government Reform; Select Intelligence
Dist. Offices: San Antonio, 210-921-3130; San Antonio, 210-784-5023; Del Rio, 830-422-2040; Eagle Pass, 210-784-5023; Socorro, 915-235-6421

Texas

Kenny Marchant (R-24th) *MARCH-unt* **202-225-6605**
2369 RHOB   7th Term/56%   10/99/92   Fax: 225-0074
marchant.house.gov   **twitter** repkenmarchant
CoS .... Brian Thomas **LD** .... John Deoudes
Sch .... Nicholas Smith **CD** .... Rob Damschen
Bio: b. 2/23/51 Bonham, TX; Nazarene; BA Bethany Nazarene Col., 1974; Home Builder; m. Donna
Comm.: Ethics; Ways & Means
Dist. Offices: Irving, 972-556-0162

Roger Williams (R-25th)   **202-225-9896**
1323 LHOB   3rd Term/58%   8/99/96   Fax: 225-9692
williams.house.gov   **twitter** reprwilliams
CoS .... Colby Hale **LD** .... Sean Dillon
Sch .... Hanna Allred **CD** .... Vince Zito
Bio: b. 9/13/49 Evanston, IL; Christian; BS TX Christian Univ., 1972; Car Dealership Owner, Professional Baseball Player; m. Patty
Comm.: Financial Services
Dist. Offices: Austin, 512-473-8910; Cleburne, 817-774-2575

Michael C. Burgess (R-26th)   **202-225-7772**
2336 RHOB   8th Term/66%   10/97/99   Fax: 225-2919
burgess.house.gov   **twitter** michaelcburgess
CoS .... Kelle Strickland **Dep CoS** .... James Decker
Sch .... Amanda Stevens **CD** .... Lesley Fulop
Bio: b. 12/23/50 Rochester, MN; Episcopal; MD Univ. of TX, 1977; Physician; m. Laura
Comm.: Energy & Commerce; Rules
Dist. Offices: Lake Dallas, 940-497-5031

Blake Farenthold (R-27th) *FAIR-enth-old* **202-225-7742**
2331 RHOB   4th Term/62%   6/98/99   Fax: 226-1134
farenthold.house.gov   **twitter** farenthold
CoS .... Bob Haueter **LD** .... Blake Adami
Sch .... Alana McRaney **CD** .... Elizabeth Peace
Bio: b. 12/12/61 Corpus Christi, TX; Episcopal; JD St. Mary's Univ., 1989; Attorney, Business Owner; m. Debbie
Comm.: Judiciary; Oversight & Government Reform; Transportation & Infrastructure
Dist. Offices: Corpus Christi, 361-884-2222; Victoria, 361-894-6446

Henry Cuellar (D-28th)   **202-225-1640**
2209 RHOB   7th Term/64%   31/70/99   Fax: 225-1641
cuellar.house.gov   **twitter** RepCuellar
CoS .... Cynthia Gaona **LD** .... Ryan Ehly
Sch .... Andrea Trevino **CD** .... Victoria Glynn
Bio: b. 9/19/55 Laredo, TX; Catholic; PhD Univ. of TX, 1998; Attorney, Customs Broker; m. Imelda
Comm.: Appropriations
Dist. Offices: San Antonio, 210-271-2851; Mission, 956-424-3942; Laredo, 956-725-0639; Rio Grande City, 956-487-5603

Gene Green (D-29th)   **202-225-1688**
2470 RHOB   13th Term/72%   86/89/94   Fax: 225-9903
green.house.gov   **twitter** RepGeneGreen
CoS .... Rhonda Jackson **LD** .... Sergio Espinosa
Sch .... Joseph Puente **Press** .... Joseph Puente
Bio: b. 10/17/47 Houston, TX; Methodist; BBA Univ. of Houston, 1971; Attorney; m. Helen
Comm.: Energy & Commerce
Dist. Offices: Houston, 281-999-5879; Houston, 713-330-0761

Texas

Eddie Bernice Johnson (D-30th) 202-225-8885
2468 RHOB   13th Term/78%   100/98/87   Fax: 226-1477
ebjohnson.house.gov   twitter RepEBJ
CoS .... Murat Gokcigdem LD .... Vacant
Sch .... Murat Gokcigdem CD ....Treshonda Sheffey
Bio: b. 12/3/35 Waco, TX; Baptist; MPA Southern Methodist Univ., 1976; Businesswoman, Nurse; div.
Comm.: Science, Space & Technology (Rnk. Mem.); Transportation & Infrastructure
Dist. Offices: Dallas, 214-922-8885

John Carter (R-31st) 202-225-3864
2110 RHOB   8th Term/58%   6/97/97   Fax: 225-5886
carter.house.gov   twitter JudgeCarter
CoS ....Jonas Miller LD ....Grady Bourn
Sch ....Carole Richmond Press..............Shannon Black
Bio: b. 11/6/41 Houston, TX; Lutheran; JD Univ of TX, 1969; Judge; m. Erika
Comm.: Appropriations
Dist. Offices: Round Rock, 512-246-1600; Temple, 254-933-1392

Pete Sessions (R-32nd) 202-225-2231
2233 RHOB   11th Term/71%   11/99/98   Fax: 225-5878
sessions.house.gov   twitter PeteSessions
CoS .... Kyle Matous LD ....Jennifer Lackey
Sch ....Katherine Runkle Press............Caroline Boothe
Bio: b. 3/22/55 Waco, TX; United Methodist; BS Southwestern Univ., 1978; Phone Company Executive; m. Karen
Comm.: Rules (Chair)
Dist. Offices: Dallas, 972-392-0505

Marc Veasey (D-33rd) 202-225-9897
1519 LHOB   3rd Term/73%   89/93/96   Fax: 225-9702
veasey.house.gov   twitter RepVeasey
CoS .... Jane Hamilton LD ....Ashley Baker
EA .... Jane Phipps CD .... Nelly Decker
Bio: b. 1/3/71 Ft. Worth, TX; Baptist; BS TX Wesleyan Univ., 1995; Real Estate Broker, Congressional Aide; m. Tonya
Comm.: Armed Services; Science, Space & Technology
Dist. Offices: Dallas, 214-741-1387; Ft. Worth, 817-920-9086

Filemon Vela (D-34th) *FEE-lay-mon VAY-la* 202-225-9901
437 CHOB   3rd Term/63%   63/86/96   Fax: 225-9770
vela.house.gov   twitter repfilemonvela
CoS .... Perry Finney Brody LD ....Julie Merberg
Sch ....Liza Lynch Press............ Mickeala Carter
Bio: b. 2/13/63 Harlingen, TX; Catholic; JD Univ. of TX, 1987; Attorney; m. Rose
Comm.: Agriculture; Homeland Security
Dist. Offices: Brownsville, 956-544-8352; San Benito, 956-276-4497; Alice, 361-230-9776; Weslaco, 956-520-8273

Lloyd Doggett (D-35th) 202-225-4865
2307 RHOB   12th Term/63%   94/98/98   Fax: 225-3073
doggett.house.gov   twitter RepLloydDoggett
CoS .... Michael Mucchetti LD .... Vacant
Sch .... Christina Nunez CD ....Jaimie Woo
Bio: b. 10/6/46 Austin, TX; Methodist; JD Univ. of TX, 1970; Attorney; m. Libby
Comm.: Ways & Means
Dist. Offices: Austin, 512-916-5921; San Antonio, 210-704-1080

Texas

Brian Babin (R-36th)　　　**202-225-1555**
316 CHOB　　2nd Term/89%　6/99/97　　Fax: 226-0396
babin.house.gov　　　　　　　**twitter** repbrianbabin
CoS .... Stuart Burns　**LD** .... Ben Couhig
Sch .... Beth Barber　**CD** .... Jimmy Milstead
Bio: b. 3/23/48 Port Arthur, TX; Southern Baptist; DDS Univ. of TX, 1976; TXNG, 1969-71; USAR, 1971-75; USAF, 1976-79; Dentist; m. Roxanne
Comm.: Science, Space & Technology; Transportation & Infrastructure
Dist. Offices: Deer Park, 832-780-0966; Orange, 409-883-8075; Woodville, 844-303-8934; Tyler, 903-593-5130

Utah
utah.gov

Pop.: 2,995,919　**Rank:** 31st
Caucasian: 91%　**African-Am.:** 1%
Nat. Am.: 2%　**Asian:** 3%　**Other:** 3%
Hisp.: 14%
Reg. Voters: 1,387,468
Party registration not required
Land Area: 82,170 sq. mi.　**Rank:** 12th

Number of US House Seats: 4 Rep.

State Legislature
le.state.ut.us
Senate: 24R/5D　House: 62R/13D
Session: 01/23/17 – 3/9/2017

Gov. Gary R. Herbert (R)　　**801-538-1000**
Next Election: 2020　3rd Term/67%　Fax: 801-538-1557
twitter governorherbert
Bio: b. 5/7/47 American Fork, UT; Mormon; Attended Brigham Young Univ.; UTARNG, 1970-76; Realtor; m. Jeanette

350 North State Street, Suite 200, Salt Lake City, UT 84114
Washington Office: 202-403-8616

SENATE

Orrin G. Hatch (R)　　　**202-224-5251**
SH-104　　7th Term/65%　　67/86/99　　Fax: 224-6331
hatch.senate.gov　　　　　　**twitter** SenOrrinHatch
CoS .... Matt Sandgren　**LD** .... John Tanner
Sch .... Ruth Montoya　**CD** .... JP Freire
Bio: b. 3/22/34 Pittsburgh, PA; Mormon; JD Univ. of Pittsburgh, 1962; Attorney; m. Elaine
Comm.: Finance (Chair); Health, Education, Labor & Pensions; Judiciary; Special Aging; Joint Taxation (Vice Chair); President Pro Tempore
Dist. Offices: Salt Lake City, 801-524-4380; Ogden, 801-625-5672; Provo, 801-375-7881; Cedar City, 435-586-8435

Mike Lee (R)　　　　**202-224-5444**
SR-361A　　2nd Term/68%　38/75/90　　Fax: 228-1168
lee.senate.gov　　　　　　　**twitter** SenMikeLee
CoS .... Allyson Bell　**LD** .... Christy Woodruff
Sch .... Linda Patino　**Press** .... Jillian Wheeler
Bio: b. 6/4/71 Mesa, AZ; Mormon; JD Brigham Young Univ., 1997; Attorney, Gubernatorial Aide; m. Sharon
Comm.: Commerce, Science & Transportation; Energy & Natural Resources; Judiciary; Joint Economic (Vice Chair)
Dist. Offices: Salt Lake City, 801-524-5933; St. George, 435-628-5514; Ogden, 801-625-5676

Rob Bishop (R-1st)   202-225-0453
123 CHOB   8th Term/63%   8/97/95   Fax: 225-5857
robbishop.house.gov   twitter RepRobBishop
CoS .... Devin Wiser **LD** .... Adam Stewart
Sch ....Carolyn Turner **CD** .... Lee Lonsberry
Bio: b. 7/13/51 Salt Lake City, UT; Mormon; BA Univ. of UT, 1974; Educator, Public Official; m. Jeralynn
Comm.: Armed Services; Natural Resources (Chair)
Dist. Offices: Ogden, 801-625-0107

Chris Stewart (R-2nd)   202-225-9730
323 CHOB   3rd Term/58%   9/98/99   Fax: 225-9627
stewart.house.gov   twitter repchrisstewart
CoS ....Brian Steed **LD** ....Gordon Larsen
Sch .... Daryn Frischknecht **CD** ....Allison Leavitt
Bio: b. 7/15/60 Logan, UT; Mormon; BS UT St. Univ., 1984; USAF, 1984-98; Author, Business Owner; m. Evie
Comm.: Appropriations; Select Intelligence
Dist. Offices: Salt Lake City, 801-364-5550; St. George, 435-627-1500

Jason Chaffetz (R-3rd) *CHAY-fits*   202-225-7751
2236 RHOB   5th Term/74%   10/96/96   Fax: 225-5629
chaffetz.house.gov   twitter jasoninthehouse
CoS .... Amber Talley **LD** ....Clay White
EA .... Danielle Suber **CD** .... Jennifer Scott
Bio: b. 3/26/67 Los Gatos, CA; Mormon; BA Brigham Young Univ., 1989; Business Owner; m. Julie
Comm.: Judiciary; Oversight & Government Reform (Chair)
Dist. Offices: Provo, 801-851-2500

Mia Love (R-4th)   202-225-3011
217 CHOB   2nd Term/53%   8/98/97   Fax: 225-5638
love.house.gov   twitter RepMiaLove
CoS .... Muffy Day **LD** .... Stefanie Dearie
Sch ....Kayla Herron **CD** .... Richard Piatt
Bio: b. 12/6/75 Brooklyn, NY; Mormon; BFA Univ. of Hartford, 1997; Homemaker, Flight Attendant; m. Jason
Comm.: Financial Services
Dist. Offices: West Jordan, 801-996-8729

VERMONT
vermont.gov

Pop.: 626,042   **Rank:** 49th
Caucasian: 95%   **African-Am.:** 1%
Nat. Am.: 0%   **Asian:** 2%   **Other:** 2%   **Hisp.:** 2%
Reg. Voters: 466,408
Party registration not required
Land Area: 9,217 sq. mi.   **Rank:** 43rd

Number of US House Seats: 1 Dem.

State Legislature
leg.state.vt.us
Senate: 20D/7R/3 Other   House: 84D/52R/14 Other
Session: 01/04/17 – 5/8/2017

. Burlington

Montpelier ★

1

· Rutland

Gov. Phil Scott (R)   802-828-3333
Next Election 2018   1st Term/53%   Fax: 802-828-3339
twitter GovPhilScott
Bio: b. 8/4/58; Barre, VT; Unspecified; BA Univ. of VT, 1980; Construction Company Owner; Construction Worker; m. Diana McTeague

109 State Street, Pavilion Office Building, Montpelier, VT 05609

VERMONT

Patrick J. Leahy (D)   **202-224-4242**
SR-437   8th Term/61%   93/99/97   Fax: 224-3479
leahy.senate.gov   **twitter** SenatorLeahy
CoS ....John Dowd   **LD**...................Erica Chabot
Sch...........Kevin McDonald   **CD** ....David Carle
Bio: b. 3/31/40 Montpelier, VT; Catholic; JD Georgetown Univ., 1964; Attorney; m. Marcelle
Comm.: Agriculture, Nutrition & Forestry; Appropriations (Rnk. Mem.); Judiciary; Rules & Administration; Joint Library
Dist. Offices: Burlington, 802 863-2525; Montpelier, 802 229-0569

Bernard Sanders (I)   **202-224-5141**
SD-332   2nd Term/71%   63/96/29   Fax: 228-0776
sanders.senate.gov   **twitter** sensanders
CoS ......Michaeleen Crowell   **LD**...............Caryn Compton
Sch ....Jacob Gillison   **CD** ....Michael Briggs
Bio: b. 9/8/41 Brooklyn, NY; Jewish; AB Univ. of Chicago, 1964; Educator; m. Jane
Comm.: Budget (Rnk. Mem.); Energy & Natural Resources; Environment & Public Works; Health, Education, Labor & Pensions; Veterans' Affairs
Dist. Offices: Burlington, 802-862-0697; St. Johnsbury, 802-748-9269

HOUSE

Peter Welch (D-At Large)   **202-225-4115**
2303 RHOB   6th Term/90%   100/98/97   Fax: 225-6790
welch.house.gov   **twitter** PeterWelch
CoS ....Bob Rogan   **LD**.................Patrick Satalin
Sch ....Patrick Etka   **CD** ....Kirsten Hartman
Bio: b. 5/2/47 Springfield, MA; Catholic; JD Univ. of CA - Berkeley, 1973; Attorney; m. Margaret Cheney
Comm.: Energy & Commerce; Oversight & Government Reform
Dist. Offices: Burlington, 802-652-2450

VIRGINIA
virginia.gov

Pop.: 8,382,993   **Rank:** 12th
Caucasian: 70%   **African-Am.:** 20%
Nat. Am.: 1%   **Asian:** 7%
Other: 3%   **Hisp.:** 9%

(map of Virginia with districts labeled 10, 11, 8, 6, 7, 1, 9, 5, 4, 3, 2; cities: Roanoke, Richmond, Hampton, Norfolk)

Reg. Voters: 5,630,352   *Party registration not required*
Land Area: 39,490 sq. mi.   **Rank:** 36th

Number of US House Seats: 7 Rep./4 Dem.

State Legislature
virginia.gov
Senate: 21R/19D   House: 66R/33D/1Vac
Session: 01/11/17 – 2/25/2017

Gov. Terry McAuliffe (D)   **804-786-2211**
Next Election: 2017 1st Term/48%   Fax: 804-371-6351
twitter governorva
Bio: b. 2/9/57 Syracuse, NY; Catholic; JD Georgetown Univ., 1984; Businessman; m. Dorothy

State Capitol, 3rd Floor, Richmond, VA 23219
Washington Office: 202-783-1769

VIRGINIA

Mark Warner (D)   **202-224-2023**
SR-475   2nd Term/49%   92/94/88   Fax: 224-6295
warner.senate.gov   twitter MarkWarner
CoS .... Mike Harney   **LD** ....Elizabeth Falcone
Sch ....Andrea Friedhoff   **CD** ....Kevin Hall
Bio: b. 12/15/54 Indianapolis, IN; Presbyterian; JD Harvard
Univ., 1980; Businessman; m. Lisa Collis
Comm.: Banking, Housing, & Urban Affairs; Budget; Finance;
Rules & Administration; Select Intelligence (Vice Chair)
Dist. Offices: Richmond, 804-775-2314; Norfolk, 757-441-
3079; Abingdon, 276-628-8158; Roanoke, 540-857-2676

Tim Kaine (D)   **202-224-4024**
SR-231   1st Term/53%   96/93/91   Fax: 228-6363
kaine.senate.gov   twitter timkaine
Acting CoS ...... John Knapp   **LD** .... Mary Naylor
Sch ....Kate McCarroll   **CD** .... Amy Dudley
Bio: b. 2/26/58 St. Paul, MN; Catholic; JD Harvard Univ.,
1983; Attorney; m. Anne Holton
Comm.: Armed Services; Budget; Foreign Relations; Health,
Education, Labor & Pensions
Dist. Offices: Richmond, 804-771-2221; Virginia Beach, 757-
518-1674; Abingdon, 276-525-4790; Danville, 434-792-0976;
Vienna, 703-442-0670

Rob Wittman (R-1st)   **202-225-4261**
2055 RHOB   6th Term/61%   8/99/99   Fax: 225-4382
wittman.house.gov   twitter RobWittman
CoS .... Jamie Jones Miller   **LD** .... Brent Robinson
Sch .... Carolyn King   **CD** ....Greg Lemon
Bio: b. 2/3/59 Washington, DC; Episcopal; PhD VA Com-
monwealth Univ., 2002; Environmental Health Specialist;
m. Kathryn
Comm.: Armed Services, Natural Resources
Dist. Offices: Yorktown, 757-874-6687; Stafford, 540-659-
2734; Tappahannock, 804-443-0668

Scott W. Taylor (R-2nd)   **202-225-4215**
412 CHOB   1st Term/62%   Fax: 225-4218
taylor.house.gov   twitter Scotttaylorva
CoS ....John Thomas   **LD** ....Reginal Darby
Sch .... Beth Kaczmarek   **CD** .... Scott Weldon
Bio: b. 6/27/79 Baltimore, MD; Christian; ALB Harvard, 2013;
USN, 1997-2005; Business Owner, Real Estate Broker; single
Comm.: Appropriations
Dist. Offices: Virginia Beach, 888-217-9979

Robert C. Scott (D-3rd)   **202-225-8351**
1201 LHOB   13th Term/67%   100/98/99   Fax: 225-8354
bobbyscott.house.gov   twitter BobbyScott
CoS ....Joni Ivey   **LD** .... David Dailey
Sch ....Randi Petty   **Press**........... Gabrielle Brown
Bio: b. 4/30/47 Washington, DC; Episcopal; JD Boston Col.,
1973; MANG, 1970-74; USAR, 1974-76; Attorney; div.
Comm.: Education & the Workforce (Rnk. Mem.)
Dist. Offices: Newport News, 757-380-1000

A.Donald McEachin (D-4th)   **202-225-6365**
314 CHOB   1st Term/58%   Fax: 226-1170
mceachin.house.gov   twitter Donald_McEachin
CoS .... Abbi Easter   **Dep CoS**.........Keenan Austin
Sch .... Tara Rountree   **CD** ....Jamitress Bowden
Bio: b. 10/10/61 Nuremberg, Germany; Baptist; MDiV VA
Union, 2008; Attorney; m. Colette Wallace
Comm.: Armed Services; Natural Resources
Dist. Offices: TBA

VIRGINIA

Tom Garrett (R-5th)　　　　　**202-225-4711**
415 CHOB　　1st Term/58%　　　　　Fax: 225-5681
tomgarrett.house.gov　　　　　twitter Rep_Tom_Garrett
CoS .... Kevin Reynolds **LD** .... Nicholas O'Boyle
Sch .... Tripp Grant **CD** .... Andrew Griffin
Bio: b. 3/27/72 Atlanta, GA; Non-Denominational Christian; JD Univ. of Richmond, 2003; USA, 1995-2000; Attorney, Aide; m. Flanna
Comm.: Education & the Workforce; Foreign Affairs; Homeland Security
Dist. Offices: Charlottesville, 434-973-9631; Danville, 434-791-2596; Farmville, 434-395-0120

Robert W. Goodlatte (R-6th)
　GOOD-lat　　　　　　　　　**202-225-5431**
2309 RHOB　13th Term/67%　8/99/97　Fax: 225-9681
goodlatte.house.gov　　　　　twitter repgoodlatte
CoS .... Pete Larkin **LD** .... Lindsay Black
Sch .... Mary Pritschau **CD** .... Beth Breeding
Bio: b. 9/22/52 Holyoke, MA; Christian Science; JD Washington & Lee Univ., 1977; Attorney, Congressional Aide; m. Maryellen
Comm.: Agriculture; Judiciary (Chair)
Dist. Offices: Roanoke, 540-857-2672; Staunton, 540-885-3861; Harrisonburg, 540-432-2391; Lynchburg, 434-845-8306

Dave Brat (R-7th)　　　　　**202-225-2815**
1628 LHOB　3rd Term/58%　8/99/94　Fax: 225-0011
brat.house.gov　　　　　twitter RepDaveBrat
CoS .... Mark Kelly **LD** .... Zoe O'Herin
Sch .... Sarah Grace Walt **CD** .... Juliana Heerschap
Bio: b. 7/27/64 Dearborn, MI; Presbyterian; PhD American Univ., 1995; Professor, Management Consultant; m. Laura
Comm.: Budget; Education & the Workforce; Small Business
Dist. Offices: Glen Allen, 804-747-4073; Spotsylvania, 540-507-7216

Don Beyer, Jr. (D-8th)　　　　　**202-225-4376**
1119 LHOB　2nd Term/69%　98/99/93　Fax: 225-0017
beyer.house.gov　　　　　twitter RepDonBeyer
CoS .... Ann O'Hanlon **LD** .... Zach Cafritz
Sch .... Sophia Khan **Press** .... Aaron Fritschner
Bio: b. 6/20/50 Free Territory of Trieste; Episcopal; BA Williams Col., 1972; Car Dealership Owner; m. Megan Carroll Beyer
Comm.: Natural Resources; Science, Space & Technology; Joint Economic
Dist. Offices: Alexandria, 703-658-5403

Morgan Griffith (R-9th)　　　　　**202-225-3861**
2202 RHOB　4th Term/69%　13/97/99　Fax: 225-0076
morgangriffith.house.gov　　　　　twitter repmgriffith
CoS .... Kelly **LD** .... Robert Hamill
　　　　　Lungren-McCollum
Sch .... Kevin Baird **CD** .... Jessica Paska
Bio: b. 3/15/58 Philadelphia, PA; Protestant; JD Washington & Lee Univ., 1983; Attorney; m. Hilary
Comm.: Energy & Commerce
Dist. Offices: Abingdon, 276-525-1405; Christiansburg, 540-381-5671

Barbara Comstock (R-10th)　　　　　**202-225-5136**
229 CHOB　2nd Term/53%　7/95/98　Fax: 225-0437
comstock.house.gov　　　　　twitter RepComstock
CoS .... Susan Falconer **LD** .... Michael Mansour
Sch .... Kasha Nielsen **Press** .... Arthur Bryant
Bio: b. 6/30/59 Springfield, MA; Catholic; JD Georgetown Univ., 1986; Public Affairs Firm Owner, Lobbyist, Attorney; m. Chip
Comm.: House Administration; Science, Space & Technology; Transportation & Infrastructure; Joint Economic
Dist. Offices: Sterling, 703-404-6903

VIRGINIA

Gerald E. Connolly (D-11th)   **202-225-1492**
2238 RHOB   5th Term/Unc.   91/97/98   Fax: 225-3071
connolly.house.gov   twitter GerryConnolly
CoS ....James Walkinshaw LD ....Collin Davenport
Sch ....Lauren Covintgton CD ....Jamie Smith
Bio: b. 3/30/50 Boston, MA; Catholic; MPA Harvard Univ.,
1979; Congressional Aide, Public Official; m. Catherine
Comm.: Foreign Affairs; Oversight & Government Reform
Dist. Offices: Annandale, 703-256-3071; Woodbridge,
571-408-4407

WASHINGTON
access.wa.gov

Pop.: 7,170,351
Rank: 13th
Caucasian: 80%
African-Am.: 4%
Nat. Am.: 2%   **Asian:** 8%
Other: 5%   **Hisp.:** 12%
Reg. Voters: 4,262,193
Party registration not required
Land Area: 66,456 sq. mi.   **Rank:** 20th

Number of US House Seats: 6 Dem./4 Rep.

State Legislature
leg.wa.gov
Senate: 25D/23R/1Vac   House: 50D/48R
Session: 01/09/17 – 4/23/2017

Gov. Jay Inslee (D)   **360-902-4111**
Next Election: 2020 2nd Term/54%   Fax: 360-753-4110
twitter govinslee
Bio: b. 2/9/51 Seattle, WA; Protestant; JD Willamette Univ.,
1976; Attorney; m. Trudi

PO Box 40002, Olympia, WA 98504-0002
Washington Office: 202-624-3691

SENATE

Patty Murray (D)   **202-224-2621**
SR-154   5th Term/59%   87/99/99   Fax: 224-0238
murray.senate.gov   twitter PattyMurray
CoS ....Mike Spahn LD .... Vacant
Sch .... Beth Burke CD .... Eli Zupnick
Bio: b. 10/11/50 Bothell, WA; Catholic; BA WA St. Univ.,
1972; Parenting Instructor, Homemaker, Secretary; m. Rob
Comm.: Appropriations; Budget; Health, Education, Labor
& Pensions (Rnk. Mem.); Veterans' Affairs; Minority As-
sistant Leader
Dist. Offices: Seattle, 206-553-5545; Vancouver, 360-696-
7797; Spokane, 509-624-9515; Yakima, 509-453-7462

Maria Cantwell (D)   **202-224-3441**
SH-511   3rd Term/60%   87/100/100 Fax: 228-0514
cantwell.senate.gov   twitter SenatorCantwell
CoS .... Travis Lumpkin LD .... Pete Modaff
Sch ....Ben Caryl CD .... Reid Walker
Bio: b. 10/13/58 Indianapolis, IN; Catholic; BA Miami Univ.
of OH, 1980; Businesswoman; single
Comm.: Commerce, Science & Transportation; Energy &
Natural Resources (Rnk Mem.); Finance; Small Business &
Entrepreneurship; Indian Affairs
Dist. Offices: Seattle, 206-220-6400; Spokane, 509-353-2507;
Vancouver, 360-696-7838; Richland, 509-946-8106; Everett,
425-259-6515; Tacoma, 253-572-3636

WASHINGTON

HOUSE

Suzan DelBene (D-1st)
Like "Susan" dell-BEN-ay   **202-225-6311**
2442 RHOB   4th Term/57%   94/97/99   Fax: 226-1606
delbene.house.gov   **twitter** RepDelBene
CoS .... Aaron Schmidt **LD** .... Ben Barasky
Sch .... Melissa Plummer **CD** .... Ramsey Cox
Bio: b. 2/17/62 Selma, AL; Episcopal; MBA Univ. of WA,
1990; Business Executive; m. Kurt
Comm.: Budget; Ways & Means
Dist. Offices: Bothell, 425-485-0085; Mount Vernon, 360-416-7879

Rick Larsen (D-2nd)   **202-225-2605**
2113 RHOB   9th Term/65%   98/98/99   Fax: 225-4420
larsen.house.gov   **twitter** RepRickLarsen
CoS .... Kimberly Johnston **LD** .... Terra Sabag
Sch .... Erin Schneider **CD** .... Douglas Wagoner
Bio: b. 6/15/65 Arlington, WA; Methodist; MPA Univ. of MN,
1990; Public Official, Lobbyist; m. Tiia Karlen
Comm.: Armed Services; Transportation & Infrastructure
Dist. Offices: Everett, 425-252-3188; Bellingham, 360-733-4500

Jaime Herrera Beutler (R-3rd)
JAY-me HER-air-ah BUT-ler   **202-225-3536**
1107 LHOB   4th Term/60%   8/95/60   Fax: 225-3478
herrerabeutler.house.gov   **twitter** herrerabeutler
CoS .... Casey Bowman **LD** .... Jordan Evich
Sch .... Angie Riesterer **Press** .... Amy Pennington
Bio: b. 11/3/78 Glendale, CA; Christian; BA Univ. of WA,
2004; Congressional Aide; m. Daniel Beutler
Comm.: Appropriations
Dist. Offices: Vancouver, 360-695-6292

Dan Newhouse (R-4th)   **202-225-5816**
1318 LHOB   2nd Term/58%   6/97/99   Fax: 225-3251
newhouse.house.gov   **twitter** RepNewhouse
CoS .... Carrie Meadows **LD** .... Jason Herbert
Sch .... Hailey Ghee **CD** .... Will Boyington
Bio: b. 7/10/55 Yakima, WA; Presbyterian; BS WA St. Univ.,
1977; Farmer; m. Carol
Comm.: Appropriations; Rules
Dist. Offices: Yakima, 509-452-3243; Richland, 509-713-7374

Cathy McMorris Rodgers (R-5th)   **202-225-2006**
1314 LHOB   7th Term/59%   6/99/99   Fax: 225-3392
mcmorrisrodgers.house.gov   **twitter** cathymcmorris
CoS .... Ian Field **LD** .... Megan Perez
Sch .... Jessica Sunday **CD** .... Kara Hauck
Bio: b. 5/22/69 Salem, OR; Christian; MBA Univ. of WA, 2002;
Orchardist, Legislative Aide; m. Brian Rodgers
Comm.: Energy & Commerce
Dist. Offices: Spokane, 509-353-2374; Colville, 509-684-3481; Walla Walla, 509-529-9358

Derek Kilmer (D-6th)   **202-225-5916**
1520 LHOB   3rd Term/62%   91/96/99   Fax: 226-3575
kilmer.house.gov   **twitter** RepDerekKilmer
CoS .... Jonathan Smith **LD** .... Aaron Wasserman
Sch .... Julia O'Connor **CD** .... Jason Phelps
Bio: b. 1/1/74 Port Angeles, WA; Methodist; DPhil Oxford
Univ., 2003; Nonprofit Executive, Management Consultant;
m. Jennifer
Comm.: Appropriations
Dist. Offices: Tacoma, 253-272-3515; Bremerton, 360-373-9725

WASHINGTON

Pramila Jayapal (D-7th)
pra-MIL-a JYE-a-paul
319 CHOB   1st Term/57%   **202-225-3106**
jayapal.house.gov   Fax: 225-6197
CoS .... Carmen Frias **LD** .... Ven Neralla   **twitter** PramilaJayapal
Sch .... Makenzie Mastrud **CD** .... Omer Farooque
Bio: b. 9/21/65 Chennai, India; Unspecified; MBA Northwestern Univ.; Advocacy Group Director; m. Steve Williamson
Comm.: Budget; Judiciary
Dist. Offices: Seattle, 206-674-0040

Dave Reichert (R-8th) *RIKE-ert*   **202-225-7761**
1127 LHOB   7th Term/59%   12/84/95   Fax: 225-4282
reichert.house.gov   **twitter** davereichert
CoS .... Chad Ramey **LD** .... Lindsay Manson
EA .... Nichole Hancock **Press**.......... Breanna Deutsch
Bio: b. 8/29/50 Detroit Lakes, MN; Lutheran - Missouri Synod; AA Concordia Lutheran Col., 1970; USAFR, 1971-76; Law Enforcement Official; m. Julie
Comm.: Ways & Means
Dist. Offices: Issaquah, 425-677-7414; Wenatchee, 509-885-6615

Adam Smith (D-9th)   **202-225-8901**
2264 RHOB   11th Term/74%   100/97/78   Fax: 225-5893
adamsmith.house.gov   **twitter** RepAdamSmith
CoS .... Shana Chandler **LD** .... Jonathan Pawlow
Sch .... Savannah Romero **CD** .... Rebecca Bryant
Bio: b. 6/15/65 Washington, DC; Episcopal; JD Univ. of WA, 1990; Prosecutor; m. Sara
Comm.: Armed Services (Rnk. Mem.)
Dist. Offices: Renton, 425-793-5180

Denny Heck (D-10th)   **202-225-9740**
425 CHOB   3rd Term/59%   93/96/99   Fax: 225-0129
dennyheck.house.gov   **twitter** RepDennyHeck
CoS .... Jami Burgess **LD** .... Brendan Woodbury
Sch .... Paige Langer **CD** .... Kati Rutherford
Bio: b. 7/29/52 Vancouver, WA; Lutheran; BA Evergreen St. Col., 1973; Broadcaster, Gubernatorial Aide, Business Owner; m. Paula
Comm.: Financial Services; Select Intelligence
Dist. Offices: Lacey, 360-459-8514; Lakewood, 253-533-8332

WEST VIRGINIA
wv.gov

Pop.: 1,844,128   **Rank:** 38th
Caucasian: 94%   **African-Am.:** 4%
Nat. Am.: 0%   **Asian:** 1%   **Other:** 2%
Hisp.: 2%
Reg. Voters: 1,275,241
Dem.: 52%   **Rep.:** 29%
Other: 19%
Land Area: 24,038 sq. mi.
Rank: 41st

Number of US House Seats: 3 Rep.

State Legislature
legis.state.wv.us
Senate: 21R/12D/1Vac   House: 63R/37D
Session: 02/08/17 – 4/8/2017

WEST VIRGINIA

Gov. Jim Justice (D) **304-558.2000**
Next Election 2020   1st Term/49%   Fax: none
twitter WVGovernor
Bio: b. 4/27/51; Charleston, WV; Unspecified; MBA Marshall Univ., 1976; Coal Company Owner, Resort Owner; m. Cathy

1900 Kanawha Boulevard East, Charleston, WV 25305

SENATE

Joe Manchin III (D) **202-224-3954**
SH-306   2nd Term/61%   69/52/98   Fax: 228-0002
manchin.senate.gov   twitter Sen_JoeManchin
CoS ....Joel Brubaker **LD** ....Adam Tomlinson
Sch ....Lauren Russell **Press**................ Kelley Moore
Bio: b. 8/24/47 Fairmont, WV; Catholic; BA WV Univ., 1970; Business Owner; m. Gayle
Comm.: Appropriations; Energy & Natural Resources; Veterans' Affairs; Select Intelligence
Dist. Offices: Charleston, 304-347-5372; Martinsburg, 304-262-9285; Morgantown, 304-292-2310; Beckley, 304-347-5372

Shelley Moore Capito (R) *CAP-ih-toe* **202-224-6472**
SR-172   1st Term/62%   54/83/99   Fax: 224-7665
capito.senate.gov   twitter SenCapito
CoS ....Joel Brubaker **LD** ....Adam Tomlinson
Sch .... Ashley Berrana **CD** .... Lauren Russell
Bio: b. 11/26/53 Glen Dale, WV; Presbyterian; MEd Univ. of VA, 1976; Career Counselor; m. Charles L. Capito, Jr.
Comm.: Appropriations; Commerce, Science & Transportation; Environment & Public Works; Rules & Administration; Joint Library
Dist. Offices: Charleston, 304-342-5855; Martinsburg, 304-264-4626; Fairmont, 304-368-0567

HOUSE

David B. McKinley (R-1st) **202-225-4172**
2239 RHOB   4th Term/69%   9/96/99   Fax: 225-7564
mckinley.house.gov   twitter RepMcKinley
CoS .... Mike Hamilton **LD** .... Margie Almanza
Sch .... Lou Hrkman **CD** .... John Stapleton
Bio: b. 3/28/47 Wheeling, WV; Episcopal; BSCE Purdue Univ., 1969; Business Owner, Civil Engineer; m. Mary
Comm.: Energy & Commerce
Dist. Offices: Wheeling, 304-232-3801; Morgantown, 304-284-8506; Parkersburg, 304-422-5972

Alex Mooney (R-2nd) **202-225-2711**
1232 LHOB   2nd Term/58%   8/98/98   Fax: 225-7856
mooney.house.gov   twitter RepAlexMooney
CoS .... Brian Chatwin **LD** .... Nicholas Butterfield
Sch .... Anita Itnyre **CD** .... Vacant
Bio: b. 6/7/71 Washington, DC; Catholic; BA Dartmouth Col., 1993; Public Affairs Firm Owner, Congressional Aide; m. Grace Gonzales Mooney
Comm.: Financial Services
Dist. Offices: Charleston, 304-925-5964; Martinsburg, 304-264-8810

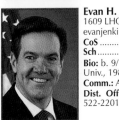

Evan H. Jenkins (R-3rd) **202-225-3452**
1609 LHOB   2nd Term/68%   6/96/99   Fax: 225-9061
evanjenkins.house.gov   twitter RepEvanJenkins
CoS ....Patrick Howell **LD** .... Brian Barnard
Sch ....Brittany Fortier **CD** .... Rebecca Neal
Bio: b. 9/12/60 Huntington, WV; Presbyterian; JD Samford Univ., 1987; Attorney; m. Elizabeth
Comm.: Appropriations
Dist. Offices: Beckley, 304-250-6177; Huntington, 304-522-2201

WISCONSIN
wisconsin.gov

Pop.: 5,771,337 **Rank:** 20th
Caucasian: 88% **African-Am.:** 7%
Nat. Am.: 1% **Asian:** 3%
Other: 2% **Hisp.:** 7%
Reg. Voters: 3,729,681
Party registration not required
Land Area: 54,158 sq. mi. **Rank:** 25th

Number of US House Seats: 5 Rep./3 Dem.

State Legislature
legis.state.wi.us
Senate: 18R/13D House: 64R/35D
Session: 01/04/17 – 12/31/2017

Gov. Scott Walker (R) **608-266-1212**
Next Election: 2018 2nd Term/52% Fax: 608-267-8983
twitter govwalker

Bio: b. 11/2/67 Colorado Springs, CO; Christian; Attended
Marquette Univ.; Financial Developer; m. Tonette

115 East State Capitol, Madison, WI 53707
Washington Office: 202-624-5870

SENATE

Ron Johnson (R) **202-224-5323**
SH-328 2nd Term/50% 43/96/93 Fax: 228-6965
ronjohnson.senate.gov **twitter** SenRonJohnson
CoS ....Tony Blando **LD** ....Sean Riley
Sch ....Jennifer O'Neil **CD** ....Ben Voelkel
Bio: b. 4/8/55 Mankato, MN; Lutheran; BS Univ. of MN,
1977; Business Owner; m. Jane
Comm.: Budget; Commerce, Science & Transportation;
Foreign Relations; Homeland Security & Governmental
Affairs (Chair)
Dist. Offices: Oshkosh, 920-230-7250; Milwaukee, 414-
276-7282

Tammy Baldwin (D) **202-224-5653**
SH-709 1st Term/51% 87/91/100 Fax: 224-9787
baldwin.senate.gov **twitter** SenatorBaldwin
CoS ....Bill Murat **LD** .... Dan McCarthy
Sch ....Carolyn Walser **CD** .... John Kraus
Bio: b. 2/11/62 Madison, WI; Not Stated; JD Univ. of WI,
1989; Attorney; single
Comm.: Appropriations; Commerce, Science & Transporta-
tion; Health, Education, Labor & Pensions
Dist. Offices: Madison, 608-264-5338; Milwaukee, 414-297-
4451; La Crosse, 608-796-0045

HOUSE

Paul D. Ryan (R-1st) **202-225-3031**
1233 LHOB 10th Term/65% 100/100/1 Fax: 225-3393
paulryan.house.gov **twitter** SpeakerRyan
CoS ....Danyell Tremmel **LD** .... Katie Donnell
Sch .... Tory Wickiser **Press**...............Ian Martorana
Bio: b. 1/29/70 Janesville, WI; Catholic; BA Miami Univ. of
OH, 1992; Economic Policy Analyst, Congressional Aide;
m. Janna
Comm.: Speaker
Dist. Offices: Janesville, 608-752-4050; Kenosha, 262-654-
1901; Racine, 262-637-0510

Mark Pocan (D-2nd) *poe-CAN* **202-225-2906**
1421 LHOB 3rd Term/69% 98/100/96 Fax: 225-6942
pocan.house.gov **twitter** repmarkpocan
CoS .... Glenn Wavrunek **Dep CoS**..............Alicia Molt
Sch ....Nick Greene **CD** .... David Kolovson
Bio: b. 8/14/64 Kenosha, WI; Not Stated; BA Univ. of WI,
1986; Business Owner; m. Philip Frank
Comm.: Appropriations
Dist. Offices: Madison, 608-258-9800; Beloit, 608-365-8001

WISCONSIN

Ron Kind (D-3rd)　　　　　　**202-225-5506**
1502 LHOB　11th Term/Unc.　90/93/92　Fax: 225-5739
kind.house.gov　　　　　　**twitter** RepRonKind
CoS ....Mike Goodman **LD** ....Elizabeth Stower
Sch ....Aaron White **CD** ....Amanda Sherman
Bio: b. 3/16/63 La Crosse, WI; Lutheran; JD Univ. of MN,
1990; District Attorney; m. Tawni
Comm.: Ways & Means
Dist. Offices: LaCrosse, 608-782-2558; Eau Claire, 715-
831-9214

Gwen Moore (D-4th)　　　　　　**202-225-4572**
2252 RHOB　7th Term/77%　100/99/90　Fax: 225-8135
gwenmoore.house.gov　　　　　**twitter** RepGwenMoore
CoS ....Sean Gard **LD** ....Vacant
Sch ....Vacant **CD** ....Eric Harris
Bio: b. 4/18/51 Racine, WI; Baptist; BA Marquette Univ.,
1978; Public Official, Civic Activist; single
Comm.: Financial Services
Dist. Offices: Milwaukee, 414-297-1140

Jim Sensenbrenner (R-5th)　　　　**202-225-5101**
2449 RHOB　20th Term/67%　9/98/100　Fax: 225-3190
sensenbrenner.house.gov　　　　**twitter** JimPressOffice
CoS ....Bart Forsyth **LD** ....Amy Bos
Sch ....Jacob Peterson **CD** ....Nicole Tieman
Bio: b. 6/14/43 Chicago, IL; Anglican Catholic; JD Univ. of
WI, 1968; Attorney; m. Cheryl
Comm.: Foreign Affairs; Judiciary
Dist. Offices: Brookfield, 262-784-1111

Glenn Grothman (R-6th)　　　　**202-225-2476**
1217 LHOB　2nd Term/57%　9/98/99　Fax: 225-2356
grothman.house.gov　　　　　**twitter** RepGrothman
CoS ....Rachel Ver Velde **Dep CoS** ....Ryan Croft
Sch ....Samantha Baker **Press** ....Bernadette Green
Bio: b. 7/3/55 Milwaukee, WI; Lutheran; JD Univ. of WI,
1983; Attorney; single
Comm.: Budget; Education & the Workforce; Oversight &
Government Reform
Dist. Offices: Fond du Lac, 920-907-0624

Sean P. Duffy (R-7th)　　　　　**202-225-3365**
2330 RHOB　4th Term/62%　6/98/91　Fax: 225-3240
duffy.house.gov　　　　　　**twitter** repseanduffy
CoS ....Pete Meachum **Dep CoS** ....Andy Taylor
Sch ....Alana Wilson **CD** ....Mark Bednar
Bio: b. 10/3/71 Hayward, WI; Catholic; JD William Mitch-
ell Col. of Law, 1999; Attorney, Prosecutor; m. Rachel
Campos-Duffy
Comm.: Financial Services
Dist. Offices: Wausau, 715-298-9344; Superior, 715-392-3984

Mike Gallagher (R-8th)　　　　**202-225-5665**
1007 LHOB　1st Term/63%　　　　Fax: 225-5729
gallagher.house.gov　　　　　**twitter** RepGallagher
CoS ....McKay Daniels **LD** ....Jennifer Shirley
Sch ....Nicole Tardif **CD** ....Madison Wiberg
Bio: b. 3/3/84 Green Bay; Catholic; PhD Georgetown, 2015;
USMC, 2006-13; Catholic; single
Comm.: Armed Services; Homeland Security
Dist. Offices: Appleton, 920-380-0061

WYOMING
wyoming.gov

Pop.: 586,107   **Rank:** 50th
Caucasian: 93%
African-Am.: 1%
Nat. Am.: 3%   **Asian:** 1%
Other: 2%   **Hisp.:** 10%
Reg. Voters: 284,203
Dem.: 19%   **Rep.:** 70%
Other: 11%
Land Area: 97,093 sq. mi.
Rank: 9th

Number of US House Seats: 1 Rep.

State Legislature
legisweb.state.wy.us
Senate: 27R/3D   House: 51R/9D
Session: 01/10/17 – 3/6/2017

Gov. Matt Mead (R)   307-777-7434
Next Election: 2018 2nd Term/59%   Fax: 307-632-3909
twitter govmattmead
Bio: b. 3/11/62 Jackson, WY; Episcopal; JD Univ. of WY, 1987; Attorney; m. Carol

State Capitol, 200 West 24th Street,
Cheyenne, WY 82002-0010

SENATE

Michael B. Enzi (R)   202-224-3424
SR-379A   4th Term/72%   55/94/98   Fax: 228-0359
enzi.senate.gov   twitter SenatorEnzi
CoS ....Tara Shaw **LD** .... Landon Stropko
Sch ....Alana Hyman **CD** ....Coy Knobel
Bio: b. 2/1/44 Bremerton, WA; Presbyterian; MS Univ. of Denver, 1968; WYANG, 1967-73; Accountant, Businessman; m. Diana
Comm.: Budget (Chair); Finance; Health, Education, Labor & Pensions; Homeland Security & Governmental Affairs; Small Business & Entrepreneurship
Dist. Offices: Gillette, 307-682-6268; Cheyenne, 307-772-2477; Casper, 307-261-6572; Cody, 307-527-9444

John Barrasso (R)   202-224-6441
SD-307   2nd Term/76%   53/96/99   Fax: 224-1724
barrasso.senate.gov   twitter senjohnbarrasso
CoS ....Dan Kunsman **LD** .... Bryn Stewart
Sch ....Kathi Wise **CD** ...Bronwyn Lance Chester
Bio: b. 7/21/52 Reading, PA; Presbyterian; MD Georgetown Univ., 1978; Orthopedic Surgeon; m. Bobbi
Comm.: Energy & Natural Resources; Environment & Public Works (Chair); Foreign Relations; Indian Affairs
Dist. Offices: Casper, 307-261-6413; Cheyenne, 307-772-2451; Rock Springs, 307-362-5012; Riverton, 307-856-6642; Jackson, 307 739-9507

HOUSE

Liz Cheney (R-At Large)   202-225-2311
416 CHOB   1st Term/62%   Fax: 225-3057
cheney.house.gov   twitter Liz_Cheney
CoS ....Kara Ahern **LD** .... Scott Hughes
Sch ....Molly Stevens **CD** .... Amy Edmonds
Bio: b. 7/28/66 Madison; Methodist; JD Univ. of Chicago, 1996; Attorney, Aide; m. Phillip Perry
Comm.: Armed Services; Natural Resources; Rules
Dist. Offices: Casper, 307-261-6595; Cheyenne, 307-772-2592; Sheridan, 307-673-4608

AMERICAN SAMOA
Pago Pago ★

americansamoa.gov

Pop.: 55,519   **Rank:** n/a
Caucasian: 1%   **Asian:** 4%
Pacific Islander: 93%   **Other:** 2%
Reg. Voters: 16776   *Party registration not required*
Land Area: 77 sq. mi.   **Rank:** n/a

Number of US House Seats: 1 Rep. (Non-voting)

State Legislature
americansamoa.gov
Senate: 18 Non.   House: 21 Non.

Gov. Lolo Matalasi Moliga (I)   **684-633-4116**
Next Election: 2016 1st Term/53%   Fax: 684-633-2269

Bio: b. 2/28/47 Ta'u, Manua; Congregational Christian; MPA San Diego State Univ., 1975; Businessman, Public Official; m. Cynthia

A.P. Lutali Executive Office Building, Utulei, Pago Pago, AS 96799

DELEGATE

Aumua Amata Coleman Radewagen   **202-225-8577**
   (R-At Large) *ow-MU-ah ah-MAH-tah COLE-man RAD-uh-wag-en*
1339 LHOB   2nd Term/75%   Fax: 225-8757
radewagen.house.gov   **twitter** RepAmata
CoS ....Leafaina Tavai Yahn **LD** ....Casey Brinck
Sch ....Nancy Dehlinger **CD** ....Casey Brinck
Bio: b. 12/29/47 Pago Pago, AS; Catholic; BA Univ. of GU, 1975; Community Activist; m. Fred Radewagen
Comm.: Natural Resources; Small Business; Veterans' Affairs
Dist. Offices: Pago Pago, 684-633-3601

DISTRICT OF COLUMBIA
dc.gov

Pop.: 672,228   **Rank:** n/a
Caucasian: 44%   **African-Am.:** 48%   **Nat. Am.:** 1%
Asian: 4%   **Other:** 3%   **Hisp.:** 11%
Reg. Voters: 482,357
Dem.: 76%   **Rep.:** 6%   **Other:** 18%
Land Area: 61 sq. mi.   **Rank:** n/a

Number of US House Seats: 1 Dem. (Non-voting)

State Legislature
dccouncil.us
Council: 11D/2 Other

Mayor Muriel E. Bowser (D)   **202-727-2643**
Next Election: 2018 1st Term/54%   Fax: 727-2357
twitter teammuriel
Bio: b. 8/2/72 Washington, DC; Christian; MPP American Univ.; Public Official; single

1350 Pennsylvania Avenue, NW, Suite 316, Washington, DC 20004

DELEGATE

Eleanor Holmes Norton (D-At Large)   **202-225-8050**
2136 RHOB   14th Term/89%   Fax: 225-3002
norton.house.gov   **twitter** eleanornorton
CoS .... Raven Reeder **LD** ....Bradley Truding
Sch .... Try Coburn **CD** .... Benjamin Fritsch
Bio: b. 6/13/37 Washington, DC; Episcopal; LLB Yale Univ., 1964; Attorney; div.
Comm.: Oversight & Government Reform; Transportation & Infrastructure
Dist. Offices: Washington, 202-408-9041; Washington, 202 678-8900

GUAM

guam.gov

Pop.: 159,358 **Rank:** n/a
Chamorro: 37% **Filipino:** 26% **Pacific Islander:** 12%
Caucasian: 7% **Other:** 8%
Reg. Voters: 51,973 *Party registration not required*
Land Area: 210 sq. mi. **Rank:** n/a

Number of US House Seats: 1 Dem. (Non-voting)

State Legislature
guamlegislature.com
Senate: 9D/6R

Gov. Eddie Baza Calvo (R)   **671-472-8931**
Next Election: 2018 2nd Term/64%   Fax: 671-477-4826
twitter governorcalvo

Bio: b. 8/29/61 Tamuning, GU; Catholic; BBA Col. of Notre
Dame (CA), 1983; Business Executive; m. Christine

Ricardo J. Bordallo Governor's Complex, Adelup, GU 96910
Washington Office: 202-434-4855

DELEGATE

Madeleine Z. Bordallo *bore-DAA-yo*   **202-225-1188**
(D-At Large)
2441 RHOB   8th Term/54%   Fax: 226-0341
bordallo.house.gov   **twitter**
CoS .... Matthew Herrmann **LD** .... Vacant
Sch .... Rosanne Meno **CD** .... Adam Carbullido
Bio: b. 5/31/33 Graceville, MN; Catholic; Attended Col. of
St. Catherine, 1953; Public Official; wid.
Comm.: Armed Services; Natural Resources
Dist. Offices: Hagatna, 671-477-4272

NORTHERN MARIANA ISLANDS

gov.mp

Pop.: 55,883 **Rank:** n/a
Asian: 50% **Pacific Islander:** 35% **Caucasian:** 2%
Other: 13%
Reg. Voters: 17,986 *Party registration not required*
Land Area: 179 sq. mi. **Rank:** n/a

Number of US House Seats: 1 Dem. (Non-voting)

State Legislature
cnmileg.gov.mp
Senate: 7R/2 Other   House: 15R/5 Other

Gov. Ralph Deleon Guerrero
Torres (R)   **670-664-2280**
Next Election: 2018 1st Term   Fax: 670-664-2211

Bio: b. 8/6/79 Saipan, MP; Not Stated; BS Boise St. Univ.,
2001; Public Official; m. Diann Mendiola Tudela

Caller Box 10007, Saipan, MP 96950

DELEGATE

Gregorio Kilili Camacho Sablan   **202-225-2646**
(D-At Large) *greg-OREO key-LEE-lee ka-MAH-cho sab-LAHN*
2411 RHOB   5th Term/Unc.   Fax: 226-4249
sablan.house.gov   **twitter**
CoS .... Bob Schwalbach **LD** .... Seth Maiman
Sch .... Agnes Cornibert **CD** .... Bob Schwalbach
Bio: b. 1/19/55 Saipan, MP; Catholic; Attended Univ. of
HI, 1989-90; USAR, 1981-86; Gubernatorial Aide, Public
Official; m. Andrea
Comm.: Education & the Workforce; Natural Resources;
Veterans' Affairs
Dist. Offices: Saipan, 670 323-2647; Rota, 670 532-2647;
Tinian, 670 433-2647

PUERTO RICO

★ San Juan

pr.gov

Pop.: 3,474,182   **Rank:** n/a
Caucasian: 70%   **African-Am.:** 8%
Other: 22%   **Hisp.:** 99%
Reg. Voters: 2,402,943   *Party registration not required*
Land Area: 3,425 sq. mi.   **Rank:** n/a

Number of US House Seats: 1 NPP/Rep. (Non-voting)

State Legislature
oslpr.org
Senate: 21NPP/4PDP/2 Other   House: 34NPP/16PDP/1 Other

Gov. Ricardo Rosselló (NPP)   717-721-7000
Next Election 2020   1st Term/42%   Fax: 787-721-5072
twitter ricardorossello
Bio: b. 3/7/79; San Juan, PR; Unspecified; PhD Univ. of Michigan, 2007; Neurobiologist; Biomedical Engineer; m. Beatriz Areizaga

La Fortaleza, PO Box 9020082, San Juan, PR 00902-0082
Washington Office: 202-778-0710

RESIDENT COMMISSIONER

Jenniffer González-Colón
(NPP/R-At Large)   202-225-2615
1529 LHOB   1st Term/49%   Fax: 225-2154
gonzalez-colon.house.gov   **twitter** RepJenniffer
CoS .... Luis Baco   **LD** .... Alex Sarnowski
Sch .... Natalia Gandia   **CD** ...... Marieli Padró Raldiris
Bio: b. 8/5/76 San Juan; Catholic; LLM Interamerican University of Puerto Rico School of Law; Attorney; single
Comm.: Natural Resources; Small Business; Veterans' Affairs
Dist. Offices: San Juan, 787-723-6333

VIRGIN ISLANDS

★ Charlotte Amalie

vi.gov

Pop.: 106,405   **Rank:** n/a
Caucasian: 16%   **African-Am.:** 76%   **Other:** 6%
Reg. Voters: 45,550   *Party registration not required*
Land Area: 134 sq. mi.   **Rank:** n/a

Number of US House Seats: 1 Dem. (Non-voting)

State Legislature
legvi.org
Senate: 11D/4 Other

Gov. Ken Mapp (I)   340-774-0001
Next Election: 2018   1st Term/63%   Fax: 340-693-4309
Bio: b. New York, NY; Not Stated; MPA Harvard Univ.; Police Officer; single

21-22 Kongens Gade, Charlotte Amalie, St. Thomas, VI 00802
Washington Office: 202-624-3560

DELEGATE

Stacey Plaskett (D-At Large)   202-225-1790
331 CHOB   2nd Term/98%   Fax: 225-5517
plaskett.house.gov   **twitter** staceyplaskett
CoS .... Jerome Murray   **LD** .... Angeline Jabbar
Sch .... Nicole Adair   **CD** .... Richard Motta
Bio: b. 5/13/66 New York, NY; Lutheran; JD American Univ., 1994; Attorney, Congressional Aide, County Prosecutor; m. Jonathan Buckney-Small
Comm.: Agriculture; Oversight & Government Reform
Dist. Offices: Frederiksted, 340-778-5900; St. Thomas, 340-774-4408

SENATE STANDING COMMITTEES

AGRICULTURE, NUTRITION AND FORESTRY

202-224-2035—SR-328A—Fax: 228-2125
ag.senate.gov

Republicans (11)
Pat Roberts, KS, Chair
Thad Cochran, MS
Mitch McConnell, KY
John Boozman, AR
John Hoeven, ND
Joni Ernst, IA
Charles E. Grassley, IA
John Thune, SD
Steve Daines, MT
David Perdue, GA
Luther Strange, AL

Democrats (10)
Debbie Stabenow, MI, Rnk. Mem.
Patrick J. Leahy, VT
Sherrod Brown, OH
Amy Klobuchar, MN
Michael Bennet, CO
Kirsten Gillibrand, NY
Joe Donnelly, IN
Heidi Heitkamp, ND
Bob Casey, PA
Chris Van Hollen, MD

Maj. Staff Dir.: Joel Leftwich—Min. Staff Dir.: Joseph Shultz

SUBCOMMITTEES

Commodities, Risk Management, and Trade
202-224-2035—SR-328A—Fax: 228-2125
Rep: Boozman, Chair; Cochran; Hoeven; Grassley; Thune; Daines; Perdue
Dem: Heitkamp, Rnk. Mem.; Brown; Bennet; Gillibrand; Donnelly; Van Hollen

Conservation, Forestry, and Natural Resources
202-224-2035—SR-328A—Fax: 228-2125
Rep: Daines, Chair; Cochran; McConnell; Boozman; Grassley; Strange
Dem: Bennet, Rnk. Mem.; Leahy; Klobuchar; Donnelly; Casey

Livestock, Marketing and Agriculture Security
202-224-2035—SR-328A—Fax: 228-2125
Rep: Perdue, Chair; McConnell; Ernst; Grassley; Thune; Daines
Dem: Gillibrand, Rnk. Mem.; Leahy; Klobuchar; Heitkamp; Casey

Nutrition, Agricultural Research, and Specialty Crops
202-224-2035—SR-328A—Fax: 228-2125
Rep: Strange, Chair; McConnell; Boozman; Hoeven; Ernst; Perdue
Dem: Casey, Rnk. Mem.; Leahy; Brown; Gillibrand; Van Hollen

Rural Development and Energy
202-224-2035—SR-328A—Fax: 228-2125
Rep: Ernst, Chair; Cochran; Boozman; Hoeven; Thune; Daines; Strange
Dem: Van Hollen, Rnk. Mem.; Brown; Klobuchar; Bennet; Donnelly; Heitkamp

APPROPRIATIONS

202-224-7257—S-128 Capitol—Fax: 228-0904
appropriations.senate.gov

Republicans (16)
Thad Cochran, MS, Chair
Mitch McConnell, KY
Richard C. Shelby, AL
Lamar Alexander, TN
Susan Collins, ME
Lisa Murkowski, AK
Lindsey Graham, SC
Roy Blunt, MO
Jerry Moran, KS
John Hoeven, ND
John Boozman, AR
Shelley Moore Capito, WV
James Lankford, OK
Steve Daines, MT
John N. Kennedy, LA
Marco Rubio, FL

Democrats (15)
Patrick J. Leahy, VT, Rnk. Mem.
Patty Murray, WA
Dianne Feinstein, CA
Richard J. Durbin, IL
Jack Reed, RI
Jon Tester, MT
Tom Udall, NM
Jeanne Shaheen, NH
Jeff Merkley, OR
Chris Coons, DE
Brian Schatz, HI
Tammy Baldwin, WI
Christopher S. Murphy, CT
Joe Manchin III, WV
Chris Van Hollen, MD

Maj. Staff Dir.: Bruce Evans—Min. Staff Dir.: Charles Kieffer

Agriculture, Rural Development, Food and Drug Administration, and Related Agencies
202-224-8090—TBA—Fax: 202-228-2320
Rep: Hoeven, Chair; Cochran; McConnell; Collins; Blunt; Moran; Rubio
Dem: Merkley, Rnk. Mem.; Feinstein; Tester; Udall; Leahy; Baldwin
Maj. Clerk: Carlisle Clarke
Min. Clerk: Jessica Schulken

Commerce, Justice, Science, and Related Agencies
202-224-5202—SD 142—Fax: 202-228-1624
Rep: Shelby, Chair; Alexander; Murkowski; Collins; Graham; Boozman; Capito; Lankford; Kennedy
Dem: Shaheen, Rnk. Mem.; Leahy; Feinstein; Reed; Coons; Schatz; Manchin; Van Hollen
Maj. Clerk: Jeremy Weirich
Min. Clerk: Jean Toal Eisen

Defense
202-224-7255—SD 122—Fax: 202-224-0110
Rep: Cochran, Chair; McConnell; Shelby; Alexander; Collins; Murkowski; Graham; Blunt; Daines; Moran
Dem: Durbin, Rnk. Mem.; Leahy; Feinstein; Murray; Reed; Tester; Udall; Schatz; Baldwin
Maj. Clerk: Brian Potts
Min. Clerk: Erik Raven

Energy and Water Development
202-224-8119—SD 184—Fax: 202-228-2322
Rep: Alexander, Chair; Cochran; McConnell; Shelby; Collins; Murkowski; Graham; Hoeven; Kennedy
Dem: Feinstein, Rnk. Mem.; Murray; Tester; Durbin; Udall; Shaheen; Merkley; Coons
Maj. Clerk: Tyler Owens
Min. Clerk: Doug Clapp

Financial Services and General Government
202-224-1133—SD 184—Fax: 202-224-0058
Rep: Capito, Chair; Moran; Boozman; Lankford; Daines
Dem: Coons, Rnk. Mem.; Durbin; Manchin; Van Hollen
Maj. Clerk: Dale Cabaniss
Min. Clerk: Marianne Upton

Homeland Security
202-224-6870—SD 135—Fax: 202-228-1621
Rep: Boozman, Chair; Cochran; Shelby; Murkowski; Hoeven; Lankford; Kennedy
Dem: Tester, Rnk. Mem.; Shaheen; Leahy; Murray; Baldwin; Manchin
Maj. Clerk: Kathy Kraninger
Min. Clerk: Stephanie Gyota

Interior, Environment, and Related Agencies
202-228-0774—SD 131—Fax: 202-228-2345
Rep: Murkowski, Chair; Cochran; Alexander; Blunt; Hoeven; McConnell; Daines; Capito
Dem: Udall, Rnk. Mem.; Feinstein; Leahy; Reed; Tester; Merkley; Van Hollen
Maj. Clerk: Leif Fonnesbeck
Min. Clerk: Rachael Taylor

Labor, Health and Human Services, Education, and Related Agencies
202-224-9145—SD 131—Fax: 202-224-1360
Rep: Blunt, Chair; Cochran; Shelby; Alexander; Graham; Moran; Capito; Lankford; Kennedy; Rubio
Dem: Murray, Rnk. Mem.; Durbin; Reed; Shaheen; Merkley; Schatz; Baldwin; Murphy; Manchin
Maj. Clerk: Laura Friedel
Min. Clerk: Alex Keenan

Legislative Branch
202-224-7256—S 128—Fax: 202-224-2100
Rep: Lankford, Chair; Kennedy; Rubio
Dem: Murphy, Rnk. Mem.; Van Hollen
Maj. Staff: Rachelle Schroeder
Min. Staff: Melissa Zimmerman

SUBCOMMITTEES (Appropriations)

Military Construction, Veterans Affairs, and Related Agencies
202-224-8224—SD 125—Fax: 202-228-2325
Rep: Moran, Chair; McConnell; Murkowski; Hoeven; Collins;
   Boozman; Capito; Rubio
Dem: Schatz, Rnk. Mem.; Tester; Murray; Reed; Udall; Baldwin;
   Murphy
Maj. Staff Dir.: Bob Henke
Min. Clerk: Christina Evans

State, Foreign Operations, and Related Programs
202-224-7284—SD 127—Fax: 202-224-2255
Rep: Graham, Chair; McConnell; Blunt; Boozman; Moran;
   Lankford; Daines; Rubio
Dem: Leahy, Rnk. Mem.; Durbin; Shaheen; Coons; Merkley;
   Murphy; Van Hollen
Maj. Clerk: Paul Grove
Min. Clerk: Tim Reiser

Transportation, Housing and Urban Development, and Related Agencies
202-224-7281—SD 142—Fax: 202-228-0249
Rep: Collins, Chair; Shelby; Alexander; Blunt; Boozman; Capito;
   Daines; Graham; Hoeven
Dem: Reed, Rnk. Mem.; Murray; Durbin; Feinstein; Coons; Schatz;
   Murphy; Manchin
Maj. Clerk: Heideh Shahmoradi
Min. Clerk: Dabney Hegg

ARMED SERVICES
202-224-3871—SR-228—Fax: 202-228-0036
armed-services.senate.gov

Republicans (14)	Democrats (13)
John McCain, AZ, Chair	Jack Reed, RI, Rnk. Mem.
James M. Inhofe, OK	Bill Nelson, FL
Roger Wicker, MS	Claire McCaskill, MO
Deb Fischer, NE	Jeanne Shaheen, NH
Tom Cotton, AR	Kirsten Gillibrand, NY
Mike Rounds, SD	Richard Blumenthal, CT
Joni Ernst, IA	Joe Donnelly, IN
Thom Tillis, NC	Mazie K. Hirono, HI
Dan Sullivan, AK	Tim Kaine, VA
David Perdue, GA	Angus King, ME (Ind.)
Lindsey Graham, SC	Martin Heinrich, NM
Ted Cruz, TX	Elizabeth Warren, MA
Ben Sasse, NE	Gary Peters, MI
Luther Strange, AL	

Maj. Staff Dir.: Christian Brose
Min. Staff Dir.: Elizabeth King

SUBCOMMITTEES

Airland
202-224-3871—SR 228—Fax: 202-228-0036
Rep: Cotton, Chair; Inhofe; Wicker; Tillis; Sullivan; Cruz; Sasse
Dem: King, Rnk. Mem.; McCaskill; Blumenthal; Donnelly; Warren;
   Peters
Maj. Lead Prof. Staff Mem.: James Hickey
Min. Lead Prof. Staff Mem.: Creighton Greene

Cybersecurity
202-224-3871--SR 228--Fax: 202-228-0036
Rep: Rounds, Chair; Fischer; Perdue; Graham; Sasse
Dem: Nelson, Rnk. Mem.; McCaskill; Gillibrand; Blumenthal

Emerging Threats and Capabilities
202-224-3871—SR-228—Fax: 202-228-0036
Rep: Ernst, Chair; Wicker; Fischer; Perdue; Cruz
Dem: Heinrich, Rnk. Mem.; Nelson; Shaheen; Peters
Maj. Lead Prof. Staff Mem.: Tom Goffus
Min. Lead Prof. Staff Mem.: Michael Noblet

Personnel
202-224-3871—SR-228—Fax: 202-228-0036
Rep: Tillis, Chair; Ernst; Graham; Sasse
Dem: Gillibrand, Rnk. Mem.; McCaskill; Warren
Maj. Lead Prof. Staff Mem.: Samantha Clark
Min. Lead Prof. Staff Mem.: Gary Leeling

Readiness and Management Support
202-224-3871—SR-228—Fax: 202-228-0036
Rep: Inhofe, Chair; Rounds; Ernst; Perdue; Strange
Dem: Kaine, Rnk. Mem.; Shaheen; Hirono
Maj. Lead Prof. Staff Mem.: Brad Patout
Min. Lead Prof. Staff Mem.: John Quirk V

Seapower
202-224-3871—SR-228—Fax: 202-228-0036
Rep: Wicker, Chair; Cotton; Rounds; Tillis; Sullivan; Strange
Dem: Hirono, Rnk. Mem.; Shaheen; Blumenthal; Kaine; King
Maj. Lead Prof. Staff Mem.: Jason Potter
Min. Lead Prof. Staff Mem.: Creighton Greene

Strategic Forces
202-224-3871—SR-228—Fax: 202-228-0036
Rep: Fischer, Chair; Inhofe; Cotton; Sullivan; Cruz; Graham
Dem: Donnelly, Rnk. Mem.; Heinrich; Warren; Peters
Maj. Lead Prof. Staff Mem.: Rob Soofer
Min. Lead Prof. Staff Mem.: Jonathan Epstein

BANKING, HOUSING, AND URBAN AFFAIRS

202-224-7391—SD-534—Fax: 224-5137
banking.senate.gov

Republicans (12)
Michael D. Crapo, ID, Chair
Richard C. Shelby, AL
Bob Corker, TN
Patrick J. Toomey, PA
Dean Heller, NV
Tim Scott, SC
Tom Cotton, AR
Mike Rounds, SD
David Perdue, GA
Thom Tillis, NC
Ben Sasse, NE
John N. Kennedy, LA

Democrats (11)
Sherrod Brown, OH, Rnk. Mem.
Jack Reed, RI
Robert Menendez, NJ
Jon Tester, MT
Mark Warner, VA
Elizabeth Warren, MA
Heidi Heitkamp, ND
Joe Donnelly, IN
Brian Schatz, HI
Chris Van Hollen, MD
Catherine Cortez Masto, NV

Maj. Staff Dir. & General Counsel: Gregg Richard
Min. Staff Dir.: Mark Powden

SUBCOMMITTEES

Economic Policy
202-224-2315—SH 713—Fax: 202-228-6321
Rep: Cotton, Chair; Toomey; Perdue; Tillis; Kennedy
Dem: Heitkamp, Rnk. Mem.; Menendez; Warren; Donnelly
Maj. Staff Dir.: Scott Riplinger
Min. Staff Dir.: David Hallock

Financial Institutions and Consumer Protection
202-224-2315—SH 713—Fax: 202-228-6321
Rep: Toomey, Chair; Shelby; Corker; Heller; Scott; Sasse; Cotton; Perdue; Kennedy
Dem: Warren, Rnk. Mem.; Reed; Tester; Warner; Donnelly; Schatz; Van Hollen; Cortez Masto
Maj. Staff Dir.: Geoffrey Okamoto
Min. Staff Dir.: Ellen Freedman

Housing, Transportation, and Community Development
202-224-4744—SH 528—Fax: 202-228-2197
Rep: Scott, Chair; Shelby; Heller; Rounds; Tillis; Kennedy
Dem: Menendez, Rnk. Mem.; Reed; Heitkamp; Schatz; Van Hollen
Maj. Staff Dir.: Travis Norton
Min. Staff Dir.: Rebecca Schatz

National Security and International Trade and Finance
202-224-2023—SR 459A—Fax: 202-224-6295
Rep: Sasse, Chair; Corker; Cotton; Rounds; Perdue
Dem: Donnelly, Rnk. Mem.; Warner; Heitkamp; Schatz
Maj. Staff Dir.: Bryan Blom
Min. Staff Dir.: Tracee Sutton

Securities, Insurance, and Investment
202-224-4642—SH 528—Fax: 202-224-4680
Rep: Heller, Chair; Shelby; Corker; Toomey; Scott; Sasse; Rounds; Tillis
Dem: Warner, Rnk. Mem.; Reed; Menendez; Tester; Warren;
    Van Hollen; Cortez Masto
Maj. Staff Dir.: Gregg Richard
Min. Staff Dir.: Milan Dalal

BUDGET

202-224-0642—SD-624—Fax: 228-2007
budget.senate.gov

Republicans (12)
Michael B. Enzi, WY, Chair
Charles E. Grassley, IA
Michael D. Crapo, ID
Lindsey Graham, SC
Patrick J. Toomey, PA
Ron Johnson, WI
Bob Corker, TN
David Perdue, GA
Cory Gardner, CO
John N. Kennedy, LA
John Boozman, AR
Luther Strange, AL

Democrats (11)
Bernard Sanders, VT (Ind.),
    Rnk. Mem.
Patty Murray, WA
Ron Wyden, OR
Debbie Stabenow, MI
Sheldon Whitehouse, RI
Mark Warner, VA
Jeff Merkley, OR
Tim Kaine, VA
Angus King, ME (Ind.)
Chris Van Hollen, MD
Kamala Harris, CA

Maj. Staff Dir.: Eric Ueland
Min. Staff Dir.: Warren Gunnels

NO SUBCOMMITTEES

COMMERCE, SCIENCE, AND TRANSPORTATION

202-224-1251—SD-512—Fax: 224-1259
commerce.senate.gov

Republicans (14)
John Thune, SD, Chair
Roger Wicker, MS
Roy Blunt, MO
Ted Cruz, TX
Deb Fischer, NE
Jerry Moran, KS
Dan Sullivan, AK
Dean Heller, NV
James M. Inhofe, OK
Mike Lee, UT
Ron Johnson, WI
Shelley Moore Capito, WV
Cory Gardner, CO
Todd Young, IN

Democrats (13)
Bill Nelson, FL, Rnk. Mem.
Maria Cantwell, WA
Amy Klobuchar, MN
Richard Blumenthal, CT
Brian Schatz, HI
Edward J. Markey, MA
Cory Booker, NJ
Tom Udall, NM
Gary Peters, MI
Tammy Baldwin, WI
Tammy Duckworth, IL
Maggie Hassan, NH
Catherine Cortez Masto, NV

Maj. Staff Dir.: Nick Rossi
Min. Staff Dir.: Kim Lipsky

Aviation Operations, Safety, and Security
202-224-9000-SH-427-Fax: 202-228-2339
Rep: Blunt, Chair; Wicker; Cruz; Fischer; Moran; Sullivan; Heller; Inhofe; Lee; Capito; Gardner; Young
Dem: Cantwell, Rnk. Mem; Klobuchar; Blumenthal; Schatz; Markey; Booker; Udall; Peters; Baldwin; Hassan; Duckworth
Maj. Policy Dir.: Bailey Edwards
Min. Prof. Staff Member: Jenny Solomon

Communications, Technology, Innovation, and the Internet
202-224-9340-SH 428-Fax: 202-228-0327
Rep: Wicker, Chair; Blunt; Cruz; Fischer; Moran; Sullivan; Heller; Inhofe; Lee; Johnson; Capito; Gardner; Young
Dem: Schatz, Rnk. Mem.; Cantwell; Klobuchar; Blumenthal; Markey; Booker; Udall; Peters; Baldwin; Duckworth; Hassan; Cortez Masto
Maj. Policy Dir.: David Quinalty
Min. Chief Counsel: John Branscome

Consumer Protection, Product Safety, Insurance and Data Security
202-224-1270-SH 428-Fax: 202-228-0327
Rep: Moran, Chair; Blunt; Cruz; Fischer; Heller; Inhofe; Lee; Capito; Young
Dem: Blumenthal, Rnk. Mem.; Klobuchar; Markey; Booker; Udall; Duckworth; Hassan; Cortez Masto
Maj. Counsel: Peter Feldman
Min. Chief Counsel: Christian Tamotsu Fjeld

Oceans, Atmosphere, Fisheries, and Coast Guard
202-224-4912-SH-420A-Fax: 202-228-4262
Rep: Sullivan, Chair; Wicker; Fischer; Inhofe; Lee; Johnson; Gardner; Young
Dem: Peters, Rnk. Mem.; Cantwell; Blumenthal; Schatz; Markey; Booker; Baldwin
Maj. Policy Dir.: Fren Gibbons
Min. Counsel: Jeff Lewis

Space, Science, and Competitiveness
202-224-0415-SH-427-Fax: 202-228-2239
Rep: Cruz, Chair; Moran; Sullivan; Lee; Johnson; Capito; Gardner
Dem: Markey, Rnk. Mem.; Schatz; Udall; Peters; Baldwin; Hassan
Maj. Policy Dir.: Bailey Edwards
Min. Staff Dir.: Nicholas Cummings

Surface Transportation and Merchant Marine Infrastructure, Safety and Security
202-224-9000-SH-427-Fax: 202-228-2239
Rep: Fischer, Chair; Wicker; Blunt; Heller; Inhofe; Johnson; Capito; Gardner; Young
Dem: Booker, Rnk. Mem.; Cantwell; Klobuchar; Blumenthal; Udall; Baldwin; Duckworth; Hassan
Maj. Policy Dir.: Fern Gibbons
Min. Counsel: Devon Barnhart

ENERGY AND NATURAL RESOURCES

202-224-4971—SD-304—Fax: 224-6163

energy.senate.gov

Republicans (12)
Lisa Murkowski, AK, Chair
John Barrasso, WY
Jim Risch, ID
Mike Lee, UT
Jeff Flake, AZ
Steve Daines, MT
Cory Gardner, CO
Lamar Alexander, TN
John Hoeven, ND
Bill Cassidy, LA
Rob Portman, OH
Luther Strange, AL

Democrats (11)
Maria Cantwell, WA,
  Rnk. Mem.
Ron Wyden, OR
Bernard Sanders, VT (Ind.)
Debbie Stabenow, MI
Al Franken, MN
Joe Manchin III, WV
Martin Heinrich, NM
Mazie K. Hirono, HI
Angus King, ME (Ind.)
Tammy Duckworth, IL
Catherine Cortez Masto, NV

Maj. Staff Dir.: Colin Hayes
Min. Staff Dir.: Angela Becker-Dippmann

SUBCOMMITTEES

Energy
202-224-4971—SD 304—Fax: 202-224-6163
Rep: Gardner, Chair; Risch; Flake; Daines; Alexander; Hoeven;
  Cassidy; Portman; Strange
Dem: Manchin, Rnk. Mem.; Wyden; Sanders; Franken; Heinrich;
  King; Duckworth; Cortez Masto

Water and Power
202-224-4971—SD 304—Fax: 202-224-6163
Rep: Flake, Chair; Barrasso; Risch; Lee; Cassidy; Portman; Strange
Dem: King, Rnk. Mem.; Wyden; Sanders; Franken; Manchin;
  Duckworth

Public Lands, Forests, and Mining
202-224-4971—SD 304—Fax: 202-224-6163
Rep: Lee, Chair; Barrasso; Risch; Flake; Daines; Gardner;
  Alexander; Hoeven; Cassidy; Strange
Dem: Wyden, Rnk. Mem.; Stabenow; Franken; Manchin; Heinrich;
  Hirono; Cortez Masto

National Parks
202-224-4971—SD 304—Fax: 202-224-6163
Rep: Daines, Chair; Barrasso; Lee; Gardner; Alexander; Hoeven;
  Portman
Dem: Hirono, Rnk. Mem.; Sanders; Stabenow; Heinrich; King;
  Duckworth

ENVIRONMENT AND PUBLIC WORKS

202-224-6176—SD-410—Fax: 224-5167

epw.senate.gov

Republicans (11)
John Barrasso, WY, Chair
James M. Inhofe, OK
Shelley Moore Capito, WV
John Boozman, AR
Roger Wicker, MS
Deb Fischer, NE
Jerry Moran, KS
Mike Rounds, SD
Joni Ernst, IA
Dan Sullivan, AK
Richard C. Shelby, AL

Democrats (10)
Thomas R. Carper, DE,
  Rnk. Mem.
Benjamin L. Cardin, MD
Bernard Sanders, VT (Ind.)
Sheldon Whitehouse, RI
Jeff Merkley, OR
Kirsten Gillibrand, NY
Cory Booker, NJ
Edward J. Markey, MA
Tammy Duckworth, IL
Kamala Harris, CA

Maj. Staff Dir.: Richard Russell
Min. Staff Dir. & Chief Counsel: Gabrielle Batkin

Clean Air and Nuclear Safety
202-224-6176—SD-410—Fax: 224-5167
Rep: TBA
Dem: TBA
Maj. Staff Dir.: Brian Clifford

Fisheries, Water, and Wildlife
202-224-6176—SD-410—Fax: 224-5167
Rep: TBA
Dem: TBA

Superfund, Waste Management, and Regulatory Oversight
202-224-6176—SD-410—Fax: 224-5167
Rep: TBA
Dem: TBA
Maj. Prof. Staff Mem.: Peter Stegner

Transportation and Infrastructure
202-224-6176—SD-410—Fax: 224-5167
Rep: TBA
Dem: TBA

FINANCE

202-224-4515—SD-219—Fax: 228-0554
finance.senate.gov

Republicans (14)
Orrin G. Hatch, UT, Chair
Charles E. Grassley, IA
Michael D. Crapo, ID
Pat Roberts, KS
Michael B. Enzi, WY
John Cornyn, TX
John Thune, SD
Richard M. Burr, NC
Johnny Isakson, GA
Rob Portman, OH
Patrick J. Toomey, PA
Dean Heller, NV
Tim Scott, SC
Bill Cassidy, LA

Democrats (12)
Ron Wyden, OR, Rnk. Mem.
Debbie Stabenow, MI
Maria Cantwell, WA
Bill Nelson, FL
Robert Menendez, NJ
Thomas R. Carper, DE
Benjamin L. Cardin, MD
Sherrod Brown, OH
Michael Bennet, CO
Bob Casey, PA
Mark Warner, VA
Claire McCaskill, MO

Maj. Staff Dir.: Chris Campbell
Min. Staff Dir.: Joshua Sheinkman

SUBCOMMITTEES

Energy, Natural Resources, and Infrastructure
202-224-4515—SD-219—Fax: 228-0554
Rep: Heller, Chair; Grassley; Crapo; Enzi; Cornyn; Burr; Scott; Cassidy
Dem: Bennet, Rnk. Mem.; Cantwell; Nelson; Menendez; Carper;
   Warner
Maj. Staff Dir.: Phillip Pinegar—Min. Staff Dir.: Ryan Abraham

Fiscal Responsibility and Economic Growth
202-224-4515—SD-219—Fax: 228-0554
Rep: Scott, Chair; Hatch
Dem: Wyden, Rnk. Mem.
Maj. Staff Dir.: Zachary Rudisill—Min. Staff Dir: Vacancy

Health Care
202-224-4515—SD-219—Fax: 228-0554
Rep: Toomey, Chair; Grassley; Roberts; Enzi; Thune; Burr; Isakson;
   Portman; Cassidy
Dem: Stabenow, Rnk. Mem.; Menendez; Cantwell; Carper; Cardin;
   Brown; Warner; Wyden
Maj. Staff Dir.: Brad Grantz—Min. Staff Dir.: Elizabeth Jurinka

International Trade, Customs, and Global Competitiveness
202-224-4515—SD-219—Fax: 228-0554
Rep: Cornyn, Chair; Grassley; Roberts; Isakson; Thune; Heller
Dem: Casey, Rnk. Mem.; Stabenow; Nelson; McCaskill
Maj. Staff Dir.: Paul Poteet—Min. Staff Dir.: Vacancy

Social Security, Pensions, and Family Policy
202-224-4515—SD-219—Fax: 228-0554
Rep: Cassidy, Chair; Portman; Crapo; Toomey
Dem: Brown, Rnk. Mem.; Casey
Maj. Staff Dir.: Scott Riplinger
Min. Staff Dir.: Tom Klouda

Taxation and IRS Oversight
202-224-4515—SD-219—Fax: 228-0554
Rep: Portman, Chair; Crapo; Roberts; Enzi; Cornyn; Thune; Burr;
  Isakson; Toomey; Scott
Dem: Warner, Rnk. Mem.; Carper; Cardin; McCaskill; Menendez;
  Bennet; Casey; Cantwell
Maj. Staff Dir.: Mike Quickel
Min. Staff Dir.: Vacancy

FOREIGN RELATIONS

202-224-4651—SD-446—Fax: 224-0836
foreign.senate.gov

Republicans (11)
Bob Corker, TN, Chair
Jim Risch, ID
Marco Rubio, FL
Ron Johnson, WI
Jeff Flake, AZ
Cory Gardner, CO
Todd Young, IN
John Barrasso, WY
Johnny Isakson, GA
Rob Portman, OH
Rand Paul, KY

Democrats (10)
Benjamin L. Cardin, MD,
  Rnk. Mem.
Robert Menendez, NJ
Jeanne Shaheen, NH
Chris Coons, DE
Tom Udall, NM
Christopher S. Murphy, CT
Tim Kaine, VA
Edward J. Markey, MA
Jeff Merkley, OR
Cory Booker, NJ

Maj. Staff Dir.: Chris Tuttle
Min. Staff Dir.: Jessica Lewis

SUBCOMMITTEES

Africa and Global Health Policy
202-224-4651—SD-446—Fax: 224-0836
Rep: Flake, Chair; Young; Barrasso; Isakson; Paul
Dem: Booker, Rnk. Mem.; Coons; Udall; Merkley
Min. Prof. Staff: Heather Flynn

East Asia, The Pacific, and International Cybersecurity Policy
202-224-4651—SD-446—Fax: 224-0836
Rep: Gardner, Chair; Risch; Rubio; Barrasso; Isakson
Dem: Markey, Rnk. Mem.; Merkley; Murphy; Kaine
Min. Counsel: Michael Schiffer

Europe and Regional Security Cooperation
202-224-4651—SD-446—Fax: 224-0836
Rep: Johnson, Chair; Risch; Barrasso; Portman; Paul
Dem: Murphy, Rnk. Mem.; Markey; Menendez; Shaheen
Min. Staff Prof.: Damian Murphy

**Multilateral International Development, Multilateral Institutions,
and International Economic, Energy, and Environmental Policy**
202-224-4651—SD-446—Fax: 224-0836
Rep: Young, Chair; Flake; Gardner; Barrasso; Portman
Dem: Merkley, Rnk. Mem.; Udall; Coons; Markey

Near East, South Asia, Central Asia, and Counterterrorism
202-224-4651—SD-446—Fax: 224-0836
Rep: Risch, Chair; Rubio; Johnson; Young; Portman
Dem: Kaine, Rnk. Mem.; Menendez; Murphy; Booker
Min. Staff Prof.: Dana Stroul

**State Department and USAID Management, International
Operations, and Bilateral International Development**
202-224-4651—SD-446—Fax: 224-0836
Rep: Isakson, Chair; Risch; Rubio; Portman; Paul
Dem: Shaheen, Rnk. Mem.; Coons; Booker; Udall
Min. Staff Prof.: Janet Stormes

Western Hemisphere, Transnational Crime, Civilian Security, Democracy, Human Rights, and Global Women's Issues
202-224-4651—SD-446—Fax: 224-0836
Rep: Rubio, Chair; Johnson; Flake; Gardner; Isakson
Dem: Menendez, Rnk. Mem.; Udall; Shaheen; Kaine
Min. Staff Prof.: Brandon Yoder

HEALTH, EDUCATION, LABOR AND PENSIONS

202-224-5375—SD-428—Fax: 202-228-5044
help.senate.gov

Republicans (12)
Lamar Alexander, TN, Chair
Michael B. Enzi, WY
Richard M. Burr, NC
Johnny Isakson, GA
Rand Paul, KY
Susan Collins, ME
Bill Cassidy, LA
Todd Young, IN
Orrin G. Hatch, UT
Pat Roberts, KS
Lisa Murkowski, AK
Tim Scott, SC

Democrats (11)
Patty Murray, WA, Rnk. Mem.
Bernard Sanders, VT (Ind.)
Bob Casey, PA
Al Franken, MN
Michael Bennet, CO
Sheldon Whitehouse, RI
Tammy Baldwin, WI
Christopher S. Murphy, CT
Elizabeth Warren, MA
Tim Kaine, VA
Maggie Hassan, NH

Maj. Staff Dir.: David Cleary
Min. Staff Dir.: Evan Schatz

SUBCOMMITTEES

Children and Families
202-224-2823—SH 404—Fax: 202-224-7475
Rep: Paul, Chair; Murkowski; Burr; Cassidy; Young; Hatch; Roberts
Dem: Casey, Rnk. Mem.; Sanders; Franken; Bennet; Kaine; Hassan
Maj. Staff Dir.: Natalie Burkhalter
Min. Staff Dir.: Larry Smar

Employment and Workplace Safety
202-224-2621—SH 143—Fax: 202-228-1017
Rep: Isakson, Chair; Roberts; Scott; Burr; Paul; Young
Dem: Franken, Rnk. Mem.; Casey; Whitehouse; Baldwin; Warren
Maj. Staff Dir.: Tommy Nguyen
Min. Staff Dir.: Michael Waske

Primary Health and Retirement Security
202-224-9243—SD 428—Fax: 202-228-0404
Rep: Enzi, Chair; Burr; Collins; Cassidy; Young; Hatch; Roberts; Scott; Murkowski
Dem: Sanders, Rnk. Mem.; Bennet; Whitehouse; Baldwin; Murphy; Warren; Kaine; Hassan
Maj. Staff Prof.: Elizabeth Schwartz
Min. Staff Prof.: Sophie Kasimow

HOMELAND SECURITY AND GOVERNMENTAL AFFAIRS

202-224-4751—SD-340—Fax: 224-9603
hsgac.senate.gov

Republicans (8)
Ron Johnson, WI, Chair
John McCain, AZ
Rob Portman, OH
Rand Paul, KY
James Lankford, OK
Michael B. Enzi, WY
John Hoeven, ND
Steve Daines, MT

Democrats (7)
Claire McCaskill, MO, Rnk. Mem.
Thomas R. Carper, DE
Jon Tester, MT
Heidi Heitkamp, ND
Gary Peters, MI
Maggie Hassan, NH
Kamala Harris, CA

Maj. Staff Dir.: Chris Nixon
Min. Staff Dir.: Gabrielle Batkin

Federal Spending Oversight and Emergency Management
202-224-4751—SH-601—Fax: 202-224-9603
Rep: Paul, Chair; Lankford; Enzi; Hoeven
Dem: Peters, Rnk. Mem.; Hassan; Harris
Maj. Staff Dir.: Brandon Booker
Min. Staff Dir.: Marianna Boyd

Investigations
202-224-3721—SR-199—Fax: 202-224-7042
Rep: Portman, Chair; Lankford; McCain; Paul; Daines
Dem: Carper, Rnk. Mem.; Tester; Heitkamp; Peters
Maj. Staff Dir.: Brian Callanan
Min. Staff Dir.: Margaret Daum

Regulatory Affairs and Federal Management
202-224-4551—SD-340—Fax: 202-224-2271
Rep: Lankford, Chair; McCain; Portman; Enzi; Daines
Dem: Heitkamp, Rnk. Mem.; Carper; Hassan; Harris
Maj. Staff Dir.: John Cuaderes
Min. Staff Dir.: Eric Bursch

JUDICIARY

202-224-5225—SD-224—Fax: 224-9102
judiciary.senate.gov

Republicans (11)
Charles E. Grassley, IA, Chair
Orrin G. Hatch, UT
Lindsey Graham, SC
John Cornyn, TX
Mike Lee, UT
Ted Cruz, TX
Ben Sasse, NE
Jeff Flake, AZ
Michael D. Crapo, ID
Thom Tillis, NC
John N. Kennedy, LA

Democrats (9)
Dianne Feinstein, CA,
  Rnk. Mem.
Patrick J. Leahy, VT
Richard J. Durbin, IL
Sheldon Whitehouse, RI
Amy Klobuchar, MN
Al Franken, MN
Chris Coons, DE
Richard Blumenthal, CT
Mazie K. Hirono, HI

Maj. Staff Dir. & Chief Counsel: Kolan Davis
Min. Staff Dir. & Chief Counsel: Jennifer Duck

SUBCOMMITTEES

Antitrust, Competition Policy and Consumer Rights
202-224-3406—SD-224—Fax: 202-224-9516
Rep: Lee, Chair; Grassley; Hatch; Graham; Tillis
Dem: Klobuchar, Rnk. Mem.; Leahy; Franken; Blumenthal
Maj. Chief Counsel: William Ranney Levi
Min. Counsel: Elizabeth Farrar

Border Security and Immigration
202-224-6498—SD-224—Fax: 202-224-9516
Rep: Cornyn, Chair; Tillis; Kennedy; Grassley; Cruz; Flake; Crapo; Lee
Dem: Durbin, Rnk. Mem.; Feinstein; Leahy; Klobuchar; Franken;
  Blumenthal; Hirono
Maj. Chief Counsel: Danielle Cutrona
Min. Counsel: Rebecca Kelly

Constitution
202-224-1158—SD-224—Fax: 202-224-9516
Rep: Cruz, Chair; Cornyn; Crapo; Sasse; Graham
Dem: Blumenthal, Rnk. Mem.; Durbin; Franken; Coons
Maj. Chief Counsel: Noah Phillips
Min. Chief Counsel: Joe Zogby

Crime and Terrorism
202-228-3740—SD-224—Fax: 202-224-9516
Rep: Graham, Chair; Cornyn; Cruz; Sasse; Kennedy
Dem: Whitehouse, Rnk. Mem.; Durbin; Klobuchar; Coons
Maj. Counsel: Lee Holmes
Min. Counsel: Ayo Griffin

Oversight, Agency Action, Federal Rights and Federal Courts
202-224-2823—SH-702—Fax: 202-224-9516
Rep: Sasse, Chair; Grassley; Crapo; Kennedy; Hatch; Lee; Flake; Tillis
Dem: Coons, Rnk. Mem.; Leahy; Whitehouse; Klobuchar; Franken; Blumenthal; Hirono
Maj. Chief Counsel: Ryan Newman
Min. Staff Dir.: Sam Simon

Privacy, Technology and the Law
202-228-3177—SD-224—Fax: 202-224-9516
Rep: Flake, Chair; Hatch; Lee; Tillis; Crapo; Kennedy
Dem: Franken, Rnk. Mem.; Leahy; Whitehouse; Coons; Hirono
Maj. Chief Counsel: Gary Barnett
Min. Chief Counsel: Vacancy

RULES AND ADMINISTRATION

202-224-6352—SR-305—Fax: 224-3036
rules.senate.gov

Republicans (10)
Richard C. Shelby, AL, Chair
Lamar Alexander, TN
Mitch McConnell, KY
Thad Cochran, MS
Pat Roberts, KS
Roy Blunt, MO
Ted Cruz, TX
Shelley Moore Capito, WV
Roger Wicker, MS
Deb Fischer, NE

Democrats (9)
Amy Klobuchar, MN, Rnk. Mem.
Dianne Feinstein, CA
Charles E. Schumer, NY
Richard J. Durbin, IL
Tom Udall, NM
Mark Warner, VA
Patrick J. Leahy, VT
Angus King, ME (Ind.)
Catherine Cortez Masto, NV

Maj. Staff Dir.: Bill Duhnke
Min. Staff Dir.: Jennifer Griffith

NO SUBCOMMITTEES

SMALL BUSINESS AND ENTREPRENEURSHIP

202-224-5175—SR-428A—Fax: 224-5619
sbc.senate.gov

Republicans (10)
Jim Risch, ID, Chair
Marco Rubio, FL
Rand Paul, KY
Tim Scott, SC
Joni Ernst, IA
James M. Inhofe, OK
Todd Young, IN
Michael B. Enzi, WY
Mike Rounds, SD
John N. Kennedy, LA

Democrats (9)
Jeanne Shaheen, NH, Rnk. Mem.
Maria Cantwell, WA
Benjamin L. Cardin, MD
Heidi Heitkamp, ND
Edward J. Markey, MA
Cory Booker, NJ
Chris Coons, DE
Mazie K. Hirono, HI
Tammy Duckworth, IL

Maj. Staff Dir.: Skiffington Holderness
Min. Staff Dir.: Sean Moore

NO SUBCOMMITTEES

VETERANS' AFFAIRS

202-224-9126—SR-412—Fax: 224-9575
veterans.senate.gov

Republicans (8)
Johnny Isakson, GA, Chair
Jerry Moran, KS
John Boozman, AR
Dean Heller, NV
Bill Cassidy, LA
Mike Rounds, SD
Thom Tillis, NC
Dan Sullivan, AK

Democrats (7)
Jon Tester, MT, Rnk. Mem.
Patty Murray, WA
Bernard Sanders, VT (Ind.)
Sherrod Brown, OH
Richard Blumenthal, CT
Mazie K. Hirono, HI
Joe Manchin III, WV

Maj. Staff Dir.: Thomas Bowman
Min. Staff Dir.: Tony McClain

NO SUBCOMMITTEES

INDIAN AFFAIRS

202-224-2251—SH-838—Fax: 224-2589
indian.senate.gov

Republicans (8)
John Hoeven, ND, Chair
John Barrasso, WY
John McCain, AZ
Lisa Murkowski, AK
James Lankford, OK
Steve Daines, MT
Michael D. Crapo, ID
Jerry Moran, KS

Democrats (7)
Tom Udall, NM, Vice Chair
Maria Cantwell, WA
Jon Tester, MT
Al Franken, MN
Brian Schatz, HI
Heidi Heitkamp, ND
Catherine Cortez Masto, NV

Maj. Staff Dir. & Chief Counsel: Mike Andrews
Min. Staff Dir. & Chief Counsel: Jennifer Romero

NO SUBCOMMITTEES

SELECT ON ETHICS

202-224-2981—SH-220—Fax: 224-7416
ethics.senate.gov

Republicans (3)
Johnny Isakson, GA, Chair
Pat Roberts, KS
Jim Risch, ID

Democrats (3)
Chris Coons, DE, Vice Chair
Brian Schatz, HI
Jeanne Shaheen, NH

Staff Dir. & Chief Counsel: Deborah Sue Mayer

NO SUBCOMMITTEES

SELECT ON INTELLIGENCE

202-224-1700—SH-211—Fax: 224-1772
intelligence.senate.gov

Republicans (8)
Richard M. Burr, NC, Chair
Jim Risch, ID
Marco Rubio, FL
Susan Collins, ME
Roy Blunt, MO
James Lankford, OK
Tom Cotton, AR
John Cornyn, TX

Democrats (7)
Mark Warner, VA, Vice Chair
Dianne Feinstein, CA
Ron Wyden, OR
Martin Heinrich, NM
Angus King, ME (Ind.)
Joe Manchin III, WV
Kamala Harris, CA

Maj. Staff Dir.: Chris Joyner
Min. Staff Dir.: David Grannis

NO SUBCOMMITTEES

SPECIAL ON AGING

202-224-5364—SD-G31—Fax: 224-9926
aging.senate.gov

Republicans (9)
Susan Collins, ME, Chair
Orrin G. Hatch, UT
Jeff Flake, AZ
Tim Scott, SC
Thom Tillis, NC
Bob Corker, TN
Richard M. Burr, NC
Marco Rubio, FL
Deb Fischer, NE

Democrats (8)
Bob Casey, PA, Rnk. Mem.
Bill Nelson, FL
Sheldon Whitehouse, RI
Kirsten Gillibrand, NY
Richard Blumenthal, CT
Joe Donnelly, IN
Elizabeth Warren, MA
Catherine Cortez Masto, NV

Maj. Staff Dir.: Kevin Kelley
Min. Staff Dir.: Kate Mevis

NO SUBCOMMITTEES

HOUSE STANDING COMMITTEES
AGRICULTURE

202-225-2171—1301 LHOB—Fax: 225-0917
agriculture.house.gov

Republicans (26)
K. Michael Conaway, 11th-TX, Chair
Robert W. Goodlatte, 6th-VA
Frank D. Lucas, 3rd-OK
Steve King, 4th-IA
Mike D. Rogers, 3rd-AL
Glenn Thompson, 5th-PA
Bob Gibbs, 7th-OH
Austin Scott, 8th-GA
Rick Crawford, 1st-AR
Scott DesJarlais, 4th-TN
Vicky Hartzler, 4th-MO
Jeff Denham, 10th-CA
Doug LaMalfa, 1st-CA
Rodney Davis, 13th-IL
Ted Yoho, 3rd-FL
Rick W. Allen, 12th-GA
Mike Bost, 12th-IL
David Rouzer, 7th-NC
Ralph Abraham, 5th-LA
Trent Kelly, 1st-MS
James R. Comer, 1st-KY
Roger Marshall, 1st-KS
Don Bacon, 2nd-NE
John J. Faso, 19th-NY
Neal Dunn, 2nd-FL
Jodey C. Arrington, 19th-TX

Democrats (20)
Collin C. Peterson, 7th-MN, Rnk. Mem.
David Scott, 13th-GA
Jim Costa, 16th-CA
Tim Walz, 1st-MN
Marcia L. Fudge, 11th-OH
Jim McGovern, 2nd-MA
Filemon Vela, 34th-TX
Michelle Lujan Grisham, 1st-NM
Ann McLane Kuster, 2nd-NH
Rick Nolan, 8th-MN
Cheri Bustos, 17th-IL
Sean Patrick Maloney, 18th-NY
Stacey Plaskett, At Large-VI
Alma Adams, 12th-NC
Dwight Evans, 2nd-PA
Al Lawson, 5th-FL
Tom O'Halleran, 1st-AZ
Jimmy Panetta, 20th-CA
Darren Soto, 9th-FL
Lisa Blunt Rochester, At Large-DE

Maj. Staff Dir.: Matt Schertz
Min. Staff Dir.: Anne Simmons

SUBCOMMITTEES

Biotechnology, Horticulture, and Research
Rep: Davis, Chair; Gibbs; Denham; Yoho; Rouzer; Bacon; Dunn; Arrington
Dem: Lujan Grisham, Rnk. Mem.; Lawson; Panetta; Costa; McGovern; Blunt Rochester

Commodity Exchanges, Energy, and Credit
Rep: Scott, Chair; Goodlatte; Rogers; LaMalfa; Davis; Comer; Marshall; Faso
Dem: Scott, Rnk. Mem.; Maloney; Kuster; Plaskett; O'Halleran; Soto

Conservation and Forestry
Rep: Lucas, Chair; Thompson; Denham; LaMalfa; Allen; Bost; Abraham; Kelly
Dem: Fudge, Rnk. Mem.; Walz; Kuster; Nolan; O'Halleran; Vela

General Farm Commodities and Risk Management
Rep: Crawford, Chair; Lucas; Rogers; Gibbs; Scott; DesJarlais; Allen; Bost; Abraham; Bacon; Dunn; Arrington
Dem: Nolan, Rnk. Mem.; Walz; Bustos; Blunt Rochester; Scott; Maloney; Plaskett; Lawson; O'Halleran

Livestock and Foreign Agriculture
Rep: Rouzer, Chair; Goodlatte; King; DesJarlais; Hartzler; Yoho; Kelly; Marshall
Dem: Costa, Rnk. Mem.; Vela; Bustos; Plaskett; Evans; Vacancy

Nutrition
Rep: Thompson, Chair; King; Crawford; DesJarlais; Hartzler; Davis; Yoho; Rouzer; Comer; Marshall; Faso; Arrington
Dem: McGovern, Rnk. Mem.; Adams; Evans; Fudge; Lujan Grisham; Lawson; Panetta; Soto; Maloney

APPROPRIATIONS

202-225-2771—H-305 Capitol—Fax: 225-5078
appropriations.house.gov

Republicans (30)
Rodney Frelinghuysen, 11th-NJ, Chair
Harold Rogers, 5th-KY
Robert B. Aderholt, 4th-AL
Kay Granger, 12th-TX
Mike Simpson, 2nd-ID
John Culberson, 7th-TX
John Carter, 31st-TX
Ken Calvert, 42nd-CA
Tom Cole, 4th-OK
Mario Diaz-Balart, 25th-FL
Charlie Dent, 15th-PA
Tom Graves, 14th-GA
Kevin Yoder, 3rd-KS
Steve Womack, 3rd-AR
Jeff Fortenberry, 1st-NE
Tom Rooney, 17th-FL
Chuck Fleischmann, 3rd-TN
Jaime Herrera Beutler, 3rd-WA
David Joyce, 14th-OH
David Valadao, 21st-CA
Andy Harris, 1st-MD
Martha Roby, 2nd-AL
Mark Amodei, 2nd-NV
Chris Stewart, 2nd-UT
David Young, 3rd-IA
Evan H. Jenkins, 3rd-WV
Steven M. Palazzo, 4th-MS
Dan Newhouse, 4th-WA
John Moolenaar, 4th-MI
Scott W. Taylor, 2nd-VA

Democrats (22)
Nita M. Lowey, 17th-NY, Rnk. Mem.
Marcy Kaptur, 9th-OH
Peter J. Visclosky, 1st-IN
José E. Serrano, 15th-NY
Rosa DeLauro, 3rd-CT
David E. Price, 4th-NC
Lucille Roybal-Allard, 40th-CA
Sanford D. Bishop, Jr., 2nd-GA
Barbara Lee, 13th-CA
Betty McCollum, 4th-MN
Tim Ryan, 13th-OH
C.A. Dutch Ruppersberger, 2nd-MD
Debbie Wasserman Schultz, 23rd-FL
Henry Cuellar, 28th-TX
Chellie Pingree, 1st-ME
Mike Quigley, 5th-IL
Derek Kilmer, 6th-WA
Matt Cartwright, 17th-PA
Grace Meng, 6th-NY
Mark Pocan, 2nd-WI
Katherine M. Clark, 5th-MA
Pete Aguilar, 31st-CA

Maj. Staff Dir./Clerk: Nancy Fox
Min. Staff Dir./Clerk: Shalanda Young

SUBCOMMITTEES

Agriculture, Rural Development, Food and Drug Administration
Rep: Aderholt, Chair; Yoder; Rooney; Valadao; Harris; Young; Palazzo
Dem: DeLauro, Rnk. Mem.; DeLauro; Pingree; Pocan

Commerce, Justice, Science, and Related Agencies
Rep: Culberson, Chair; Rogers; Aderholt; Carter; Roby; Palazzo; Jenkins
Dem: Serrano, Rnk. Mem.; Kilmer; Cartwright; Meng

Defense
Rep: Granger, Chair; Rogers; Calvert; Cole; Womack; Aderholt; Carter; Diaz-Balart; Graves; Roby
Dem: Visclosky, Rnk. Mem.; McCollum; Ryan; Ruppersberger; Kaptur; Cuellar

Energy and Water Development, and Related Agencies
Rep: Simpson, Chair; Calvert; Fleischmann; Fortenberry; Granger; Herrera Beutler; Joyce; Newhouse
Dem: Kaptur, Rnk. Mem.; Visclosky; Wasserman Schultz; Aguilar; Serrano

Financial Services and General Government
Rep: Graves, Chair; Yoder; Herrera Beutler; Amodei; Stewart; Young; Moolenaar
Dem: Quigley, Rnk. Mem.; Serrano; Cartwright; Bishop

Homeland Security
Rep: Carter, Chair; Culberson; Fleischmann; Harris; Palazzo; Newhouse; Taylor
Dem: Roybal-Allard, Rnk. Mem.; Cuellar; Price; Ruppersberger

Interior, Environment, and Related Agencies
Rep: Calvert, Chair; Simpson; Cole; Joyce; Stewart; Amodei; Jenkins
Dem: McCollum, Rnk. Mem.; Pingree; Kilmer; Kaptur

SUBCOMMITTEES (Appropriations)

Labor, Health and Human Services, Education, and Related Agencies
Rep: Cole, Chair; Simpson; Womack; Fleischmann; Harris; Roby; Herrera Beutler; Moolenaar
Dem: DeLauro, Rnk. Mem.; Roybal-Allard; Lee; Pocan; Clark;

Legislative Branch
Rep: Yoder, Chair; Amodei; Newhouse; Moolenaar; Taylor
Dem: Ryan, Rnk. Mem.; McCollum; Wasserman Schultz

Military Construction, Veterans Affairs, and Related Agencies
Rep: Dent, Chair; Fortenberry; Rooney; Valadao; Womack; Jenkins; Taylor
Dem: Wasserman Schultz, Rnk. Mem.; Bishop; Lee; Ryan

State, Foreign Operations, and Related Programs
Rep: Rogers, Chair; Granger; Diaz-Balart; Dent; Rooney; Fortenberry; Stewart
Dem: Lowey, Rnk. Mem.; Lee; Ruppersberger; Meng; Price

Transportation, Housing and Urban Development, and Related Agencies
Rep: Diaz-Balart, Chair; Dent; Joyce; Culberson; Young; Valadao; Graves
Dem: Price, Rnk. Mem.; Quigley; Clark; Aguilar

ARMED SERVICES

202-225-4151—2126 RHOB—Fax: 225-9077
armedservices.house.gov

Republicans (34)
Mac Thornberry, 13th-TX, Chair
Walter B. Jones, 3rd-NC
Joe Wilson, 2nd-SC
Frank A. LoBiondo, 2nd-NJ
Rob Bishop, 1st-UT
Michael R. Turner, 10th-OH
Mike D. Rogers, 3rd-AL
Trent Franks, 8th-AZ
Bill Shuster, 9th-PA
K. Michael Conaway, 11th-TX
Doug Lamborn, 5th-CO
Rob Wittman, 1st-VA
Duncan Hunter, 50th-CA
Mike Coffman, 6th-CO
Vicky Hartzler, 4th-MO
Austin Scott, 8th-GA
Mo Brooks, 5th-AL
Paul Cook, 8th-CA
Jim Bridenstine, 1st-OK
Brad Wenstrup, 2nd-OH
Bradley Byrne, 1st-AL
Sam Graves, 6th-MO
Elise Stefanik, 21st-NY
Martha McSally, 2nd-AZ
Steve Knight, 25th-CA
Steve Russell, 5th-OK
Scott DesJarlais, 4th-TN
Ralph Abraham, 5th-LA
Trent Kelly, 1st-MS
Mike Gallagher, 8th-WI
Matt Gaetz, 1st-FL
Don Bacon, 2nd-NE
Jim Banks, 3rd-IN
Liz Cheney, At Large-WY

Democrats (28)
Adam Smith, 9th-WA, Rnk. Mem.
Robert A. Brady, 1st-PA
Susan A. Davis, 53rd-CA
Jim Langevin, 2nd-RI
Rick Larsen, 2nd-WA
Jim Cooper, 5th-TN
Madeleine Z. Bordallo, At Large-GU
Joe Courtney, 2nd-CT
Niki Tsongas, 3rd-MA
John Garamendi, 3rd-CA
Jackie Speier, 14th-CA
Marc Veasey, 33rd-TX
Tulsi Gabbard, 2nd-HI
Beto O'Rourke, 16th-TX
Donald Norcross, 1st-NJ
Ruben Gallego, 7th-AZ
Seth Moulton, 6th-MA
Colleen Hanabusa, 1st-HI
Carol Shea-Porter, 1st-NH
Jacky Rosen, 3rd-NV
A. Donald McEachin, 4th-VA
Salud Carbajal, 24th-CA
Anthony G. Brown, 4th-MD
Stephanie Murphy, 7th-FL
Ro Khanna, 17th-CA
Tom O'Halleran, 1st-AZ
Tom Suozzi, 3rd-NY
Vacancy

Maj. Staff Dir.: Bob Simmons
Min. Staff Dir.: Paul Arcangeli

Emerging Threats And Capabilities
202-225-4151-2340 RHOB-Fax: 202-226-0105
Rep: Stefanik, Chair; Shuster; Wenstrup; Abraham; Cheney; Wilson;
  LoBiondo; Franks; Lamborn; Scott
Dem: Langevin, Rnk. Mem.; Larsen; Cooper; Speier; Veasey;
  Gabbard; O'Rourke; Murphy
Maj. Staff Dir.: Vacant
Min. Staff Dir.: Vacant

Military Personnel
202-225-4151-2340 RHOB-Fax: 202-226-0105
Rep: Coffman, Chair; Jones; Wenstrup; Russell; Bacon; McSally;
  Abraham; Kelly
Dem: Speier, Rnk. Mem.; Brady; Tsongas; Gallego; Shea-Porter; Rosen
Maj. Clerk: Colin Bosse
Min. Counsel: William "Spencer" Johnson

Oversight And Investigations
202-225-4151-2120 RHOB-Fax: 202-225-7102
Rep: Hartzler, Chair; Conaway; Gaetz; Banks; Cheney; Scott
Dem: Moulton, Rnk. Mem.; O'Halleran; Suozzi
Maj. Clerk: Anna Waterfield
Min. Staff Dir.: Vacant

Readiness
202-225-4151-2340 RHOB-Fax: 202-226-0789
Rep: Wilson, Chair; Bishop; Scott; Russell; Rogers; Hartzler;
  Stefanik; McSally; DesJarlais; Kelly; Gallagher
Dem: Bordallo, Rnk. Mem.; Courtney; Gabbard; Shea-Porter;
  McEachin; Carbajal; Brown; Murphy; Khanna
Maj. Clerk: Jodi Brignola
Min. Staff Dir.: Vacant

Seapower And Projection Forces
202-225-4151-2340 RHOB-Fax: 202-226-0105
Rep: Wittman, Chair; Conaway; Hartzler; Byrne; DesJarlais;
  Gallagher; Hunter; Cook; Bridenstine; Knight; Abraham
Dem: Courtney, Rnk. Mem.; Davis; Langevin; Bordallo; Garamendi;
  Norcross; Moulton; Hanabusa; McEachin
Maj. Clerk: Jodi Brignola
Min. Staff Dir.: Phil MacNaughton

Strategic Forces
202-225-4151-2340 RHOB-Fax: 202-226-0105
Rep: Rogers, Chair; Franks; Lamborn; Hunter; Brooks; Bridenstine;
  Turner; Coffman; Byrne; Graves
Dem: Cooper, Rnk. Mem.; Davis; Larsen; Garamendi; O'Rourke;
  Norcross; Hanabusa; Khanna
Maj. Clerk: Michael Gancio
Min. Counsel: Leonor Tomero

Tactical Air And Land Forces
202-225-4151-2340 RHOB-Fax: 202-226-0105
Rep: Turner, Chair; LoBiondo; Cook; Graves; McSally; Knight; Kelly;
  Gaetz; Bacon; Banks; Jones; Bishop; Wittman; Brooks
Dem: Tsongas, Rnk. Mem.; Langevin; Cooper; Veasey; Gallego;
  Rosen; Carbajal; Brown; O'Halleran; Suozzi
Maj. Staff Dir.: Vacant
Min. Staff Dir.: Vacant

BUDGET

202-226-7270—207 CHOB—Fax: 226-7174
budget.house.gov

Republicans (22)
Diane Black, 6th-TN, Chair
Mario Diaz-Balart, 25th-FL
Tom Cole, 4th-OK
Tom McClintock, 4th-CA
Todd Rokita, 4th-IN
Rob Woodall, 7th-GA
Mark Sanford, 1st-SC
Steve Womack, 3rd-AR
Dave Brat, 7th-VA
Glenn Grothman, 6th-WI
Gary Palmer, 6th-AL
Bruce Westerman, 4th-AR
James B. Renacci, 16th-OH
Bill Johnson, 6th-OH
Jason Smith, 8th-MO
Jason Lewis, 2nd-MN
Jack Bergman, 1st-MI
John J. Faso, 19th-NY
Lloyd K. Smucker, 16th-PA
Matt Gaetz, 1st-FL
Jodey C. Arrington, 19th-TX
Drew Ferguson, 3rd-GA

Democrats (14)
John Yarmuth, 3rd-KY,
    Rnk. Mem.
Barbara Lee, 13th-CA
Michelle Lujan Grisham,
    1st-NM
Seth Moulton, 6th-MA
Hakeem Jeffries, 8th-NY
Brian Higgins, 26th-NY
Suzan DelBene, 1st-WA
Debbie Wasserman Schultz,
    23rd-FL
Brendan F. Boyle, 13th-PA
Ro Khanna, 17th-CA
Pramila Jayapal, 7th-WA
Salud Carbajal, 24th-CA
Shelia Jackson Lee, 18th-TX
Jan Schakowsky, 9th-IL

Maj. Staff Dir.: Rick May
Min. Staff Dir.: Ellen Balif

NO SUBCOMMITTEES

EDUCATION AND THE WORKFORCE

202-225-4527—2176 RHOB—Fax: 225-9571
edworkforce.house.gov

Republicans (23)
Virginia Foxx, 5th-NC, Chair
Joe Wilson, 2nd-SC
Duncan Hunter, 50th-CA
Phil Roe, 1st-TN
Glenn Thompson, 5th-PA
Tim Walberg, 7th-MI
Brett Guthrie, 2nd-KY
Todd Rokita, 4th-IN
Lou Barletta, 11th-PA
Luke Messer, 6th-IN
Bradley Byrne, 1st-AL
Dave Brat, 7th-VA
Glenn Grothman, 6th-WI
Steve Russell, 5th-OK
Elise Stefanik, 21st-NY
Rick W. Allen, 12th-GA
Jason Lewis, 2nd-MN
Francis Rooney, 19th-FL
Paul Mitchell, 10th-MI
Tom Garrett, 5th-VA
Lloyd K. Smucker, 16th-PA
Drew Ferguson, 3rd-GA
Vacancy

Democrats (17)
Robert C. Scott, 3rd-VA, Rnk. Mem.
Susan A. Davis, 53rd-CA
Raúl M. Grijalva, 3rd-AZ
Joe Courtney, 2nd-CT
Marcia L. Fudge, 11th-OH
Jared Polis, 2nd-CO
Gregorio Kilili Camacho Sablan,
    At Large-MP
Frederica S. Wilson, 24th-FL
Suzanne Bonamici, 1st-OR
Mark Takano, 41st-CA
Alma Adams, 12th-NC
Mark DeSaulnier, 11th-CA
Donald Norcross, 1st-NJ
Lisa Blunt Rochester, At Large-DE
Raja Krishnamoorthi, 8th-IL
Carol Shea-Porter, 1st-NH
Adriano Espaillat, 13th-NY

Maj. Staff Dir.: Brandon Renz
Min. Staff Dir.: Denise Forte

SUBCOMMITTEES

Early Childhood, Elementary, and Secondary Education
Rep: Rokita, Chair; Hunter; Roe; Thompson; Messer; Brat; Garrett
Dem: Polis, Rnk. Mem.; Grijalva; Fudge; Bonamici; Davis; Wilson

Health, Employment, Labor, and Pensions
Rep: Walberg, Chair; Wilson; Roe; Rokita; Barletta; Allen; Lewis;
    Rooney; Mitchell; Smucker; Ferguson; Vacancy
Dem: Sablan, Rnk. Mem.; Wilson; Norcross; Blunt Rochester;
    Shea-Porter; Espaillat; Courtney; Fudge; Bonamici

Higher Education and Workforce Training
Rep: Guthrie, Chair; Thompson; Barletta; Messer; Byrne; Grothman;
    Stefanik; Allen; Lewis; Mitchell; Garrett; Smucker
Dem: Davis, Rnk. Mem.; Courtney; Adams; DeSaulnier;
    Krishnamoorthi; Polis; Sablan; Takano; Blunt Rochester; Espaillat

Workforce Protections
Rep: Byrne, Chair; Wilson; Hunter; Brat; Grothman; Stefanik;
    Rooney; Ferguson; Vacancy
Dem: Takano, Rnk. Mem.; Grijalva; Adams; DeSaulnier; Norcross;
    Krishnamoorthi; Shea-Porter

ENERGY AND COMMERCE

202-225-2927—2125 RHOB—Fax: 225-1919
energycommerce.house.gov

Republicans (31)
Greg Walden, 2nd-OR, Chair
Joe L. Barton, 6th-TX
John Shimkus, 15th-IL
Tim Murphy, 18th-PA
Michael C. Burgess, 26th-TX
Marsha Blackburn, 7th-TN
Fred Upton, 6th-MI
Steve Scalise, 1st-LA
Bob Latta, 5th-OH
Cathy McMorris Rodgers, 5th-WA
Gregg Harper, 3rd-MS
Leonard Lance, 7th-NJ
Brett Guthrie, 2nd-KY
Pete Olson, 22nd-TX
David B. McKinley, 1st-WV
Adam Kinzinger, 16th-IL
Morgan Griffith, 9th-VA
Gus Bilirakis, 12th-FL
Bill Johnson, 6th-OH
Billy Long, 7th-MO
Larry Bucshon, 8th-IN
Bill Flores, 17th-TX
Susan W. Brooks, 5th-IN
Markwayne Mullin, 2nd-OK
Richard Hudson, 8th-NC
Chris Collins, 27th-NY
Kevin Cramer, At Large-ND
Earl L. "Buddy" Carter, 1st-GA
Ryan A. Costello, 6th-PA
Tim Walberg, 7th-MI
Mimi Walters, 45th-CA

Democrats (24)
Frank Pallone, Jr., 6th-NJ,
   Rnk. Mem.
Bobby L. Rush, 1st-IL
Anna G. Eshoo, 18th-CA
Eliot L. Engel, 16th-NY
Gene Green, 29th-TX
Diana DeGette, 1st-CO
Mike Doyle, 14th-PA
Jan Schakowsky, 9th-IL
G.K. Butterfield, 1st-NC
Doris Matsui, 6th-CA
Kathy Castor, 14th-FL
John Sarbanes, 3rd-MD
Jerry McNerney, 9th-CA
Peter Welch, At Large-VT
Ben Ray Luján, 3rd-NM
Paul Tonko, 20th-NY
Yvette D. Clarke, 9th-NY
Dave Loebsack, 2nd-IA
Kurt Schrader, 5th-OR
Joseph P. Kennedy III, 4th-MA
Tony Cárdenas, 29th-CA
Raul Ruiz, 36th-CA
Scott Peters, 52nd-CA
Debbie Dingell, 12th-MI

Maj. Staff Dir.: Ray Baum
Min. Staff Dir.: Jeff Carroll

SUBCOMMITTEES

Communications and Technology
Rep: Blackburn, Chair; Lance; Shimkus; Scalise; Latta; Guthrie;
   Olson; Kinzinger; Bilirakis; Johnson; Long; Flores; Brooks;
   Collins; Cramer; Walters; Costello; Walden
Dem: Doyle, Rnk. Mem.; Welch; Clarke; Loebsack; Ruiz; Dingell;
   Rush; Eshoo; Engel; Butterfield; Matsui; McNerney; Pallone

Energy and Power
Rep: Upton, Chair; Olson; Barton; Shimkus; Murphy; Latta; Harper;
   McKinley; Kinzinger; Griffith; Johnson; Long; Bucshon; Flores;
   Mullin; Hudson; Cramer; Walberg; Walden
Dem: Rush, Rnk. Mem.; McNerney; Peters; Green; Doyle; Castor;
   Sarbanes; Welch; Tonko; Loebsack; Schrader; Kennedy;
   Butterfield; Pallone

Environment and the Economy
Rep: Shimkus, Chair; McKinley; Barton; Murphy; Blackburn;
   Harper; Olson; Johnson; Flores; Hudson; Cramer; Latta; Walberg;
   Carter
Dem: Tonko, Rnk. Mem.; Ruiz; Peters; Green; DeGette; McNerney;
   Cárdenas; Dingell; Matsui; Pallone

Health

Rep: Burgess, Chair; Guthrie; Barton; Upton; Shimkus; Murphy; Blackburn; McMorris Rodgers; Lance; Griffith; Bilirakis; Long; Bucshon; Brooks; Mullin; Hudson; Collins; Carter; Walden

Dem: Green, Rnk. Mem.; Engel; Schakowsky; Butterfield; Matsui; Castor; Sarbanes; Luján; Schrader; Kennedy; Cárdenas; Eshoo; DeGette; Pallone

Oversight and Investigations

Rep: Murphy, Chair; Griffith; Barton; Burgess; Brooks; Collins; Walberg; Walters; Bucshon; Costello; Carter; Walden

Dem: DeGette, Rnk. Mem.; Schakowsky; Castor; Tonko; Clarke; Ruiz; Peters; Pallone

Digital Commerce and Consumer Protection

Rep: Latta, Chair; Harper; Upton; Burgess; Lance; Guthrie; McKinley; Kinzinger; Bilirakis; Bucshon; Mullin; Walters; Costello; Walden

Dem: Schakowsky, Rnk. Mem.; Luján; Clarke; Cárdenas; Dingell; Matsui; Welch; Kennedy; Green; Pallone

ETHICS

202-225-7103—1015 LHOB—Fax: 225-7392
ethics.house.gov

Republicans (5)	**Democrats (5)**
Susan W. Brooks, 5th-IN, Chair	Ted Deutch, 22nd-FL, Rnk. Mem.
Patrick Meehan, 7th-PA	Yvette D. Clarke, 9th-NY
Trey Gowdy, 4th-SC	Jared Polis, 2nd-CO
Kenny Marchant, 24th-TX	Anthony G. Brown, 4th-MD
Leonard Lance, 7th-NJ	Steve Cohen, 9th-TN

Staff Dir. & Chief Counsel: Tom Rust

NO SUBCOMMITTEES

FINANCIAL SERVICES

202-225-7502—2129 RHOB—Fax: 226-0682
financialservices.house.gov

Republicans (34)
Jeb Hensarling, 5th-TX, Chair
Peter T. King, 2nd-NY
Ed Royce, 39th-CA
Frank D. Lucas, 3rd-OK
Patrick T. McHenry, 10th-NC
Steve Pearce, 2nd-NM
Bill Posey, 8th-FL
Blaine Luetkemeyer, 3rd-MO
Bill Huizenga, 2nd-MI
Sean P. Duffy, 7th-WI
Steve Stivers, 15th-OH
Randy Hultgren, 14th-IL
Dennis A. Ross, 15th-FL
Robert Pittenger, 9th-NC
Ann Wagner, 2nd-MO
Andy Barr, 6th-KY
Keith Rothfus, 12th-PA
Luke Messer, 6th-IN
Scott Tipton, 3rd-CO
Roger Williams, 25th-TX
Bruce Poliquin, 2nd-ME
Mia Love, 4th-UT
French Hill, 2nd-AR
Tom Emmer, 6th-MN
Lee Zeldin, 1st-NY
Dave Trott, 11th-MI
Barry Loudermilk, 11th-GA
Alex Mooney, 2nd-WV
Tom MacArthur, 3rd-NJ
Warren Davidson, 8th-OH
Ted Budd, 13th-NC
David Kustoff, 8th-TN
Claudia Tenney, 22nd-NY
Trey Hollingsworth, 9th-IN

Democrats (26)
Maxine Waters, 43rd-CA,
    Rnk. Mem.
Carolyn B. Maloney, 12th-NY
Nydia M. Velázquez, 7th-NY
Brad Sherman, 30th-CA
Gregory W. Meeks, 5th-NY
Michael E. Capuano, 7th-MA
William Lacy Clay, 1st-MO
Stephen F. Lynch, 8th-MA
David Scott, 13th-GA
Al Green, 9th-TX
Emanuel Cleaver II, 5th-MO
Gwen Moore, 4th-WI
Keith Ellison, 5th-MN
Ed Perlmutter, 7th-CO
Jim Himes, 4th-CT
Bill Foster, 11th-IL
Dan Kildee, 5th-MI
John Delaney, 6th-MD
Kyrsten Sinema, 9th-AZ
Joyce Beatty, 3rd-OH
Denny Heck, 10th-WA
Juan C. Vargas, 51st-CA
Josh Gottheimer, 5th-NJ
Vicente Gonzalez, 15th-TX
Charlie Crist, 13th-FL
Ruben Kihuen, 4th-NV

Maj. Staff Dir.: Kirsten Mork
Min. Staff Dir.: Charla Ouertatani

SUBCOMMITTEES

Capital Markets, Securities, and Investments
Rep: Huizenga, Chair; Hultgren; King; McHenry; Duffy; Stivers;
  Wagner; Messer; Poliquin; Hill; Emmer; Mooney; MacArthur;
  Davidson; Budd; Hollingsworth
Dem: Maloney, Rnk. Mem.; Sherman; Meeks; Lynch; Scott; Ellison;
  Himes; Foster; Sinema; Vargas; Gottheimer; Gonzalez

Financial Institutions and Consumer Credit
Rep: Luetkemeyer, Chair; Rothfus; Royce; Lucas; Posey; Ross;
  Pittenger; Barr; Tipton; Williams; Love; Trott; Loudermilk; Kustoff;
  Tenney
Dem: Clay, Rnk. Mem.; Heck; Crist; Maloney; Velázquez; Meeks;
  Capuano; Scott; Green; Moore; Ellison

Housing and Insurance
Rep: Duffy, Chair; Ross; Royce; Pearce; Posey; Luetkemeyer; Stivers;
  Hultgren; Rothfus; Zeldin; Trott; MacArthur; Budd
Dem: Cleaver, Rnk. Mem.; Velázquez; Capuano; Kildee; Beatty;
  Delaney; Kihuen; Sherman; Clay; Lynch

Monetary Policy and Trade
Rep: Barr, Chair; Williams, Vice Chair; Lucas; Huizenga; Pittenger;
  Love; Hill; Emmer; Mooney; Davidson; Tenney; Hollingsworth
Dem: Moore, Rnk. Mem.; Heck; Crist; Sherman; Meeks; Green;
  Foster; Kildee; Vargas

Oversight and Investigations
Rep: Wagner, Chair; Tipton; King; McHenry; Ross; Messer; Zeldin;
  Trott; Loudermilk; Kustoff; Tenney; Hollingsworth
Dem: Green, Rnk. Mem.; Cleaver; Beatty; Ellison; Moore; Capuano;
  Crist; Gottheimer; Gonzalez

Terrorism and Illicit Finance
Rep: Pearce, Chair; Pittenger; Rothfus; Messer; Tipton; Williams;
    Poliquin; Love; Hill; Emmer; Zeldin; Davidson; Budd; Kustoff
Dem: Perlmutter, Rnk. Mem.; Himes; Foster; Kildee; Delaney;
    Sinema; Vargas; Gottheimer; Gonzalez; Kihuen; Maloney

FOREIGN AFFAIRS

202-225-5021—2170 RHOB—Fax: 226-5394
foreignaffairs.house.gov

Republicans (26)
Ed Royce, 39th-CA, Chair
Christopher H. Smith, 4th-NJ
Ileana Ros-Lehtinen, 27th-FL
Dana Rohrabacher, 48th-CA
Steve Chabot, 1st-OH
Joe Wilson, 2nd-SC
Michael McCaul, 10th-TX
Ted Poe, 2nd-TX
Darrell Issa, 49th-CA
Tom Marino, 10th-PA
Jeff Duncan, 3rd-SC
Mo Brooks, 5th-AL
Paul Cook, 8th-CA
Scott Perry, 4th-PA
Ron DeSantis, 6th-FL
Mark Meadows, 11th-NC
Ted Yoho, 3rd-FL
Adam Kinzinger, 16th-IL
Lee Zeldin, 1st-NY
Dan Donovan, 11th-NY
Jim Sensenbrenner, 5th-WI
Ann Wagner, 2nd-MO
Brian Mast, 18th-FL
Francis Rooney, 19th-FL
Brian Fitzpatrick, 8th-PA
Tom Garrett, 5th-VA

Democrats (21)
Eliot L. Engel, 16th-NY, Rnk. Mem.
Brad Sherman, 30th-CA
Gregory W. Meeks, 5th-NY
Albio Sires, 8th-NJ
Gerald E. Connolly, 11th-VA
Ted Deutch, 22nd-FL
Karen Bass, 37th-CA
William Keating, 9th-MA
David Cicilline, 1st-RI
Ami Bera, 7th-CA
Lois Frankel, 21st-FL
Tulsi Gabbard, 2nd-HI
Joaquin Castro, 20th-TX
Robin Kelly, 2nd-IL
Brendan F. Boyle, 13th-PA
Dina Titus, 1st-NV
Norma J. Torres, 35th-CA
Brad Schneider, 10th-IL
Tom Suozzi, 3rd-NY
Adriano Espaillat, 13th-NY
Ted Lieu, 33rd-CA

Maj. Staff Dir.: Tom Stechy
Min. Staff Dir.: Jason Steinbaum

SUBCOMMITTEES

Africa, Global Health, Global Human Rights, and International Organizations
Rep: Smith, Chair; Meadows; Donovan; Sensenbrenner; Garrett
Dem: Bass, Rnk. Mem.; Bera; Castro; Suozzi

Asia and the Pacific
Rep: Yoho, Chair; Rohrabacher; Chabot; Marino; Brooks; Perry;
    Kinzinger; Wagner
Dem: Sherman, Rnk. Mem.; Bera; Titus; Connolly; Deutch; Gabbard

Europe, Eurasia, and Emerging Threats
Rep: Rohrabacher, Chair; Wilson; Poe; Marino; Duncan;
    Sensenbrenner; Rooney; Fitzpatrick
Dem: Meeks, Rnk. Mem.; Sherman; Sires; Keating; Cicilline; Kelly

SUBCOMMITTEES (Foreign Affairs)

Middle East and North Africa
Rep: Ros-Lehtinen, Chair; Chabot; Issa; DeSantis; Meadows; Cook; Kinzinger; Zeldin; Donovan; Wagner; Mast; Fitzpatrick
Dem: Deutch, Rnk. Mem.; Connolly; Cicilline; Frankel; Boyle; Gabbard; Schneider; Suozzi; Lieu

Terrorism, Nonproliferation, and Trade
Rep: Poe, Chair; Wilson; Issa; Cook; Perry; Zeldin; Mast; Garrett
Dem: Keating, Rnk. Mem.; Frankel; Boyle; Titus; Torres; Schneider

Western Hemisphere
Rep: Duncan, Chair; Smith; Ros-Lehtinen; McCaul; Brooks; DeSantis; Yoho; Rooney
Dem: Sires, Rnk. Mem.; Castro; Kelly; Torres; Espaillat; Meeks

HOMELAND SECURITY

202-226-8417—H2-176 FHOB—Fax: 226-3399
homeland.house.gov

Republicans (18)
Michael McCaul, 10th-TX, Chair
Lamar Smith, 21st-TX
Peter T. King, 2nd-NY
Mike D. Rogers, 3rd-AL
Jeff Duncan, 3rd-SC
Tom Marino, 10th-PA
Lou Barletta, 11th-PA
Scott Perry, 4th-PA
John Katko, 24th-NY
Will Hurd, 23rd-TX
Martha McSally, 2nd-AZ
John Ratcliffe, 4th-TX
Dan Donovan, 11th-NY
Mike Gallagher, 8th-WI
Clay Higgins, 3rd-LA
John Rutherford, 4th-FL
Tom Garrett, 5th-VA
Brian Fitzpatrick, 8th-PA

Democrats (12)
Bennie Thompson, 2nd-MS, Rnk. Mem.
Sheila Jackson Lee, 18th-TX
Jim Langevin, 2nd-RI
Cedric L. Richmond, 2nd-LA
William Keating, 9th-MA
Donald M. Payne, Jr., 10th-NJ
Filemon Vela, 34th-TX
Bonnie Watson Coleman, 12th-NJ
Kathleen Rice, 4th-NY
Lou Correa, 46th-CA
Val B. Demings, 10th-FL
Nanette Barragán, 44th-CA

Maj. Staff Dir.: Brendan Shields
Min. Staff Dir.: I. Lanier Avant

SUBCOMMITTEES

Border and Maritime Security
Rep: McSally, Chair; Smith; Rogers; Duncan; Barletta; Hurd; Rutherford
Dem: Vela, Rnk. Mem.; Richmond; Correa; Demings; Barragán

Counterterrorism and Intelligence
Rep: King, Chair; Barletta; Perry; Hurd; Gallagher
Dem: Rice, Rnk. Mem.; Jackson Lee; Keating

Cybersecurity and Infrastructure Protection
Rep: Ratcliffe, Chair; Donovan; Katko; Gallagher; Garrett; Fitzpatrick
Dem: Richmond, Rnk. Mem.; Jackson Lee; Langevin; Demings

Emergency Preparedness, Response, and Communication
Rep: Donovan, Chair; Marino; McSally; Rutherford; Garrett
Dem: Payne, Rnk. Mem.; Langevin; Watson Coleman

Oversight and Management Efficiency
Rep: Perry, Chair; Duncan; Marino; Ratcliffe; Higgins
Dem: Correa, Rnk. Mem.; Rice; Barragán

Transportation Security
Rep: Katko, Chair; King; Rogers; Higgins; Fitzpatrick
Dem: Watson Coleman, Rnk. Mem.; Keating; Payne

HOUSE ADMINISTRATION

202-225-8281—1309 LHOB—Fax: 225-9957
cha.house.gov

Republicans (6)
Gregg Harper, 3rd-MS, Chair
Rodney Davis, 13th-IL
Barbara Comstock, 10th-VA
Mark Walker, 6th-NC
Adrian Smith, 3rd-NE
Barry Loudermilk, 11th-GA

Democrats (3)
Robert A. Brady, 1st-PA,
 Rnk. Mem.
Zoe Lofgren, 19th-CA
Jamie Raskin, 8th-MD

Maj. Staff Dir.: Sean Moran
Min. Staff Dir.: Jamie Fleet

NO SUBCOMMITTEES

JUDICIARY

202-225-3951—2138 RHOB—Fax: 225-7682
judiciary.house.gov

Republicans (24)
Robert W. Goodlatte, 6th-VA, Chair
Jim Sensenbrenner, 5th-WI
Lamar Smith, 21st-TX
Steve Chabot, 1st-OH
Darrell Issa, 49th-CA
Steve King, 4th-IA
Trent Franks, 8th-AZ
Louie Gohmert, 1st-TX
Jim Jordan, 4th-OH
Ted Poe, 2nd-TX
Jason Chaffetz, 3rd-UT
Tom Marino, 10th-PA
Trey Gowdy, 4th-SC
Raúl R. Labrador, 1st-ID
Blake Farenthold, 27th-TX
Doug Collins, 9th-GA
Ron DeSantis, 6th-FL
Ken Buck, 4th-CO
John Ratcliffe, 4th-TX
Martha Roby, 2nd-AL
Matt Gaetz, 1st-FL
Mike Johnson, 4th-LA
Andy Biggs, 5th-AZ
Vacancy

Democrats (17)
John Conyers, Jr., 13th-MI,
   Rnk. Mem.
Jerrold Nadler, 10th-NY
Zoe Lofgren, 19th-CA
Sheila Jackson Lee, 18th-TX
Steve Cohen, 9th-TN
Hank Johnson, 4th-GA
Ted Deutch, 22nd-FL
Luis V. Gutiérrez, 4th-IL
Karen Bass, 37th-CA
Cedric L. Richmond, 2nd-LA
Hakeem Jeffries, 8th-NY
David Cicilline, 1st-RI
Eric Swalwell, 15th-CA
Ted Lieu, 33rd-CA
Pramila Jayapal, 7th-WA
Jamie Raskin, 8th-MD
Brad Schneider, 10th-IL

Maj. Staff Dir. & General Counsel: Shelley Husband
Min. Staff Dir. & Chief Counsel: Perry Apelbaum

SUBCOMMITTEES

Constitution and Civil Justice
Rep: King, Chair; DeSantis; Franks; Gohmert; Gowdy
Dem: Cohen, Rnk. Mem.; Raskin; Nadler

Courts, Intellectual Property, and the Internet
Rep: Issa, Chair; Collins; Smith; Chabot; Franks; Jordan; Poe;
   Chaffetz; Marino; Labrador; Farenthold; DeSantis; Gaetz; Biggs
Dem: Nadler, Rnk. Mem.; Johnson; Deutch; Bass; Richmond;
   Jeffries; Swalwell; Lieu; Lofgren; Cohen; Gutiérrez; Vacancy

Crime, Terrorism, Homeland Security, and Investigations
Rep: Gowdy, Chair; Gohmert; Sensenbrenner; Chabot; Poe;
   Chaffetz; Ratcliffe; Roby; Johnson; Vacancy
Dem: Jackson Lee, Rnk. Mem.; Deutch; Bass; Richmond; Jeffries;
   Cicilline; Lieu

Immigration and Border Security
Rep: Sensenbrenner, Chair; Labrador; Smith; King; Jordan; Buck;
   Johnson; Biggs
Dem: Lofgren, Rnk. Mem.; Gutierrez; Jayapal; Jackson Lee; Vacancy

Regulatory Reform, Commercial, and Antitrust Law
Rep: Marino, Chair; Farenthold; Issa; Collins; Buck; Ratcliffe; Gaetz;
   Vacancy
Dem: Cicilline, Rnk. Mem.; Johnson; Swalwell; Raskin; Jayapal

NATURAL RESOURCES

202-225-2761—1324 LHOB—Fax: 225-5929
naturalresources.house.gov

Republicans (26)
Rob Bishop, 1st-UT, Chair
Don Young, At Large-AK
Louie Gohmert, 1st-TX
Doug Lamborn, 5th-CO
Rob Wittman, 1st-VA
Tom McClintock, 4th-CA
Steve Pearce, 2nd-NM
Glenn Thompson, 5th-PA
Paul Gosar, 4th-AZ
Raúl R. Labrador, 1st-ID
Scott Tipton, 3rd-CO
Doug LaMalfa, 1st-CA
Jeff Denham, 10th-CA
Paul Cook, 8th-CA
Bruce Westerman, 4th-AR
Garret Graves, 6th-LA
Jody B. Hice, 10th-GA
Aumua Amata Coleman
  Radewagen, At Large-AS
Darin LaHood, 18th-IL
Daniel Webster, 11th-FL
David Rouzer, 7th-NC
Jack Bergman, 1st-MI
Liz Cheney, At Large-WY
Mike Johnson, 4th-LA
Jenniffer González-Colón,
  At Large-PR
Vacancy

Democrats (18)
Raúl M. Grijalva, 3rd-AZ,
  Rnk. Mem.
Grace F. Napolitano, 32nd-CA
Madeleine Z. Bordallo, At
  Large-GU
Jim Costa, 16th-CA
Gregorio Kilili Camacho
  Sablan, At Large-MP
Niki Tsongas, 3rd-MA
Jared Huffman, 2nd-CA
Alan Lowenthal, 47th-CA
Don Beyer, Jr., 8th-VA
Norma J. Torres, 35th-CA
Ruben Gallego, 7th-AZ
Colleen Hanabusa, 1st-HI
Nanette Barragán, 44th-CA
Darren Soto, 9th-FL
Jimmy Panetta, 20th-CA
A. Donald McEachin, 4th-VA
Anthony G. Brown, 4th-MD
William Lacy Clay, 1st-MO

Maj. Staff Dir.: Jason Knox
Min. Staff Dir.: David Watkins

SUBCOMMITTEES

Energy and Mineral Resources
Rep: Gosar, Chair; Gohmert; Lamborn; Wittman; Pearce; Thompson;
  Tipton; Cook; Westerman; Graves; Hice; LaHood; Cheney
Dem: Lowenthal, Rnk. Mem.; Brown; Costa; Tsongas; Huffman;
  Beyer; Polis; Soto; Barragán

Federal Lands
Rep: McClintock, Chair; Young; Pearce; Thompson; Labrador;
  Tipton; Westerman, Vice Chair; LaHood; Webster; Rouzer;
  Bergman; Cheney
Dem: Hanabusa, Rnk. Mem.; Tsongas; Lowenthal; Torres; Barragán;
  Panetta; McEachin; Brown

Indian, Insular and Alaska Native Affairs
Rep: LaMalfa, Chair; Young; Denham; Cook; Radewagen; LaHood;
  Bergman; González-Colón, Vice Chair
Dem: Torres, Rnk. Mem.; Bordallo; Sablan; Gallego; Soto; Hanabusa

Oversight and Investigations
Rep: Labrador, Chair; Gohmert; Radewagen; Bergman; Johnson,
  Vice Chair; González-Colón
Dem: McEachin, Rnk. Mem.; Gallego; Huffman; Beyer; Soto

Water, Power and Oceans
Rep: Lamborn, Chair; Wittman; McClintock; Gosar; LaMalfa;
  Denham; Graves; Hice; Weber; Rouzer; Johnson
Dem: Huffman, Rnk. Mem.; Napolitano; Costa; Beyer; Barragán;
  Panetta; Bordallo; Sablan

OVERSIGHT AND GOVERNMENT REFORM

202-225-5074—2157 RHOB—Fax: 225-3974
oversight.house.gov

Republicans (24)
Jason Chaffetz, 3rd-UT, Chair
John J. Duncan, Jr., 2nd-TN
Darrell Issa, 49th-CA
Jim Jordan, 4th-OH
Mark Sanford, 1st-SC
Justin Amash, 3rd-MI
Paul Gosar, 4th-AZ
Scott DesJarlais, 4th-TN
Trey Gowdy, 4th-SC
Blake Farenthold, 27th-TX
Virginia Foxx, 5th-NC
Thomas Massie, 4th-KY
Mark Meadows, 11th-NC
Ron DeSantis, 6th-FL
Dennis A. Ross, 15th-FL
Mark Walker, 6th-NC
Rod Blum, 1st-IA
Jody B. Hice, 10th-GA
Steve Russell, 5th-OK
Glenn Grothman, 6th-WI
Will Hurd, 23rd-TX
Gary Palmer, 6th-AL
James R. Comer, 1st-KY
Paul Mitchell, 10th-MI

Democrats (18)
Elijah E. Cummings, 7th-MD,
    Rnk. Mem.
Carolyn B. Maloney, 12th-NY
Eleanor Holmes Norton,
    At Large-DC
William Lacy Clay, 1st-MO
Stephen F. Lynch, 8th-MA
Jim Cooper, 5th-TN
Gerald E. Connolly, 11th-VA
Robin Kelly, 2nd-IL
Brenda Lawrence, 14th-MI
Bonnie Watson Coleman,
    12th-NJ
Stacey Plaskett, At Large-VI
Val B. Demings, 10th-FL
Raja Krishnamoorthi, 8th-IL
Jamie Raskin, 8th-MD
Peter Welch, At Large-VT
Matt Cartwright, 17th-PA
Mark DeSaulnier, 11th-CA
John Sarbanes, 3rd-MD

Maj. Staff Dir.: Jon Skladany
Min. Staff Dir.: Dave Rapallo

SUBCOMMITTEES

Government Operations
Rep: TBA
Dem: TBA

Health Care, Benefits, and Administrative Rules
Rep: TBA
Dem: TBA

Information Technology
Rep: TBA
Dem: TBA

Interior
Rep: TBA
Dem: TBA

National Security
Rep: TBA
Dem: TBA

Transportation and Public Assets
Rep: TBA
Dem: TBA

RULES

202-225-9191—H-312 Capitol—Fax: 225-6763
rules.house.gov

Republicans (9)
Pete Sessions, 32nd-TX, Chair
Tom Cole, 4th-OK
Rob Woodall, 7th-GA
Michael C. Burgess, 26th-TX
Doug Collins, 9th-GA
Bradley Byrne, 1st-AL
Dan Newhouse, 4th-WA
Ken Buck, 4th-CO
Liz Cheney, At Large-WY

Democrats (4)
Louise M. Slaughter, 25th-NY,
  Rnk. Mem.
Jim McGovern, 2nd-MA
Alcee L. Hastings, 20th-FL
Jared Polis, 2nd-CO

Maj. Staff Dir.: Stephen Cote
Min. Staff Dir.: Don Sisson

SUBCOMMITTEES

Legislative and Budget Process
Rep: TBA
Dem: TBA

Rules and Organization of the House
Rep: TBA
Dem: TBA

SCIENCE, SPACE AND TECHNOLOGY

202-225-6371—2321 RHOB—Fax: 226-0113
science.house.gov

Republicans (22)
Lamar Smith, 21st-TX, Chair
Dana Rohrabacher, 48th-CA
Frank D. Lucas, 3rd-OK
Mo Brooks, 5th-AL
Randy Hultgren, 14th-IL
Bill Posey, 8th-FL
Thomas Massie, 4th-KY
Jim Bridenstine, 1st-OK
Randy Weber, 14th-TX
Steve Knight, 25th-CA
Brian Babin, 36th-TX
Barbara Comstock, 10th-VA
Gary Palmer, 6th-AL
Barry Loudermilk, 11th-GA
Ralph Abraham, 5th-LA
Darin LaHood, 18th-IL
Daniel Webster, 11th-FL
Jim Banks, 3rd-IN
Andy Biggs, 5th-AZ
Roger Marshall, 1st-KS
Neal Dunn, 2nd-FL
Clay Higgins, 3rd-LA

Democrats (17)
Eddie Bernice Johnson,
   30th-TX, Rnk. Mem.
Zoe Lofgren, 19th-CA
Daniel Lipinski, 3rd-IL
Suzanne Bonamici, 1st-OR
Ami Bera, 7th-CA
Elizabeth Esty, 5th-CT
Marc Veasey, 33rd-TX
Don Beyer, Jr., 8th-VA
Jacky Rosen, 3rd-NV
Jerry McNerney, 9th-CA
Ed Perlmutter, 7th-CO
Paul Tonko, 20th-NY
Bill Foster, 11th-IL
Mark Takano, 9th-CA
Colleen Hanabusa, 1st-HI
Charlie Crist, 13th-FL
Vacancy

Maj. Chief of Staff: Jennifer Brown
Min. Chief of Staff: Richard Obermann

SUBCOMMITTEES

Energy
Rep: Weber, Chair; Knight; Rohrabacher; Lucas; Brooks; Hultgren;
   Massie; Bridenstine; Lahood; Webster; Dunn
Dem: Veasey, Rnk. Mem.; Lofgren; Lipinski; Rosen; McNerney;
   Tonko; Foster; Takano
Maj. Staff Dir.: Mark Marin
Min. Staff Dir.: Adam Rosenberg

Environment
202-225-8844-2319 RHOB-Fax: 202-225-4438
Rep: Biggs, Chair; Banks; Rohrabacher; Posey; Brooks; Weber;
   Babin; Palmer; Loudermilk; Higgins
Dem: Bonamici, Rnk. Mem.; Hanabusa; Crist; Vacancy; Vacancy
Maj. Staff Dir.: Joseph Brazauskas
Min. Staff Dir.: Vacant

Oversight
202-225-8772-B374 RHOB-Fax: 202-225-7815
Rep: LaHood, Chair; Marshall; Posey; Massie; Palmer; Loudermilk;
   Higgins
Dem: Beyer, Rnk. Mem.; McNerney; Perlmutter
Maj. Staff Dir.: Ashley Callen
Min. Staff Dir.: Doug Pasternak

Research And Technology
202-225-9644-B374 RHOB-Fax: 202-225-7815
Rep: Comstock, Chair; Abraham; Lucas; Hultgren; Knight; LaHood;
   Webster; Banks; Marshall
Dem: Lipinski, Rnk. Mem.; Esty; Rosen; Bonamici; Bera; Beyer
Maj. Staff Dir.: Cliff Shannon
Min. Staff Dir.: Dahlia Sokolov

Space
202-225-8123-B374 RHOB-Fax: 202-225-7815
Rep: Babin, Chair; Brooks; Rohrabacher; Lucas; Posey; Bridenstine;
   Knight; Comstock; Abraham; Webster; Banks; Biggs; Dunn; Higgins
Dem: Bera, Rnk.; Lofgren; Beyer; Veasey; Lipinski; Perlmutter; Crist;
   Foster
Maj. Staff Dir.: Tom Hammond
Min. Staff Dir.: Vacant

SMALL BUSINESS

202-225-5821—2361 RHOB—Fax: 226-5276
smallbusiness.house.gov

Republicans (14)
Steve Chabot, 1st-OH, Chair
Steve King, 4th-IA
Blaine Luetkemeyer, 3rd-MO
Dave Brat, 7th-VA
Aumua Amata Coleman
    Radewagen, At Large-AS
Steve Knight, 25th-CA
Trent Kelly, 1st-MS
Rod Blum, 1st-IA
James R. Comer, 1st-KY
Jenniffer González-Colón,
    At Large-PR
Don Bacon, 2nd-NE
Brian Fitzpatrick, 8th-PA
Roger Marshall, 1st-KS
Vacancy

Democrats (10)
Nydia M. Velázquez, 7th-NY,
    Rnk. Mem.
Dwight Evans, 2nd-PA
Stephanie Murphy, 7th-FL
Al Lawson, 5th-FL
Yvette D. Clarke, 9th-NY
Judy Chu, 27th-CA
Alma Adams, 12th-NC
Adriano Espaillat, 13th-NY
Brad Schneider, 10th-IL
Vacancy

Maj. Staff Dir.: Kevin Fitzpatrick
Min. Staff Dir.: Adam Minehardt

SUBCOMMITTEES

Agriculture, Energy And Trade
202-225-4038-2361 RHOB-Fax:202-226-5276
Rep: Blum, Chair; King; Luetkemeyer; Radewagen; Comer; Bacon
Dem: Schneider, Rnk. Mem.; Lawson; Vacancy; Vacancy

Contracting And Workforce
202-225-4038-2361 RHOB-Fax:202-226-5276
Rep: Knight, Chair; Comer; Vacancy; Vacancy; Vacancy; Vacancy
Dem: Murphy, Rnk. Mem.; Clarke; Evans; Lawson

Economic Growth, Tax And Capital Access
202-225-4038-2361 RHOB-Fax:202-226-5276
Rep: Brat, Chair; Knight; Kelly; Gonzalez-Colon; Fitzpatrick
Dem: Evans, Rnk. Mem.; Chu; Murphy; Clarke

Health And Technology
202-225-4038-2361 RHOB-Fax:202-226-5276
Rep: Radewagen, Chair; Luetkemeyer; Brat; González-Colón;
    Fitzpatrick; Marshall
Dem: Lawson, Rnk. Mem.; Espaillat; Vacancy; Vacancy; Vacancy

Investigations, Oversight And Regulations
202-225-4038-2361 RHOB-Fax:202-226-5276
Rep: Kelly, Chair; Blum; Bacon; Marshall; Vacancy; Vacancy
Dem: Adams, Rnk. Mem.; Vacancy; Vacancy

TRANSPORTATION AND INFRASTRUCTURE

202-225-9446—2251 RHOB—Fax: 225-6782
transportation.house.gov

Republicans (34)
Bill Shuster, 9th-PA, Chair
Don Young, At Large-AK
John J. Duncan, Jr., 2nd-TN
Frank A. LoBiondo, 2nd-NJ
Sam Graves, 6th-MO
Duncan Hunter, 50th-CA
Rick Crawford, 1st-AR
Lou Barletta, 11th-PA
Blake Farenthold, 27th-TX
Bob Gibbs, 7th-OH
Daniel Webster, 11th-FL
Jeff Denham, 10th-CA
Thomas Massie, 4th-KY
Mark Meadows, 11th-NC
Scott Perry, 4th-PA
Rodney Davis, 13th-IL
Mark Sanford, 1st-SC
Rob Woodall, 7th-GA
Todd Rokita, 4th-IN
John Katko, 24th-NY
Brian Babin, 36th-TX
Garret Graves, 6th-LA
Barbara Comstock, 10th-VA
David Rouzer, 7th-NC
Mike Bost, 12th-IL
Randy Weber, 14th-TX
Doug LaMalfa, 1st-CA
Bruce Westerman, 4th-AR
Lloyd K. Smucker, 16th-PA
Paul Mitchell, 10th-MI
John J. Faso, 19th-NY
Drew Ferguson, 3rd-GA
Brian Mast, 18th-FL
Jason Lewis, 2nd-MN

Democrats (27)
Peter A. DeFazio, 4th-OR,
  Rnk. Mem.
Eleanor Holmes Norton,
  At Large-DC
Jerrold Nadler, 10th-NY
Eddie Bernice Johnson,
  30th-TX
Elijah E. Cummings, 7th-MD
Rick Larsen, 2nd-WA
Michael E. Capuano, 7th-MA
Grace F. Napolitano, 32nd-CA
Daniel Lipinski, 3rd-IL
Steve Cohen, 9th-TN
Albio Sires, 8th-NJ
John Garamendi, 3rd-CA
Hank Johnson, 4th-GA
André Carson, 7th-IN
Rick Nolan, 8th-MN
Dina Titus, 1st-NV
Sean Patrick Maloney,
  18th-NY
Elizabeth Esty, 5th-CT
Lois Frankel, 21st-FL
Cheri Bustos, 17th-IL
Jared Huffman, 2nd-CA
Julia Brownley, 26th-CA
Frederica S. Wilson, 24th-FL
Donald M. Payne Jr., 10th-NJ
Alan Lowenthal, 47th-CA
Brenda Lawrence, 14th-MI
Mark DeSaulnier, 11th-CA

Maj. Staff Dir.: Matt Sturges
Min. Staff Dir.: Kathy Dedrick

SUBCOMMITTEES

Aviation
Rep: LoBiondo, Chair; Young; Duncan; Graves; Hunter; Farenthold;
  Gibbs; Webster; Denham; Massie; Meadows; Perry; Davis;
  Sanford; Woodall; Rokita; Comstock; LaMalfa; Westerman;
  Mitchell; Lewis
Dem: Larsen, Rnk. Mem.; Johnson; Lipinski; Carson; Bustos;
  Norton; Titus; Maloney; Brownley; Payne; Lawrence; Capuano;
  Napolitano; Cohen; Johnson; Nolan

Coast Guard and Maritime Transportation
Rep: Hunter, Chair; Young; LoBiondo; Graves; Rouzer; Weber; Mast;
  Lewis
Dem: Garamendi, Rnk. Mem.; Cummings; Larsen; Huffman;
  Lowenthal; Norton

Economic Development, Public Buildings, and Emergency Management
Rep: Barletta, Chair; Crawford; Comstock; Bost; Smucker; Faso;
  Ferguson; Mast
Dem: Johnson, Rnk. Mem.; Norton; Sires; Napolitano; Capuano

SUBCOMMITTEES (Transportation)

Highways and Transit

Rep: Graves, Chair; Young; Duncan; LoBiondo; Hunter; Crawford; Barletta; Farenthold; Gibbs; Denham; Massie; Meadows; Perry; Davis; Woodall; Katko; Babin; Graves; Comstock; Rouzer; Bost; LaMalfa; Westerman; Smucker; Mitchell; Faso; Ferguson

Dem: Norton, Rnk. Mem.; Nadler; Cohen; Sires; Nolan; Titus; Maloney; Esty; Huffman; Brownley; Lowenthal; Lawrence; DeSaulnier; Johnson; Capuano; Napolitano; Lipinski; Johnson; Frankel; Bustos; Wilson

Railroads, Pipelines, and Hazardous Materials

Rep: Denham, Chair; Duncan; Graves; Barletta; Farenthold; Webster; Meadows; Perry; Sanford; Rokita; Katko; Babin; Weber; Westerman; Smucker; Mitchell; Faso; Lewis

Dem: Capuano, Rnk. Mem.; Payne; Nadler; Cummings; Cohen; Sires; Garamendi; Carson; Nolan; Esty; Bustos; Wilson; DeSaulnier; Lipinski

Water Resources and Environment

Rep: Graves, Chair; Crawford; Gibbs; Webster; Massie; Davis; Sanford; Woodall; Rokita; Katko; Babin; Rouzer; Bost; Weber; LaMalfa; Ferguson; Mast

Dem: Napolitano, Rnk. Mem.; Frankel; Wilson; Huffman; Lowenthal; Johnson; Garamendi; Titus; Maloney; Esty; Bustos; Brownley; Lawrence

VETERANS' AFFAIRS

202-225-3527—335 CHOB—Fax: 225-5486
veterans.house.gov

Republicans (14)
Phil Roe, 1st-TN, Chair
Gus Bilirakis, 12th-FL
Mike Coffman, 6th-CO
Brad Wenstrup, 2nd-OH
Aumua Amata Coleman
    Radewagen, At Large-AS
Mike Bost, 12th-IL
Jodey C. Arrington, 19th-TX
Jim Banks, 3rd-IN
Jack Bergman, 1st-MI
Neal Dunn, 2nd-FL
Clay Higgins, 3rd-LA
John Rutherford, 4th-FL
Bruce Poliquin, 2nd-ME
Jenniffer González-Colón,
    At Large-PR

Democrats (10)
Tim Walz, 1st-MN, Rnk. Mem.
Mark Takano, 41st-CA
Julia Brownley, 26th-CA
Ann McLane Kuster, 2nd-NH
Beto O'Rourke, 16th-TX
Kathleen Rice, 4th-NY
Lou Correa, 46th-CA
Scott Peters, 52nd-CA
Gregorio Kilili Camacho
    Sablan, At Large-MP
Elizabeth Esty, 5th-CT

Maj. Staff Dir.: Jon Towers
Min. Staff Dir.: Raymond Kelly

SUBCOMMITTEES

Disability Assistance and Memorial Affairs
Rep: Bost, Chair; Coffman; Radewagen; Bergman; Banks
Dem: Etsy, Rnk. Mem.; Brownley; Sablan

Economic Opportunity
Rep: Arrington, Chair; Bilirakis; Wenstrup; Banks; Rutherford
Dem: O'Rourke, Rnk. Mem.; Takano; Correa; Rice

Health
Rep: Wenstrup, Chair; Bilirakis; Radewagen; Dunn; Rutherford;
    Higgins; González-Colón
Dem: Brownley, Rnk. Mem.; Takano; Kuster; O'Rourke; Correa

Oversight and Investigations
Rep: Bergman, Chair; Bost; Poliquin; Dunn; Arrington;
    González-Colón
Dem: Kuster, Rnk. Mem.; Rice; Peters; Sablan

WAYS AND MEANS

202-225-3625—1102 LHOB—Fax: 225-2610
waysandmeans.house.gov

Republicans (24)
Kevin Brady, 8th-TX, Chair
Sam Johnson, 3rd-TX
Devin Nunes, 22nd-CA
Pat Tiberi, 12th-OH
Dave Reichert, 8th-WA
Peter Roskam, 6th-IL
Vern Buchanan, 16th-FL
Adrian Smith, 3rd-NE
Lynn Jenkins, 2nd-KS
Erik Paulsen, 3rd-MN
Kenny Marchant, 24th-TX
Diane Black, 6th-TN
Tom Reed, 23rd-NY
Mike Kelly, 3rd-PA
James B. Renacci, 16th-OH
Patrick Meehan, 7th-PA
Kristi Noem, At Large-SD
George Holding, 2nd-NC
Jason Smith, 8th-MO
Tom Rice, 7th-SC
David Schweikert, 6th-AZ
Jackie Walorski, 2nd-IN
Carlos Curbelo, 26th-FL
Mike Bishop, 8th-MI

Democrats (16)
Richard E. Neal, 1st-MA,
  Rnk. Mem.
Sander M. Levin, 9th-MI
John Lewis, 5th-GA
Lloyd Doggett, 35th-TX
Mike Thompson, 5th-CA
John B. Larson, 1st-CT
Earl Blumenauer, 3rd-OR
Ron Kind, 3rd-WI
Bill Pascrell, Jr., 9th-NJ
Joseph Crowley, 14th-NY
Danny K. Davis, 7th-IL
Linda T. Sánchez, 38th-CA
Brian Higgins, 26th-NY
Terri A. Sewell, 7th-AL
Suzan DelBene, 1st-WA
Judy Chu, 27th-CA

Maj. Staff Dir.: David Stewart
Min. Staff Dir.: Brandon Casey

SUBCOMMITTEES

Health
Rep: Tiberi, Chair; Johnson; Nunes; Roskam; Buchanan; Smith;
  Jenkins; Marchant; Black; Paulsen; Vacancy
Dem: Levin, Rnk. Mem.; Thompson; Kind; Blumenauer;
  Higgins; Sewell; Chu

Human Resources
Rep: Smith, Chair; Smith; Walorski; Curbelo; Reichert; Reed; Rice
Dem: Davis, Rnk. Mem.; Doggett; Sewell; Chu

Oversight
Rep: Buchanan, Chair; Meehan; Smith; Schweikert; Walorski;
  Curbelo; Holding
Dem: Lewis, Rnk. Mem.; Crowley; DelBene; Blumenauer

Social Security
Rep: Johnson, Chair; Rice; Schweikert; Smith; Buchanan; Kelly;
  Renacci; Walorski
Dem: Larson, Rnk. Mem.; Pascrell; Crowley; Sánchez

Tax Policy
Rep: Roskam, Chair; Reichert; Tiberi; Reed; Kelly; Renacci; Noem;
  Holding; Marchant
Dem: Doggett, Rnk. Mem.; Larson; Sánchez; Thompson; DelBene;
  Blumenauer

Trade
Rep: Reichert, Chair; Nunes; Jenkins; Paulsen; Kelly; Meehan; Reed;
  Noem; Holding; Rice
Dem: Pascrell, Rnk. Mem.; Kind; Doggett; Levin; Davis; Higgins

PERMANENT SELECT ON INTELLIGENCE

202-225-4121—HVC-304 CVC—Fax: 225-1991
intelligence.house.gov

Republicans (13)
Devin Nunes, 22nd-CA, Chair
K. Michael Conaway, 11th-TX
Peter T. King, 2nd-NY
Frank A. LoBiondo, 2nd-NJ
Tom Rooney, 17th-FL
Ileana Ros-Lehtinen, 27th-FL
Michael R. Turner, 10th-OH
Brad Wenstrup, 2nd-OH
Chris Stewart, 2nd-UT
Rick Crawford, 1st-AR
Trey Gowdy, 4th-SC
Elise Stefanik, 21st-NY
Will Hurd, 23rd-TX

Democrats (9)
Adam B. Schiff, 28th-CA,
   Rnk. Mem.
Jim Himes, 4th-CT
Terri A. Sewell, 7th-AL
André Carson, 7th-IN
Jackie Speier, 14th-CA
Mike Quigley, 5th-IL
Eric Swalwell, 15th-CA
Joaquin Castro, 20th-TX
Denny Heck, 10th-WA

Maj. Staff Dir.: Damon Nelson
Min. Staff Dir.: Michael Bahar

SUBCOMMITTEES

CIA
Rep: LoBiondo, Chair; Conaway; King; Rooney; Ros-Lehtinen;
   Stewart
Dem: Swalwell, Rnk. Mem.; Himes; Castro; Heck

Department of Defense Intelligence and Overhead Architecture
Rep: Stewart, Chair; Turner; Wenstrup; Crawford; Stefanik; Hurd
Dem: Sewell, Rnk. Mem.; Carson; Castro; Heck

Emerging Threats
Rep: King, Chair; LoBiondo; Wenstrup; Crawford; Gowdy; Hurd
Dem: Carson, Rnk. Mem.; Speier; Quigley; Swalwell

NSA and Cybersecurity
Rep: Rooney, Chair; Conaway; Ros-Lehtinen; Turner; Gowdy;
   Stefanik
Dem: Himes, Rnk. Mem.; Sewell; Speier; Quigley

JOINT ECONOMIC

202-224-5171—SD-G01—Fax: 224-0240
jec.senate.gov

Republicans (12)
Senate
Mike Lee, UT, Vice Chair
Tom Cotton, AR
Rob Portman, OH
Ted Cruz, TX
Bill Cassidy, LA
Ben Sasse, NE

House
Pat Tiberi, 12th-OH, Chair
Erik Paulsen, 3rd-MN
David Schweikert, 6th-AZ
Barbara Comstock, 10th-VA
Darin LaHood, 18th-IL
Francis Rooney, 19th-FL

Democrats (8)
Senate
Martin Heinrich, NM, Rnk. Mem.
Amy Klobuchar, MN
Maggie Hassan, NH
Gary Peters, MI

House
Carolyn B. Maloney, 12th-NY
John Delaney, 6th-MD
Alma Adams, 12th-NC
Don Beyer, Jr., 8th-VA

Rep. Staff Dir.: Whitney Daffner
Dem. Staff Dir.: Abe Rakov

NO SUBCOMMITTEES

JOINT ON THE LIBRARY

202-224-6352—SR-305—Fax: 224-1912
cha.house.gov/jointcommittees/joint-committee-library

Republicans (6)
Senate
Roy Blunt, MO, Chair
Pat Roberts, KS
Shelley Moore Capito, WV

House
Gregg Harper, 3rd-MS,
　Vice Chair
Kevin Yoder, 3rd-KS
Barry Loudermilk, 11th-GA

Democrats (4)
Senate
Charles E. Schumer, NY
Patrick J. Leahy, VT

House
Robert A. Brady, 1st-PA
Zoe Lofgren, 19th-CA

NO SUBCOMMITTEES

JOINT ON PRINTING

202-225-8281—1309 LHOB—Fax: 225-9957
cha.house.gov/jointcommittees/joint-committee-on-printing

Republicans (6)
Senate
Roy Blunt, MO, Vice Chair
Pat Roberts, KS
John Boozman, AR

House
Gregg Harper, 3rd-MS, Chair
Rodney Davis, 13th-IL
Mark Walker, 6th-NC

Democrats (4)
Senate
Charles E. Schumer, NY
Tom Udall, NM

House
Robert A. Brady, 1st-PA
Jamie Raskin, 8th-MD

NO SUBCOMMITTEES

JOINT ON TAXATION

202-225-3621—H2-502 FHOB—Fax: 225-0832
www.jct.gov

Republicans (6)
Senate
Orrin G. Hatch, UT, Vice Chair
Charles E. Grassley, IA
Michael D. Crapo, ID

House
Kevin Brady, 8th-TX, Chair
Sam Johnson, 3rd-TX
Devin Nunes, 22nd-CA

Democrats (4)
Senate
Ron Wyden, OR
Debbie Stabenow, MI

House
Richard E. Neal, 1st-MA
John Lewis, 5th-GA

NO SUBCOMMITTEES

Note: As of press time, the rosters for the Joint Committees on the Library, Printing, and Taxation were not final. Information provided here is preliminary and subject to change.

NOTES

COMMUNICATING WITH CONGRESS

TIPS FOR E-MAILING CONGRESS

Heightened security measures have dramatically increased the time it takes for a letter sent by post to reach a congressional office. More and more, citizens are using e-mails and faxes to communicate their concerns and increasingly elected officials' offices prefer electronic communications for constituent contact. As a general rule, Members of Congress are far more likely to heed your message if you are one of their constituents.

Purpose of Your E-Mail:

- State your purpose for writing in the first sentence of the e-mail.

- If your e-mail pertains to a specific piece of legislation, identify it. And make sure that you are referencing the correct legislation to the correct body of Congress. House bills are H.R. ____; Senate bills are designated as S. ____.

- Be courteous.

- If appropriate, include personal information about why the issue matters to you.

- Address only one issue in each e-mail.

Addressing Your Correspondence:

- **To a Senator**

    The Honorable (Full Name)
    United States Senate
    Washington, DC 20510

    Dear Senator (Last Name):

- **To a Representative**

    The Honorable (Full Name)
    United States House of Representatives
    Washington, DC 20515

    Dear Mr./Mrs./Ms. (Last Name):

Note: When writing to the Chair of a Committee or the Speaker of the House, it is proper to address him/her as:

        Dear Mr. Chairman or Madam Chairwoman:
        Dear Mr. Speaker or Madam Speaker:

TIPS FOR PHONING CONGRESS

Telephone calls are usually taken by a staff member. Ask to speak with the aide who handles the issue about which you wish to comment.

After identifying yourself as a constituent, tell the aide you would like to leave a brief message, such as: "Please tell Senator/Representative (Name) that I support/oppose (S.___/H.R.___)."

State your reasons for your support or opposition to the bill. Ask for your senators' or representative's position on the bill. You may also request a written response to your telephone call.

SUGGESTIONS FOR A PERSONAL VISIT

Meeting with a Member of Congress, or congressional staff, is a very effective way to convey a message about a specific issue or legislative matter. Below are some suggestions to consider when planning a visit to a congressional office.

Plan Your Visit Carefully: Be clear about what it is you want to achieve; determine in advance which Member or committee staff you need to meet with to achieve your purpose.

COMMUNICATING WITH CONGRESS

Make an Appointment: When attempting to meet with a Member, contact the Appointment Secretary/Scheduler. Explain your purpose and who you represent. It is easier for congressional staff to arrange a meeting if they know what you wish to discuss and your relationship to the area or interests represented by the Member.

Be Prompt and Patient: When it is time to meet with a Member, be punctual and be patient. It is not uncommon for a Congressman or Congresswoman to be late, or to have a meeting interrupted due to the Member's crowded schedule. If interruptions do occur, be flexible. When the opportunity presents itself, continue your meeting with a Member's staff.

Be Prepared: Whenever possible, bring to the meeting information and materials supporting your position. Members are required to take positions on many different issues. In some instances, a Member may lack important details about the pros and cons of a particular matter. It is therefore helpful to share with the Member information and examples that demonstrate clearly the impact or benefits associated with a particular issue or piece of legislation.

Be Political: Members of Congress want to represent the best interests of their district or state. Whenever possible, demonstrate the connection between what you are requesting and the interests of the Member's constituency. If possible, describe for the Member how you or your group can be of assistance to him/her. When it is appropriate, remember to ask for a commitment.

Be Responsive: Be prepared to answer questions or provide additional information in the event the Member expresses interest or asks questions. Follow up the meeting with a thank-you letter that outlines the different points covered during the meeting, and send along any additional information and materials requested.

THE ROLES OF CONGRESSIONAL STAFF

Each Member of Congress has staff to assist him/her during a term in office. To be most effective in communicating with Congress, it is helpful to know the titles and principal functions of key staff.

Commonly used titles and job functions:

Administrative Assistant (AA) or **Chief of Staff (CoS):** The AA reports directly to the Member of Congress. He/she usually has overall responsibility for evaluating the political outcomes of various legislative proposals and constituent requests. The AA is usually the person in charge of overall office operations, including the assignment of work and the supervision of key staff.

Legislative Director (LD), Senior Legislative Assistant (Sr LA), or **Legislative Counsel (LC):** The LD is usually the staff person who monitors the legislative schedule and makes recommendations regarding the pros and cons of particular issues. In some congressional offices there are several LAs and responsibilities are assigned to staff with particular expertise in specific areas. For example, depending on the responsibilities and interests of the Member, an office may include a different LA for health issues, environmental matters, taxes, etc.

Press Secretary (Press) or **Communications Director (CD):** The Press Secretary's responsibility is to build and maintain open and effective lines of communication between the Member, his/her constituency, and the general public. The Press Secretary is expected to know the benefits, demands, and special requirements of both print and electronic media, and how to most effectively promote the Member's views or position on specific issues.

Appointment Secretary (Appt), Personal Secretary, or **Scheduler (Sch):** The Appointment Secretary is usually responsible for allocating a Member's time among the many demands that arise from congressional responsibilities, staff requirements, and constituent requests. The Appointment Secretary may also be responsible for making necessary travel arrangements, arranging speaking dates, visits to the district, etc.

COMMUNICATING WITH CONGRESS

Caseworker: The Caseworker is the staff member usually assigned to help with constituent requests by preparing replies for the Member's signature. The Caseworker's responsibilities may also include helping resolve problems constituents present in relation to federal agencies, e.g., Social Security and Medicare issues, veteran's benefits, passports, etc. There are often several Caseworkers in a congressional office.

Other Staff Titles: Other titles used in a congressional office may include: Executive Assistant, Legislative Correspondent, Executive Secretary, Office Manager, and Receptionist.

HOW A BILL BECOMES LAW

1. Introduction of Legislation
There are two basic types of legislation: bills and resolutions. Bills are used to create public policy. There are three types of resolutions – joint, concurrent, and simple – that can be used to appropriate money or express a sentiment of Congress. Constitutional amendments originate in Congress as joint resolutions.

Ideas for bills can come from anyone, although only a Member of Congress can introduce legislation. All bills are assigned an identifying number. Those introduced in the House begin with H.R., and those in the Senate begin with S. Legislation appropriating money must originate in the House.

2. Committee Action
Once legislation is introduced, it is referred to the committee that has jurisdiction over its subject. A bill may be sent to a single committee (single referral), several committees at once (multiple or joint referral), from one committee to another (sequential referral), or different parts of a bill may be sent to different committees (split referral).

Because most of the work done on a bill is at the committee level, committees have a great deal of power to decide which bills will receive the most attention. The more support a bill has, especially from congressional or committee leadership or from the President, the greater its chance of receiving consideration.

3. Subcommittee Action
After it receives a bill, a committee will generally refer it to the proper subcommittee. Subcommittees have a more narrow focus than committees. Three main steps occur at this stage:

- Hearings. Witnesses are called to testify about the merits and shortcomings of a piece of legislation. Questions from committee members and testimony of witnesses are generally prepared in advance to support a particular position on a bill.
- Mark Up. At this stage, committee members may offer their own views on a bill and suggest amendments. Amendments do not have to be related to the subject of the overall bill at this stage.
- Reporting Out. When the mark up is complete, a final draft of the legislation is voted on for approval. If a majority supports the bill, it is "reported out." If the legislation does not receive majority support, the bill dies.

After a subcommittee reports out legislation, the full committee will go through the same consideration process. If the committee approves a bill, it is reported out to the full House or Senate.

4. Publication of a Written Report
After a committee votes to report a bill, the committee chair instructs the committee staff to prepare a report on the bill. This report describes the intent of the legislation, its impact on existing laws and programs, and views of dissenting members.

HOW A BILL BECOMES LAW

5. Floor Action

Next, legislation is placed on the House or Senate calendar for debate by the full chamber.

In the House, the Rules Committee sets the terms of debate. This Committee may place limits on the time for debate or on the number and type of amendments that may be offered. If the Committee does not place a rule on a bill, there is little chance of it being debated, and the bill dies. Once a bill comes to the floor, supporters and opponents are given a chance to speak. Any amendments offered on the floor must be germane, or related to the main subject of the legislation.

The Senate places fewer restrictions on debate. The terms of debate are often set by a Unanimous Consent Agreement, which is approved by party leaders. Any Senator may filibuster, or speak against a particular piece of legislation, for as long as he or she wishes. A filibuster may only be ended by invoking cloture, which requires that 60 Senators vote to end debate.

When debate concludes in either chamber, a vote takes place to approve or defeat a bill.

6. Conference Committee

Bills may originate in one chamber, and upon passage, move to the opposite chamber to repeat the approval process. Often, however, similar bills work their way through both the House and Senate at the same time. Both chambers must pass identical bills in order for the legislation to be sent to the President for approval, so the House and Senate will form a conference committee to reconcile any differences between their bills. Both chambers may instruct their conferees on acceptable compromises. Once differences are resolved and a conference report is generated, both chambers must once again vote to approve the legislation.

7. Action by the President

The President has four choices upon receiving legislation. He may:

- sign the bill into law;
- veto the bill and send it back to Congress with suggestions for reconsideration;
- take no action while Congress is in session, in which case the bill will become law in ten days;
- take no action and let the bill die after Congress has adjourned for the session. This is called a "pocket veto."

8. Overriding a Veto

If the President vetoes a bill, Congress may override his decision. A two-thirds vote in both chambers is required to overturn a veto.

LEGISLATIVE GLOSSARY

Act: Legislation that has passed both houses of Congress and been signed into law by the president.

Adjourn: To close a legislative day.

Amendment: A change in a bill or document by adding, substituting or deleting portions.

Appropriations Bill: Legislation that provides funding for government agencies and programs.

Authorization Bill: Legislation establishing or extending a program and setting funding limits and policy.

Bill: Legislation introduced in either the House or Senate that, if enacted, has the force of law.

Budget Resolution: Concurrent resolution that establishes spending and revenue targets for the upcoming fiscal year. It does not become law but provides a framework for Congress as it considers other measures.

By Request: Phrase used when a member introduces a bill at the request of an executive agency or private organization but does not necessarily endorse the legislation.

Calendar: List and schedule of bills to be considered by a committee or chamber.

Caucus: Collection of members of Congress, usually organized by party or shared interest. In the House, the party caucuses are known as the Republican Conference and Democratic Caucus. In the Senate, both are formally known as conferences.

Chairman/Chairwoman: Presiding officer of a committee or the Committee of the Whole.

Chamber: Place where the entire House or Senate meets to conduct business; also can refer to the House of Representatives or the Senate itself.

Clean Bill: A new bill, reflecting revisions made by a committee to an earlier version of the legislation.

Cloakrooms: Small rooms off the House and Senate floor where members can rest and hold informal conferences.

Closed Hearings: Hearings closed to all but members, staff and witnesses testifying; also called executive hearings.

Closed Rule: In the House, a rule that prohibits floor amendments.

Cloture: Method of limiting debate or ending a filibuster in the Senate. At least 60 senators must vote in favor before cloture can be invoked. Once cloture is invoked, there can be 30 more hours of debate.

Committee: A group of members assigned to give special consideration to certain bills that fall into subject areas within the committee's jurisdiction.

Committee of the Whole: A mechanism to expedite business in the House whereby the House itself meets as a committee, allowing for less rigid rules and a quorum of 100 instead of 218.

Companion Bills: Identical, or nearly identical, bills introduced separately in both the Senate and the House.

Concurrent Resolution: Legislation used to express the position of the House and Senate. Does not have the force of law, if enacted.

Conference Committee: Meeting between representatives and senators to resolve differences when two versions of a bill have been passed by the House and Senate. It can produce a conference report that is sent to both chambers for approval.

Congressional Record: Official transcript of the proceedings in Congress.

Continuing Resolution: A joint resolution to appropriate funds, usually for a short period of time and often in the absence of a regular appropriations bill. It is frequently used at the beginning of a fiscal year if work on appropriations measures has not been completed.

Cosponsor: Member who joins in sponsoring legislation but who is not the principal sponsor or the one who introduced the legislation.

Discharge Petition: In the House, a petition for the purpose of removing a bill from the control of a committee. A discharge petition must be signed by a majority of members.

Discretionary Spending: Funding for programs or agencies determined by Congress through the appropriations process.

Earmark: There is considerable debate about what qualifies as an earmark, but generally it is congressionally directed funding, issued through an appropriations or authorization bill, for a project in a member's district or state.

Engrossed Bill: Final copy of a bill passed by either the House or Senate with amendments. The bill is then delivered to the other chamber.

Enrolled Bill: Final copy of a bill that has passed both the House and Senate in identical form.

Extension of Remarks: When a member of Congress inserts material in the Congressional Record that is not directly related to the debate under way.

Filibuster: Tactic used in the Senate whereby a minority intentionally delays a vote by extending proceedings such as using unlimited debate. The cloture process can overcome a filibuster

Final Passage: Approval of a bill after all amendments have been voted on.

LEGISLATIVE GLOSSARY

Fiscal Year: Accounting year. For the federal government, the fiscal year begins Oct. 1.

Five-Minute Rule: Rule that allows any House member to propose an amendment and debate it for five minutes. Opponents and supporters of the amendment have five minutes to debate it.

Floor Manager: A member who attempts to direct a bill through the debate and amendment process to a final vote.

Germane: Amendments that are relevant to the underlying bill. All amendments in the House must be germane. A non-germane amendment would add new and different subject matter, or its subject matter may be irrelevant to the bill or other measure it seeks to amend. Senate rules permit non-germane amendments in all but a few specific circumstances — most often, after cloture is invoked.

Hearing: Committee sessions for receiving testimony from witnesses.

Holds: A courtesy afforded senators that allows them to delay legislation. The senator placing the hold must do so in writing, and the notice is published in the Congressional Record.

Hopper: Box on the desk of the clerk of the House where sponsors submit their bills.

Hour Rule: When the House is sitting as the full House, each member has one hour to debate amendments. In the Committee of the Whole, the five-minute rule is in effect.

Jefferson's Manual: Basic rules of parliamentary procedure drafted by Thomas Jefferson that guide both chambers.

Joint Committee: Committee composed of members of both the House and Senate.

Joint Resolution: Legislation similar to a bill that has the force of law if passed by both houses and signed by the president, generally used for special circumstances and to propose constitutional amendments.

Lame Duck: Member of Congress (or the president) who was defeated for, or did not seek, re-election but whose term has not yet expired.

Leader Time: In the Senate, 10 minutes given to the majority and minority leaders at the beginning of each day Congress is in session.

Legislative Day: In the Senate, the period of time between convening until the Senate adjourns, not necessarily a calendar day.

Lobbying: The process of attempting to influence the passage, defeat or content of legislation by individuals or a group other than members of Congress.

Logrolling: Quid pro quo process whereby members help each other get particular measures passed. One member will help another on one piece of legislation in return for similar help.

Majority Leader: Chief spokesman and strategist for the majority party, elected by members of the majority party. In the House, the majority leader is the second-ranking lawmaker, behind the Speaker.

Mandatory Spending: Funding for programs or agencies provided directly through authorization bills, such as entitlement programs.

Marking Up a Bill: Process, usually in committee, of analyzing a piece of legislation section by section and making changes.

Member: A U.S. senator or U.S. representative.

Minority Leader: Chief spokesman and strategist for the minority party, elected by members of the minority party.

Modified Open Rule: In the House, permission to offer amendments to a particular bill during floor debate under certain restrictions set by the Rules Committee, such as a time limit or a requirement that the amendments be printed ahead of time in the Congressional Record.

Motion: Proposal presented to a legislative body for consideration.

Motion to Concur: Proposal to agree to the other chamber's altered version of a measure passed by both the House and the Senate. The chamber can also vote on a motion to concur with further amendments to the measure.

Motion to Recommit: Proposal to send a bill or resolution back to a committee. The motion to recommit can contain instructions for the committee, such as amending the legislation. The minority party in the House may use the motion to recommit to propose changes immediately prior to a vote on final passage.

Motion to Table: Proposal to kill a bill or amendment by cutting off consideration of it. Such motions are not debatable.

Omnibus Bill: Legislation that combines different bills regarding a single broader subject into one measure, such as appropriations bills.

One-Day Rule: In the Senate, a requirement that measures reported from committee be held for at least one legislative day before being brought to the floor.

Open Rule: In the House, permission to offer any amendments to a particular bill during floor debate.

Override a Veto: When both the House and Senate vote by a two-thirds majority to enact a bill over a presidential veto of the legislation.

Pairing: System whereby two members jointly agree not to vote on a particular matter.

Party Unity Score: CQ's measure of the percentage of votes in which a member sides with his or her party when a majority of one party votes against a majority of the other party.

LEGISLATIVE GLOSSARY

Petition: Plea by an individual or organization for a chamber to consider particular legislation.

Pocket Veto: When the president kills a bill by withholding his signature when Congress has recessed or adjourned, preventing him from returning the measure. A true pocket veto denies Congress the opportunity to override the veto, but presidents and Congresses have disagreed about when pocket vetoes may occur.

Point of Order: An objection that language, an amendment or bill is in violation of a rule.

President of the Senate: The vice president of the United States is designated by the Constitution as the president of the Senate. That individual casts a vote only in cases of a tie.

President Pro Tempore: Senator who presides over the Senate in the absence of the vice president of the United States. The president pro tem is usually the longest-serving member of the majority party.

Previous Question: In the House, a request to end all debate and force a vote on the motion, bill or other measure under consideration.

Private Bill: Bill designed to benefit a certain individual or business.

Public Law: Designation used for legislation that has been passed by both chambers and signed by the president or enacted over a presidential veto. Private bills become private laws.

Quorum: The number of senators or representatives who must be present before a legislative body can conduct official business.

Quorum Call: In the Senate, a method of determining whether there is a quorum. Often used to suspend debate without adjourning.

Ranking Member: The leading member of the minority party on a committee. The ranking member may be referred to as the ranking Democrat or ranking Republican, depending on which party is in the minority of the relevant chamber.

Recess: Temporary halt to proceedings, with a time set for proceedings to resume. It also describes periods when the House or Senate is not in session.

Reconciliation: Process in which the budget resolution includes instructions to committees to report legislation that changes laws dealing with mandatory spending or taxes. The resulting measures are not subject to filibusters in the Senate.

Recorded Vote: Vote in which members of Congress indicate their vote for listing in the Congressional Record.

Rescission Bill: Legislation that revokes spending authority previously granted by Congress.

Resolution: A measure adopted only in one house to express the sentiment of that chamber. A simple resolution does not have the force of law.

Rider: A measure added to another, often unrelated, bill with the purpose of one piece of legislation passing on the strength of another.

Roll Call Vote: A vote in which a record is kept. The House uses electronic vote recording; the Senate uses oral voting.

Seniority: A member's rank in a chamber based on length of congressional service and other factors, including tenure in certain other elected offices. Often used to determine rank on committees.

Seriatim Consideration: Consideration of a motion line by line.

Sine Die: Final adjournment at the end of a session, of which there are two in each Congress. Bills under consideration but not enacted by the end of the Congress must be reintroduced in the next session.

Speaker: The presiding officer of the House, elected by members of that chamber.

Sponsor: The representative or senator who introduces a measure.

Suspend the Rules: Procedural action to expedite debate in the House. A motion to suspend the rules requires the votes of two-thirds of those present and is debatable for 40 minutes. Members cannot offer amendments.

Teller Vote: A vote in the House in which members file past tellers who count the votes. The total vote is recorded, but no record is kept on how each member voted. A teller vote is rarely used.

Three-Day Rule: In the House, a requirement that legislation be held for at least three calendar days (not counting weekends and holidays) before being brought to the floor. Similar to the One-Day Rule in the Senate.

Unanimous Consent: A procedure whereby a matter is considered agreed to if no member on the floor objects. It can be used to pass legislation or set the terms for floor debate. Unanimous consent motions save time by eliminating the need for a vote.

Unlimited Debate: In the Senate, the right of any senator to talk as long as desired during floor debates on a bill.

Whip: Assistant leader for each party in each chamber who keeps other members of the party informed of the legislative agenda of the leader. Also tracks sentiment among party members for certain legislation and tries to persuade members to be present and vote for measures important to the leadership.

Yield: Permission granted by the member who has the floor to another member who wishes to make a comment or ask a question.

Standard Addendum

For updates to this addendum, please send your request to
books@cqrollcall.com

Information Updates as of March 9, 2017

Committee Notes

SENATE ENVIRONMENT AND PUBLIC WORKS SUBCOMMITTEES

Clean Air And Nuclear Safety
202-224-6176—SD-410—Fax: 202-224-1273
Rep: Capito, Chair; Inhofe; Boozman; Wicker; Fischer; Moran; Ernst; Shelby
Dem: Whitehouse, Rnk. Mem.; Cardin; Sanders; Merkley;
  Gillibrand; Markey; Duckworth

Fisheries, Wildlife And Water
202-224-6176—SD-410—Fax: 202-224-1273
Rep: Boozman, Chair; Inhofe; Capito; Wicker; Fischer; Rounds; Sullivan; Shelby
Dem: Duckworth, Rnk. Mem.; Cardin; Whitehouse; Merkley;
  Gillibrand; Booker; Markey

Superfund, Waste Management And Regulatory Oversight
202-224-6176—SD-410—Fax: 202-224-1273
Rep: Rounds, Chair; Moran; Ernst; Sullivan
Dem: Harris, Rnk. Mem.; Sanders; Booker

Transportation And Infrastructure
202-224-6176—SD-410—Fax: 202-224-1273
Rep: Inhofe, Chair; Capito; Boozman; Wicker; Fischer; Moran; Ernst;
  Sullivan; Shelby
Dem: Cardin, Rnk. Mem.; Sanders; Whitehouse; Merkley;
  Gillibrand; Markey; Duckworth; Harris

HOUSE OVERSIGHT AND GOVERNMENT REFORM SUBCOMMITTEES

Government Operations
Rep: Meadows, Chair; Hice; Jordan; Sanford; Massie; Desantis; Ross; Blum
Dem: Connolly, Rnk. Mem.; Maloney; Norton; Clay; Lawrence; Watson
  Coleman

Health Care, Benefits, and Administrative Rules
Rep: Jordan, Chair; Walker; Issa; Sanford; DesJarlais; Meadows; Grothman;
  Mitchell
Dem: Krishnamoorthi, Rnk. Mem.; Cooper; Norton; Kelly; Watson Coleman;
  Plaskett

Information Technology
Rep: Hurd, Chair; Mitchell; Issa; Amash; Farenthold; Russell
Dem: Kelly, Rnk. Mem.; Raskin; Lynch; Connolly; Krishnamoorthi

Intergovernmental Affairs
Rep: Palmer, Chair; Grothman; Duncan; Gowdy; Foxx; Massie; Walker
Dem: Demings, Rnk. Mem.; DeSaulnier; Vacancy; Vacancy; Vacancy

Interior, Energy, and Environment
Rep: Farenthold, Chair; Gosar; Ross; Palmer; Comer
Dem: Plaskett, Rnk. Mem.; Raskin; Vacancy; Vacancy

National Security
Rep: DeSantis, Chair; Russell; Duncan; Amash; Gosar; Foxx: Hice; Comer
Dem: Lynch, Rnk. Mem.; Welch; Demings; DeSaulnier; Sarbanes; Vacancy;
  Vacancy

HOUSE RULES SUBCOMMITTEES

The Legislative And Budget Process
Reo: Woodall, Chair; Burgess; Byrne; Newhouse; Buck
Dem: Hastings, Rnk. Mem.; Polis

Rules And The Organization Of The House
Rep: Collins, Chair; Byrne; Newhouse; Cheney; Sessions
Dem: Slaughter, Rnk. Mem.; McGovern

HOUSE WAYS AND MEANS SUBCOMMITTEES

Updated to reflect changes due to Mike Bishop's (R-8th/MI) appointment

Health

202-225-3945--1135 LHOB--Fax: 226-1765
Rep: Tiberi, Chair; Johnson; Nunes; Roskam; Buchanan; Smith; Jenkins; Marchant; Black; Paulsen; Reed
Dem: Levin, Rnk. Mem.; Thompson; Kind; Blumenauer; Higgins; Sewell; Chu
Maj. Staff Dir.: Emily Murry
Min. Staff Dir.: Amy Hall

Human Resources

202-225-1025--B-317 RHOB--Fax: 225-9480
Rep: Smith, Chair; Smith; Walorski; Curbelo; Bishop; Reichert; Reed
Dem: Davis, Rnk. Mem.; Doggett; Sewell; Chu
Maj. Staff Dir.: Vacant
Min. Staff Dir.: Morna Miller

Oversight

202-225-5522--1136 LHOB--Fax: 225-0787
Rep: Buchanan, Chair; Schweikert; Walorski; Curbelo; Bishop; Meehan; Holding
Dem: Lewis, Rnk. Mem.; Crowley; DelBene; Blumenauer
Maj. Staff Dir.: Machalagh Carr
Min. Staff Dir.: Drew Crouch

Social Security

202-225-9263--1129 LHOB--Fax: 225-5286
Rep: Johnson, Chair; Rice; Schweikert; Buchanan; Kelly; Renacci; Smith
Dem: Larson, Rnk. Mem.; Pascrell; Crowley; Sanchez
Maj. Staff Dir.: Amy Shuart
Min. Staff Dir.: Kathryn Olson

Tax Policy

202-225-5522--1136 LHOB--Fax: 225-0787
Rep: Roskam, Chair; Reichert; Tiberi; Kelly; Renacci; Noem; Holding; Marchant; Meehan
Dem: Doggett, Rnk. Mem.; Larson; Sanchez; Thompson; DelBene; Blumenauer
Maj. Chief Tax Counsel: Barbara Angus
Min. Staff Dir.: Aruna Kalyanam

Trade

202-225-6649--1104 LHOB--Fax: 226-0158
Rep: Reichert, Chair; Nunes; Jenkins; Paulsen; Kelly; Meehan; Reed; Noem; Holding; Rice
Dem: Pascrell, Rnk. Mem.; Kind; Doggett; Levin; Davis; Higgins
Maj. Staff Dir. & Chief Counsel: Angela Ellard
Min. Staff Dir.: Jason Kearns

Office Changes